Statistics & Probability
For Business and Economic Decisions

Milad A. Tawadros

Associate Professor
Business and Economic Division
Indiana University, South Bend

PUBLISHERS
South Bend

Manufactured in the United States of America
by M & S PUBLISHERS
Box 2031, South Bend, Indiana 46615

Library of Congress Catalog Card Number: 73-85022
ISBN: 0-914084-01-1

Preface

This book is designed to include both classical and modern versions of statistics and statistical analysis. Topics which used to be covered in a traditional business and economic statistics course have been presented in chapters I and II. In these chapters, classical topics as: grouping and graphic presentation of data, measures of central location, measures of dispersion, and measures of skewness and kurtosis are presented to pave the way for a better understanding of the modern approach of statistics and statistical analysis covered in the rest of the book.

The current trend indicates that statistical applications in the decision making field depend heavily on probability, probability functions, expected value, and Bayesian theorem. All these topics are presented in chapters III through VI and are considered vital tools to apply in statistical decision making as well as in other fields as: management science, operations research, quantitative marketing, and quantitative economics. Chapters VII, VIII, and IX are designed for the application of probability in statistical decision making.

On the other hand, the book is designed for a one-semester course in statistics for both undergraduate business and economics majors, and MBA students. Part of chapter IV (the probability functions for two or more variables) and all chapter V can be omitted without loss of continuity, and an undergraduate course structured this way will not require calculus as prerequisite for this course. For the MBA students the knowledge of calculus is essential for a better understanding of the probability functions being extensively used in statistical decision problems they are facing or will be facing in their practical business life.

The author is very grateful to the publishers and authors who kindly gave permission to reproduce the statistical tables presented in the Tables section in this book.

The author is very grateful to Dr. Gerald E. Harriman, Chairman of the Business and Economic Division, IUSB, for his encouragement.

I am indebted to my family, my wife Sabah and my sons Adel, Atef, and Azmi for their patience, understanding, and encouragement during the writing of this book.

South Bend, Indiana
October, 1972

Milad A. Tawadros

Contents

Chapter I

STATISTICS: ITS NATURE

Statistics is a science that deals with quantitative or numerical data. The collection, organization, graphic presentation and calculation of measures to describe the numerical data is the function of a branch of statistics called descriptive statistics. In this chapter collection, organization and graphic presentation of data will be presented. In Chapter II measures of location, dispersion, skewness and kurtosis are calculated to assist in describing numerical data.

Statistical analysis is being used in the field of decision making. It helps in arriving at decisions based on statistical analysis or improving the process of decision making. This branch of statistics is called statistical decision making. This function can be divided into two categories: classical and non-classical. Classical statistics decision making is known as statistical inference and includes: estimation of population parameters and test of hypotheses. The non-classical approach of statistical decision making is new and has been developed in conjunction with decision theory and econometrics. Both of the classical and non-classical approaches are developed to help make decisions concerning the uncertain future. Therefore this body of statistical analysis is based on probability. Following the descriptive statistics presentation, probability and probability distributions are introduced to pave the way of applying probability to the decision making process.

Population vs. Samples:

Data can be collected to represent populations as well as samples. A population or universe is a complete set of observations that a variable may assume. For example if X as a variable assumes the heights of 10,000 students enrolled in university XYZ, then X has a population of 10,000 observations. Populations are of two types: finite and infinite. Measures calculated for populations are called parameters and denoted by Greek letters. For example, the mean of a population is denoted by the Greek letter μ (MU). The number of observations contained in a population is referred to by N.

Using populations for statistical analysis can be costly and time consuming. Therefore, samples drawn from populations are usually used instead of populations. A sample is a part of a population or universe. If we call a population a set, then a sample is a subset. Measures calculated for samples are known as statistics and denoted by Latin letters. The mean of a sample is denoted by $\bar{X}$, $\bar{Y}$, $\bar{Z}$, and so on. The number of observations contained in a sample is referred to by n.

1

Ungrouped vs. Grouped data:

Raw data collected for populations or samples are called ungrouped data. Presentation of raw data in frequency tables through the application of tally sheets is known as grouped data. Data collected from published internal or external sources, or through surveys can be organized into classes and frequencies to construct frequency distribution tables.

Example 1.1:

Let X assume the grades of 40 students in a statistics final examination. The 40 values of X are:

90	78	50	97	55	98	41	90
82	60	48	92	62	75	55	70
73	42	75	84	79	83	99	49
81	79	77	71	70	76	87	56
65	88	64	60	45	84	61	79

Suppose we want to describe the performance of the 40 students in this final examination, one may suggest any of the following ways to do so:

(1) arrange the data in ascending or descending order and report the lowest and the highest grades

(2) arrange the data in classes or groups

(3) calculate a measure that describes or represents the data, e.g. the mean

The description of the performance of the 40 students in the examination by the lowest and the highest grades is not enough since these two values represent the extremes. Grouping the raw data into classes or groups is introduced below. Calculation of measures to describe the data such as measures of central location, dispersion and others are presented in the following chapter.

The 40 grades or the ungrouped data can be classified into groups or classes through the application of tally sheets as follows:

Class	Tally	Frequency
40-49	ᴎᴎ	5
50-59	IIII	4
60-69	ᴎᴎ I	6
70-79	ᴎᴎ ᴎᴎ II	12
80-89	ᴎᴎ II	7
90-99	ᴎᴎ I	6
		—
		40

The result of grouping the data can be presented in a frequency distribution table:

FREQUENCY DISTRIBUTION
OF THE GRADES (X).

Class	f (frequency)
40-49	5
50-59	4
60-69	6
70-79	12
80-89	7
90-99	6
	—
	40

Reducing the data to a frequency distribution table has made it possible to simplify the presentation of this data, however, information concerning the individual grades has been lost. For example, in the class interval 40-49, we know that there are five students whose scores fall within the limits of this class interval, but in the absence of the raw data, we cannot determine the exact grades contained in this class interval.

Remarks about class intervals:

1. The arrangement of groups into 40-49, 50-59, . . . , 90-99 are called class intervals. Each class interval has two limits, lower limit as 40, 50, 60, . . . , 90, and upper limit as 49, 59, . . . , 99. Class intervals with unknown lower or upper limit are called open-end class intervals, e.g. less than 150 or 200 or more.

2. Class interval may be viewed as the number of units or observations contained in the class groupings, e.g., the class interval of 40-49 is 10 units. Class intervals may or may not be equal in a frequency distribution table. It is advisable to use equal class intervals in the construction of frequency distributions, however, it is not a rule.

3. The more the number of class intervals in the frequency distribution table, the more detailed information is known about the data and vice versa. There is no fixed rule to determine the number of class intervals in any frequency distribution. It is up to the investigator to decide on the number of class intervals that serves his goals in constructing the distribution table.

4. Class intervals are either discrete or continuous depending on the type of data being grouped. If the data is discrete, as the case of the previous example of the grades, then the class intervals contain a break:

   40-49
   50-59

   On the other hand, if the data represents a continuous variable, then the class intervals for continuous data have no break:

   40 and less than 50
   50 and less than 60

5. The midpoint of a class interval is the average of the values contained in this interval. To calculate the midpoint (M) simply add the lower limit and the upper limit and divide the sum by two. For example, the midpoint for a discrete class interval: 40-49 is $(40 + 49)/2 = 44.5$, and the midpoint for a continuous class interval: 40 and less than 50 is $(40 + 50)/2 \cong 45$ (because less than 50 could be 49.9999 which is approximately 50).

Graphic presentation of the frequency distribution:

Graphs are used to give more and clear visual information about the data. There are many methods to be used to draw a diagram for a frequency distribution. The most important ways are: the bar chart, the histogram, the frequency polygon, and the smooth continuous frequency curves. These four methods of graphic presentation can be used to convert a discrete data graph to a continuous data one. The construction of 4 graphs ranging from a bar chart, to a continuous curve of the frequency distribution of X, where X represents the 40 grades in the previous example, is shown below in Figures 1-1 through 1-4:

X (Grades)	frequency (f)
40-49	5
50-59	4
60-69	6
70-79	12
80-89	7
90-99	6

(a) A bar chart:

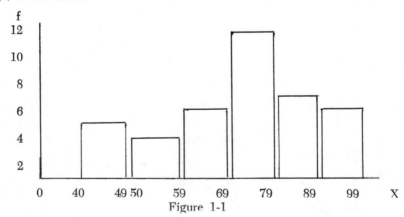

Figure 1-1

(b) A histogram:

To construct a histogram, the gaps between the class intervals must be closed. This can be done by finding the boundaries of the class intervals, e.g., for the class interval 40-49, its boundaries are 39.5 and 49.5.

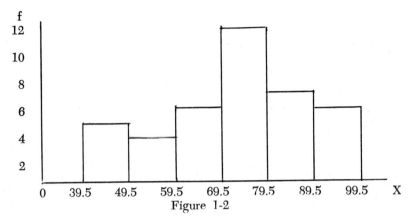

Figure 1-2

(c) A frequency polygon:
If we connect the midpoints of the class intervals of a histogram, this produces a frequency polygon:

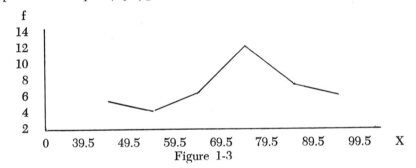

Figure 1-3

(d) A frequency distribution curve:
A smoothed frequency polygon is a continuous frequency distribution curve:

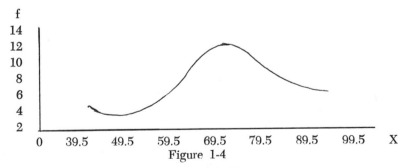

Figure 1-4

Frequency distribution curves are of different types, each represents a different frequency distribution function or model. The following are some important frequency distribution curves:

6

1. Uniform distribution curve:

If the frequencies are the same for all the class intervals, then the distribution is called a rectangular or uniform frequency distribution, as in Figure 1-5.

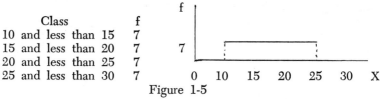

Class	f
10 and less than 15	7
15 and less than 20	7
20 and less than 25	7
25 and less than 30	7

Figure 1-5

2. Normal distribution curve:

The normal distribution is a very important distribution, it is a bell-shaped curve. The mean divides the distribution into two symmetrical halves as in Figure 1-6:

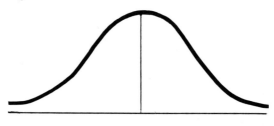

μ
Figure 1-6

3. Skewed and multimodal distribution curves:

If the distribution is not symmetrical, then it is either skewed or has more than one peak.

Skewed distributions have a long tail to the right (positively skewed) or a long tail to the left (negatively skewed) as in Figure 1-7:

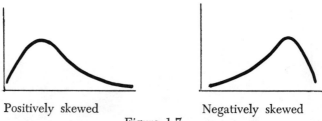

Positively skewed   Negatively skewed

Figure 1-7

A frequency distribution that has more than one peak is a multimodal distribution. A frequency distribution with two peaks is called bimodal, while a trimodal distribution has three peaks.

The material covered in this chapter about grouping the data into a frequency distribution and the graphic presentation of frequency distributions is one way to describe and simplify the raw data.

Another way to describe a mass of data is to calculate measures of different types to know more about the characteristics of the data and the shape of its frequency distribution. This is the second part of descriptive statistics and is presented in chapter II.

EXERCISES

1.1 a. Define statistics.
     b. What is the difference between statistical inference and descriptive statistics?
     c. Differentiate between a discrete and continuous variable.

1.2 Define:

a. Population	b. Sample	c. Parameter
d. Statistic	e. Histogram	f. Frequency
g. Class midpoint		polygon

1.3 The following table shows the height of 100 football players: (in inches)

74	70	71	70	77
75	76	77	71	73
72	72	72	72	73
75	76	69	74	74
71	74	72	79	75
74	71	74	71	76
71	76	73	71	73
70	74	74	75	74
76	74	72	73	73
74	75	70	75	74
71	71	72	74	72
75	73	71	72	72
74	70	75	73	71
72	75	77	74	73
76	72	72	74	69
71	74	76	72	75
70	74	73	70	69
75	77	71	75	72
78	73	74	77	70
72	76	75	69	79

a. Construct a frequency distribution:
   Class
   69-70
   71-72
   73-74
   75-76
   77-78
   79-80
b. Draw a bar chart
c. Draw a histogram, frequency polygon, and a frequency curve.

1.4 The following data represent High School I.Q. Scores for 110 students:

154	116	142	97	150	115	117	93	147	114
118	89	145	113	119	85	143	112	121	127
142	111	122	136	110	123	123	137	109	125
119	136	108	127	100	135	80	128	100	133
87	132	108	133	85	134	85	112	123	96
121	140	99	104	135	100	102	109	107	144
129	134	97	111	124	105	106	110	123	134
114	115	145	109	148	99	116	120	143	133
128	97	122	99	136	128	110	146	107	129
89	111	115	113	107	109	87	112	132	98
110	128	109	121	111	99	104	102	87	125

    a. Group the data into the following class intervals:
       80-89, 90-99, 100-109, . . . , 150-159.
    b. Draw a histogram for the grouped data.

1.5 The following table shows sales of groceries of 50 customers: (in dollars)

25.64	15.10	30.45	50.34	17.05
34.67	56.06	20.86	19.05	8.99
56.98	42.11	11.69	23.56	31.90
12.89	36.56	44.22	11.75	9.99
33.67	29.06	15.39	22.91	22.87
35.87	44.98	50.00	39.11	34.86
18.77	20.90	38.71	56.70	34.99
52.89	35.87	25.87	44.00	29.99
21.11	19.03	19.65	29.06	28.77
34.98	41.09	27.67	39.06	51.03

    a. Construct a frequency table for the data.
    b. Draw a histogram and a frequency curve for the data.

Chapter II

DESCRIPTIVE STATISTICS

As indicated in Chapter I, statistics is the science dealing with the collection, organization, analysis, and making decisions of quantitative data.

The collection, organization, and graphic presentation of numerical data help to describe a mass of data and present such data into a form suitable for deriving logical conclusions. This part of descriptive statistics is presented in Chapter I.

Analysis of data is another way to simplify quantitative data by extracting relevant information from which summarized and comprehensible numerical measures can be calculated to describe the given data. The most important measures for this purpose are: measures of location, measures of dispersion, and measures of symmetry and skewness. This is the other part of descriptive statistics which is the main topic of this chapter.

The collection, organization, graphic presentation, and the calculation of descriptive statistic measures are merely different approaches to present the data in a simple form to draw conclusions or to help in making decisions concerning the future, but the future is uncertain, therefore, the probability theory applies itself to this part of decision making in statistics which is called statistical inference. Probability and statistical inference will be presented in later chapters.

In this chapter, the three different measures of descriptive statistics are presented in the following order: Measures of location, measures of dispersion, and measures of symmetry and skewness.

I. Measures of location

A single value can be derived for a mass of data to describe the elements contained in the set or the frequency distribution representing such data. This single value is called a measure of central location or central tendency. There are three popular types, namely: averages (or means), the median, and the mode. Averages or means are subdivided into many types; four of these will be explained in detail: arithmetic, weighted arithmetic, geometric, and harmonic. In addition, there are other measures of location which are not central location; such as, quartiles, deciles, and percentiles. These measures of location are presented in Appendix II. Figure 2-1 shows a summary of measures of location.

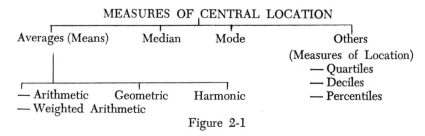

Figure 2-1

In evaluating these measures of central tendency, we shall differentiate between ungrouped data (raw data) and grouped data (frequency distribution tables). However, if we utilize computer programming to calculate the statistics of the measures of central location, it is not necessary to distinguish between ungrouped and grouped data. As a matter of fact, we do not need to develop computer programs for the grouped data at all. The computer is capable of handling an extensive number of observations without grouping the data before calculating any statistic.

A general knowledge of basic statistical methods requires, however, that the student be capable of utilizing the formulas for both ungrouped and grouped data which will be presented in this discussion.

1. AVERAGES or MEANS

An average is a single value that describes or characterizes the elements of a set of data. Averages or means are of many kinds; four of these will be considered in this chapter. These four are the arithmetic mean, the weighted arithmetic mean, the geometric mean and the harmonic mean.

A. Arithmetic Mean

In everyday activity you may hear or read the word "average"; such as, average income, average weight, average weekly working hours, average speed, etc. The concept of "average" in ordinary usage is what statisticians call the arithmetic average or arithmetic mean. In most cases the terms "arithmetic mean, arithmetic average, mean, and average" are used interchangeably in this text.

The arithmetic mean, or simply the mean, is calculated by adding the values of all the elements of the variable (X) and dividing the total or the summation (ΣX) by the number of elements or observations (N or n) contained in that variable. The general formula used to derive the mean is

$$\mu = \frac{\Sigma X}{N}$$

The Greek letter μ (MU) is used to denote the mean of the population. μ is a parameter.

$$\overline{X} = \frac{\Sigma X}{n}$$

$\overline{X}$ ("X bar") is the symbol used to denote the mean of a sample. $\overline{X}$ is a statistic.

From the general formula used to calculate the mean, one can see that the arithmetic mean is affected by each observed value of the variable including the extremes. This follows from the fact that the value of each element of the distribution (or the array) of X is a part of ΣX.

To calculate the arithmetic mean, we shall differentiate between ungrouped and grouped data.

Ungrouped Data:

1. General Method

The formula to be used to calculate the mean for ungrouped data is the same as the general formula where the mean is defined as follows:

$$\overline{X} = \frac{\sum_{i=1}^{n} X_i}{n} \quad \text{or simply} \quad \overline{X} = \frac{\Sigma X}{n}$$

For example: Let X_i be the weekly income per family in a city, then $X_1, X_2, \ldots, X_9, X_{10}$ represents the weekly income for 10 families in this city. To calculate the average weekly income for these 10 families $(\overline{X})$, one must apply the previous formulas:

$$\overline{X} = \frac{\sum_{i=1}^{n} X_i}{n} \quad \text{where } n = 10$$

$$\text{or} \quad \overline{X} = \frac{X_1 + X_2 + \ldots + X_9 + X_{10}}{10}$$

Example 2.1: Suppose that the weekly income of these 10 families is as shown in Table 2-1, and we want to calculate the average weekly income for these families.

Table 2-1
X_i (weekly income per family in dollars)*

X_1	140
X_2	250
X_3	300
X_4	90
X_5	180
X_6	200
X_7	220
X_8	150
X_9	180
X_{10}	250

1960
*source: Hypothetical

Solution:

$$\Sigma X_i = 1960$$

then $\overline{X} = \dfrac{\Sigma X}{n} = \dfrac{1960}{10} = \$196.00$ (average weekly income for the ten families)

2. Shortcut Methods:

The shortcut methods are based upon two simple mathematical facts: First, If we subtract a constant from an equation or a formula and compensate for such subtraction by adding to the formula the same constant, the equation will not change.[1]
For example: Let the equation be:

$$Y = X^2 + 10 - FX$$

If we subtract 19 and add the same constant to the right or the left side of the equation, the equation will not change:

$$Y = X^2 + 10 - FX + 19 - 19$$
or
$$Y + 19 - 19 = X^2 + 10 - FX$$

Notice that $-19 + 19 = 0$.

Second: And/OR, if we divide the formula by a constant, then compensate for such division by multiplying our formula by the same constant,[2] there will be no change. If we divide by 10 and then multiply by 10, this is exactly the same thing as multiplying by $1(\div 10 \times 10 = 1/10 \times 10 = 1)$.

One can apply the first or the second method or both and the formula will not change.

Perhaps the use of the word "shortcut" is a misnomer here. The student will see as we move along that the so-called shortcut methods are really simplifying methods. They enable us to reduce a large unwieldy number to a small value which simplifies the calculations.

For each method, a new formula to calculate the mean will be developed.

a. First Method

In this case a constant (C) will be **deducted** from each value of the variable,[3] and to compensate for that the same constant will be **added** to the mean formula which becomes:[4]

---

(1) Also, one can add and then subtract the same constant, and the formula remains the same.

(2) One can multiply and divide by a constant and the formula will not change.

(3) There is no fixed rule to determine the value of the constant.

(4) If a constant is added to each value of X, then $\overline{X} = \dfrac{\Sigma X'}{n} - C; X' = X + C;$ however, it is not practical to add to the value of X, but rather to subtract.

$$\overline{X} = \frac{\Sigma X'}{n} + C \qquad \text{where } C = \text{constant and} \\ X' = X - C$$

$$\text{or} \quad \overline{X} = C + \frac{\Sigma X'}{n}$$

Example 2.2: Let us apply this method to Example 1; where C = 200.

Solution

X	X − C = X'	
140	140 − 200 = − 60	
250	250 − 200 = 50	$\overline{X} = C + \dfrac{\Sigma X'}{n}$
300	= 100	
90	= −110	$= 200 + \dfrac{-40}{10}$
180	= − 20	
200	= 0	
220	= − 50	$= 200 - 4$
150	= − 20	$= 196$
180	= 20	
250	= 50	

$$\Sigma X' = - 40$$
$$n = 10$$
$$C = 200$$

b. Second Shortcut Method

The second shortcut method is to **divide** each value of the variable by a constant (K), and then compensate for that by **multiplying** the mean formula by the same constant.[5]
The new formula will be:

$$\overline{X} = \frac{\Sigma X''}{n} \ (K) \qquad \text{where } K = \text{constant} \\ \text{and } X'' = X/K$$

Example 2.3: Let us use the same values of the variable X as in Example 1; where K = 10.

Solution

X	$\dfrac{X}{K} = X''$	
140	$140/10 = 14$	
250	$250/10 = 25$	
300	$= 30$	
90	$= 9$	
180	$= 18$	
200	$= 20$	
220	$= 22$	$\overline{X} = \dfrac{\Sigma X''}{n}\ (K)$
150	$= 15$	
180	$= 18$	$= (196/10)\ (10)$
250	$= 25$	$= 196$

$$\Sigma X'' = 196$$
$$n = 10$$
$$K = 10$$

c. Third Shortcut Method

This method is merely a combination of the two shortcut methods previously mentioned. A constant (C) may be deducted from each value of the variable and then divided by another constant (K); however, we must compensate for the subtraction and the division by adding C and multiplying by K in the mean formula which now becomes:

$$\overline{X} = \frac{\Sigma X'''}{n}\ (K) + C \qquad \text{where C and K} = \text{constants}$$
$$\text{and } X''' = \frac{X - C}{K}$$

or $\quad \overline{X} = C + \dfrac{\Sigma X'''}{n}\ (K)$

Example 2.4: If we combine Examples 2 and 3; where C = 200 and K = 10, then:

Solution

X	X − C	$\dfrac{X - C}{K} = X'''$
140	$140 - 200 = -\ 60$	$-60/10 = -\ 6$
250	$=\ \ \ \ 50$	$50/10 =\ \ \ \ 5$
300	$=\ \ \ 100$	$=\ \ \ 10$
90	$= -110$	$= -11$
180	$= -\ 20$	$= -\ 2$
200	$=\ \ \ \ \ 0$	$=\ \ \ \ \ 0$
220	$=\ \ \ \ 20$	$=\ \ \ \ 2$
150	$= -\ 50$	$= -\ 5$
180	$= -\ 20$	$= -\ 2$
250	$=\ \ \ \ 50$	$=\ \ \ \ 5$

$$\Sigma X''' = -4$$

$$\overline{X} = C + \frac{\Sigma X'''}{n} \bullet K$$

$$= 200 + \frac{-4}{10} \bullet 10$$

$$= 200 + (-4)$$

$$= 200 - 4$$

$$= 196$$

Grouped Data:

1. General Method

Grouped data refers to any set of observations tabulated into classes with corresponding frequencies which we call frequency distribution tables. By grouping the data, the individual value of each observation has disappeared and has been included with others falling within the same class interval.

For example: Let X be a variable that assumes the following values: 10, 11, 11, 15, 16, 16, 17, 19 and 20. Grouping the values of X into three class intervals (10-14, 15-19, 20-24), a frequency distribution table is developed as shown below in Table 2-2:

Table 2-2

THE VALUES OF THE VARIABLE X, UNGROUPED AND GROUPED

Ungrouped	X	Grouped: Frequency distribution	
	10	Class	Frequency (f)
	11		
	11	10-14	3
	15	15-19	5
	16	20-24	1
	16		
	17		
	19		
	20		

In the frequency distribution (or grouped data), the first class interval (10-14) has 3 frequencies which means that there are three values of X having a magnitude between 10 and 14. In the absence of exact values of X, one can say that the 3 frequencies could be: 10, 10, 10 or 14, 14, 14 or any combination of values between 10 and 14.

Hence, the sum of the 3 values or frequencies contained in the first class interval might be as low as $10 + 10 + 10 = 30$ or as high as $14 + 14 + 14 = 42$ or any value between 30 and 42. Neither 30 nor 42 is an acceptable sum of the 3 frequencies; therefore, an average of both $\frac{30 + 42}{2}$ $= 36$ is an appropriate value of the sum for the three values contained in the first class interval.

We arrive at the same summation by multiplying the midpoint of the interval by the frequency.[6]

Applying this rule for the first class interval (10-14) of the frequency distribution in Table 2-2, the midpoint $(M) = \dfrac{10 + 14}{2} = 12$, the frequency $(f) = 3$, then the midpoint times the frequency or $Mf = 12 \times 3 = 36$. This rule will assist us in finding the summation of all the values of X that have been grouped where $\Sigma Mf \cong \Sigma X$. Accordingly, the general formula of the mean for grouped data becomes:

$$\overline{X} = \frac{\Sigma Mf}{\Sigma f}$$

where M = midpoint of class intervals
f = frequency of class intervals

Comparing the ungrouped formula

$$\overline{X} = \frac{\Sigma X}{n}$$

with the grouped formula

$$\overline{X} = \frac{\Sigma Mf}{\Sigma f}$$

we can see that: $\quad \Sigma Mf \cong \Sigma X$
and $\quad \Sigma f = n$

In most cases, the mean of the ungrouped values of X is not equal to the mean of the same values after being grouped because the exact values of X have been lost in the process of the grouping. To clarify this point, let us calculate the mean for the ungrouped and the grouped values of the variable X presented in Table 2-2.

Example 2.5:

Ungrouped Data

X
10
11
11
15
16
16
17
19
20

$\Sigma X = 135$
$n = 9$

Solution

$$\overline{X} = 135/9 = 15$$

Grouped Data

Solution

Class	Frequency (f)	Midpoint (M)	Mf
10-14	3	12	36
15-19	5	17	85
20-24	1	22	22

$\Sigma f = 9 \qquad \Sigma Mf = 143$
$\Sigma f = 9$

$$\overline{X} = \frac{\Sigma Mf}{\Sigma f}$$
$$= 143 / 9$$
$$= 15.89$$

(6) Midpoint of a class interval explained in Chapter I.

2. Shortcut Methods

The shortcut methods or simplifying methods used for the ungrouped data can be applied to grouped data. Formulas and examples to show the application of the three shortcut methods of computing the mean for the grouped data are presented as follows:

a. First Shortcut Method

A constant (C) will be **deducted** from the value of the midpoint (M) of each class in the frequency distribution table[7], and to compensate for this, the same constant must be **added** to the mean formula. The new mean formula becomes:

$$\overline{X} = C + \frac{\Sigma M'f}{\Sigma f}$$

where C = constant
and M' = M − C

Example 2.6: Assume the following frequency distribution:

Solution

Class	Frequency (f)	Midpoint (M)	M − C = M'		M'f
10-19.9	8	14.95	14.95-24.95 =	−10	−80
20-29.9	40	24.95	24.95-24.95 =	0	0
30-39.9	37	34.95		10	370
40-49.9	15	44.95		20	300

Note: The selected value of C is 24.95.

$$\Sigma M'f = \overline{590}$$

$$\overline{X} = C + \frac{\Sigma M'f}{\Sigma f} \quad \begin{aligned} &= 24.95 + 590/100 \\ &= 24.95 + 5.90 \\ &= 30.85 \end{aligned}$$

b. Second Shortcut Method

In this method the values of the midpoint of each class interval (M) will be divided by a constant (K); however, to compensate for this, the mean formula must be multiplied by the same constant.[8] The new mean formula becomes:

$$\overline{X} = \frac{\Sigma M''f}{\Sigma f} \ (K)$$

where K = constant

$$M'' = \frac{M}{K}$$

---

(7) It is advisable to let the constant C take the value of the midpoint of the class with the highest frequency.

(8) The value assigned (K) is again an arbitrary decision.

Example 2.7: The following is a frequency distribution of the annual sales (in millions of dollars) of 100 selected firms in a certain industry:

Solution

Class	Frequency (f)	Midpoint (M)	M/K=M″	M″f
5 and less than 15	10	10	10/10=1	10
15 and less than 25	30	20	20/10=2	60
25 and less than 35	29	30	30/10=3	87
35 and less than 45	14	40	4	56
45 and less than 55	17	50	5	85

$$\Sigma f = 100 \qquad \Sigma M''f = 298$$
$$\Sigma f = 100$$
$$K = 10$$

$$\overline{X} = \frac{\Sigma M''f}{\Sigma f} \ (K)$$
$$= 298/100 \times 10$$
$$= 29.8$$

c. Third Shortcut Method

This method is not new to us, it is a combination of both the first and the second shortcut methods. In other words, a constant (C) will be deducted from each value of the midpoint (M), then divided by another constant (K). The new mean formula then becomes:

$$\overline{X} = C + \frac{\Sigma M'''f}{\Sigma f} \ K \qquad \text{where C and K} = \text{constants}$$
$$M''' = \frac{M - C}{K}$$

Example 2.8: Let us apply this method to the frequency distribution in Example 2.6, where C = 24.95 and K = 10:

Solution

Class	f	M	M − C	$\frac{M-C}{K}=M'''$	M‴f	M	$\frac{M-C}{K}=M'''$	M‴f
10-19.9	8	14.95	14.95-24.95 = −10	−1	−8	14.95 $\frac{14.95-24.95}{10}$=−1	−8
20-29.9	40	24.95	= 0	0	0	24.95 = 0	0
30-39.9	37	34.95	= 10	1	37	34.95 = 1	37
40-49.9	15	44.95	= 20	2	30	44.95 = 2	30

$$\Sigma f = 100 \qquad \Sigma M'''f = 59 \qquad \Sigma M'''f = 59$$
C = 24.95
K = 10

then: $\bar{\bar{X}} = C + \left(\dfrac{\Sigma M'''f}{\Sigma f} \right) K$

$= 24.95 + (59/100) \ (10)$
$= 24.95 + 5.90$
$= 30.85$

To summarize the various methods for calculating the mean, we will apply all of them to the following example:

Example 2.9: Let the following frequency distribution represent the grades of 50 students in a statistics course:

Problem:

Solution: C = 65, K = 5

Class	f	General Method $\bar{X} = \Sigma Mf/\Sigma f$		First Shortcut $\bar{X} = C + \Sigma M'f/\Sigma f$		Second Shortcut $\bar{X} = \Sigma M''f/\Sigma f \cdot K$		Third Shortcut $\bar{X} = C + \Sigma M'''f/\Sigma f \cdot K$	
		M	Mf	M − C = M'	M'f	$\frac{M}{K} = M''$	M''f	$\frac{M-C}{K} = M'''$	M'''f
30 and under 40	1	35	35	35-65 = −30	−30	$\frac{35}{5} = 7$	7	$\frac{35-65}{5} = -6$	− 6
40 and under 50	4	45	180	45-65 = −20	−80	$\frac{45}{5} = 9$	36	$\frac{45-65}{5} = -4$	−16
50 and under 60	9	55	495	= −10	−90	= 11	99	= −2	−18
60 and under 70	18	65	1170	= 0	0	= 13	234	= 0	0
70 and under 80	10	75	750	= 10	100	= 15	150	= 2	20
80 and under 90	5	85	425	= 20	100	= 17	85	= 4	20
90 and under 100	3	95	285	= 30	90	= 19	57	= 6	18

Σf = 50

$\Sigma Mf = 3340$
$\Sigma f = 50$

$\Sigma M'f = 90$
$\Sigma f = 50$
$C = 65$

$\Sigma M''f = 668$
$\Sigma f = 50$
$K = 5$

$\Sigma M'''f = 19$
$\Sigma f = 50$
$C = 65$
$K = 5$

$\bar{X} = \Sigma Mf/\Sigma f$
$= 3340/50$
$= 66.8$

$\bar{X} = C + \Sigma M'f/\Sigma f$
$= 65 + 90/50$
$= 65 + 1.8$
$= 66.8$

$\bar{X} = \Sigma M''f/\Sigma f \cdot K$
$= 668/50 \cdot 5$
$= 668/10$
$= 66.8$

$\bar{X} = C + \Sigma M'''f/\Sigma f \cdot K$
$= 65 + 18/50 \cdot 5$
$= 65 + 18/10$
$= 66.8$

Chief Mathematical Characteristics of the Arithmetic Mean:

1. Summation of the deviations about the mean is zero, or $\Sigma(X-\overline{X}) = 0$; $X-\overline{X} = $ deviations.
2. Summation of squared deviations about the mean is minimum, or $\Sigma(X-\overline{X})^2 = $ min. This means that $\Sigma(X-\overline{X})^2$ is smaller than $\Sigma(X-K)^2$; $K \neq \overline{X}$

B. Weighted Arithmetic Mean

The value of the arithmetic mean is based on all the values of the observations contained in the variable. In our previous examples we assumed that all values had equal weights.

However, in some cases, it is very useful to assign different weights to the values of the variable. An obvious case is the different weights assigned to different types of tests and examinations. We know that there are different levels of examinations to be given to college students, including tests of five or ten minutes, one-hour examinations, and the final examination. To evaluate the course grade of a student given these different levels of tests and examinations, different weights should be assigned to each level of these examinations reflecting its importance. The weighted arithmetic mean will be the appropriate mean to be applied.

The formula of the weighted arithmetic mean is as follows:

$$\overline{X}_w = \frac{\Sigma WX}{\Sigma W}$$ where W denotes the weights assigned to the values of the variable X.

Example 2.10: In four examinations and the final, a student's grades in a business course are as follows:

1st exam	81
2nd exam	90
3rd exam	75
4th exam	95
Final	80 40

A weight is assigned to the final to be 40% of the grade[9]. Find the course grade for this student.

	Grade (X)	Weight (W)	XW
1st exam	81	15	1215
2nd exam	90	15	1350
3rd exam	75	15	1125
4th exam	95	15	1425
Final	80	40	3200
		$\Sigma W = 100$	$\Sigma XW = 8315$

$$\overline{X}_w = \frac{8315}{100} = 83.15 \cong 83$$

---

(9) The four examinations are treated as equal or having equal weights.

C. Geometric Mean

The geometric mean is used to calculate the average of ratios or rates of change. It is affected by all the values of the elements contained in the variable; however, the geometric mean gives less weight to extreme values than that given to such values by the arithmetic mean.

Ungrouped Data

The formula used to derive the geometric mean is:

$$G = \sqrt[n]{X_1 \cdot X_2 \cdot X_3 \ldots X_{n-1} \cdot X_n}$$

$$\text{or } G = \sqrt[n]{\prod_{i=1}^{n} X_i}$$

where π or (PI) is a mathematical operator defined in Appendix 1. We can use this formula to calculate the geometric mean of limited and simple values of X; e.g., if X assumes the values of 2, 8, 16, and 1, then the geometric mean of X is:

$$G = \sqrt[4]{2 \cdot 8 \cdot 16 \cdot 1}$$
$$= \sqrt[4]{256}$$
$$= \sqrt[4]{4^4}$$
$$= 4$$

If the variable X has many observations, perhaps 10, 20, or 50, and these observations are large numbers such as 193, 46, 19, 78, 901, 1062, . . . , the previous formula for calculating the geometric mean will not be appropriate. Therefore, a new formula, expressed in logarithms, can be derived from the old formula as follows:

$$G = \sqrt[n]{X_1 \cdot X_2 \cdot \ldots X_{n-1} \cdot X_n} \quad \text{(old formula)}$$
$$G = (X_1 \cdot X_2 \cdot \ldots X_{n-1} \cdot X_n)^{1/n}$$

The last formula can be expressed in logarithms:

$$\text{Log } G = 1/n(\text{Log } X_1 + \text{Log } X_2 + \ldots + \text{Log } X_n)$$

$$= 1/n \sum_{i=1}^{n} \left(\log X_i \right)$$

$$= \frac{\Sigma \log X}{n}$$

The calculation of this formula will give us the value of Log G. To find the value of G (the geometric mean), one has to find the anti log of Log G.

$$\text{Hence} \quad G = \text{Anti log} \left(\frac{\Sigma \log X}{n} \right)$$

Example 2.11: Let X be the sales ratio[10] of Dick's Department Store for the past five years. Find the geometric mean of X.

---

(10) Total sales of each year has been expressed as a ratio to total sales of a specific base year.

Solution

X	Log X
0.85	1.9294
1.01	0.0043
0.96	1.9823
1.60	0.2041
1.80	0.2553

$\Sigma \log X = \overline{0.3754}$

$$\text{Log } G = \frac{\Sigma \log X}{n}$$
$$= 0.3754/5$$
$$= .0751$$
$$G = 1.19$$

The geometric mean is 1.19; this is interpreted as an average increase of 19% in the sales of Dick's Department Store during the past five years.

The average percent change (increase or decrease) over a period of time in production, sales, stock prices, dividends, and other variables is very important to the businessman. The geometric mean helps to find such averages as shown in Example 2.11. However, the average percent change over a long period can be calculated by the following simplified formula for the geometric mean:

$$G = \sqrt[n-1]{\frac{X_n}{X_1}} - 1$$

Where n = number of periods

X_n = the value of the last period.

X_1 = the value of the first period.

This formula can be used to calculate the average percent change in sales in Example 2.11 as follows:

$$G = \sqrt[5-1]{\frac{1.80}{0.85}} - 1$$

$$= \sqrt[4]{2.1176} - 1$$
$$= 1.20 - 1$$
$$= .20 \quad \text{or } 20\% \text{ (the average increase in sales is 20\% per year)}$$

let $Y = \sqrt[4]{2.1176}$

$\log Y = \frac{1}{4} \log 2.1176$

$= \frac{1}{4} (0.32634)$

$= .08159$

$Y = 1.20$

Grouped Data

The geometric mean for grouped data may be derived by the following formula:

Log G = Σ(f log M)/ Σf   where f = frequency
                                            M = Midpoint

and   G = antilog (Log G)

An illustrative example:

Compute the geometric mean for the following frequency distribution:

Class	f	M	**Solution** log M	f log M
4 and less than 8	5	6	0.7782	3.8910
8 and less than 12	3	10	1.0000	3.0000
12 and less than 16	2	14	1.1461	2.2922
16 and less than 20	10	18	1.2553	12.5530
20 and less than 24	4	22	1.3424	5.3696

$$\Sigma f = 24$$

$$\Sigma(f \log M) = 27.1058$$
$$\Sigma f = 24$$

$$Log\ G = 27.1058/24$$
$$= 1.1294$$
$$G = 13.5$$

D. Harmonic Mean

The harmonic mean can be used instead of the weighted mean. The harmonic mean gives less weight to the extremely large values of an array and a considerable weight to the small values.

Ungrouped Data

The formula for the harmonic mean is as follows:

$$H = \frac{n}{\Sigma \dfrac{1}{X}}$$

If we set Y to equal $\dfrac{1}{X}$ then the previous formula becomes:

$$H = n/\Sigma Y \qquad\qquad Y = \text{the reciprocal of X}$$

Example 2.12: A typing contest among secretaries showed the following results:

A	65 words/minute
B	74 words/minute
C	81 words/minute
D	76 words/minute

Find the average words/minute for the group.

Solution:

X	1/X or Y	
65	.0153	
74	.0133	
81	.0122	$H = 4/.0540$
76	.0132	$= 74.074$
	.0540	$\cong 74$ words/minute

Grouped Data

For grouped data, the harmonic mean may be computed from the following formula:

$$H = \frac{\Sigma f}{\Sigma \dfrac{f}{M}}$$

f = frequency
M = midpoint

For example:
Calculate the harmonic mean for the following distribution:

Class	f	M	Solution f/M
4 and less than 8	5	6	5/6 = .833
8 and less than 12	3	10	3/10 = .300
12 and less than 16	2	14	2/14 = .143
16 and less than 20	10	18	10/18 = .556
20 and less than 24	4	22	4/22 = .182

$$\Sigma f = 24$$

2.014
H = 24/2.014
= 11.917

The Use of the Harmonic Mean

Sometimes it is not possible to assign a weight or system of weights to a variable. The advantage of the harmonic mean lies in the fact that it requires no weights and thereby avoids the problem of weight selection completely. Additionally, the harmonic mean will find application to problems involving rates of time such as miles per hour, production per day, etc.

Comparison of the Three Means (X, G, and H)

Arithmetic Mean

1. The value of the arithmetic mean is based on all observations including the extremes; however, each observation has the same weight.

2. X can be computed even if any value of the observations is zero or negative.

Geometric Mean

1. It is based on all observations; however, it gives less weight to the extremely large values.

2. If one observation of the variable is zero, G is zero; and if any observation is negative, G will be an imaginary value.
$$\sqrt{(5)\,(0)} = \sqrt{0} = 0$$
$$\sqrt{(5)\,(-2)} = \sqrt{-10}$$

Harmonic Mean

1. It is based on all observations, but it gives even less weight to the extremely large values than does the geometric mean.

2. Harmonic mean becomes indetermined if one of the observations is equal to zero.
$(1/0) = \infty$).

Relationship Among the Three Means

The relationship among the arithmetic mean, the geometric mean, and the harmonic mean can be stated as follows:

$$H \leq G \leq \overline{X}$$

Example 2.13:   If X is a variable and assumes the following values: 4, 5, 6, 9; a computation of X, G, and H will show the previous relationship among the three different types of mean:

Solution:

X	Log X	1/X
4	0.6021	.25
5	0.6990	.20
6	0.7782	.17
9	0.9542	.11

$$\Sigma X = 24 \qquad \Sigma \log G = 3.0335 \qquad \Sigma 1/X = .73$$
$$n = 4 \qquad\qquad n = 4 \qquad\qquad n = 4$$

$$\overline{X} = \frac{\Sigma X}{n} \qquad \text{Log } G = \frac{\Sigma \log G}{n} \qquad H = \frac{n}{\Sigma \frac{1}{X}}$$

$$= 24/4 \qquad\qquad = 3.0335/4$$
$$\overline{X} = 6 \qquad\qquad G = 5.72 \qquad\qquad = 4/.73 = 5.5$$

$$\text{or } H \leq G \leq \overline{X}$$
$$5.5 \leq 5.72 \leq 6.0$$

2.   MEDIAN

Although the arithmetic mean is commonly used, it is affected by extreme values in the variable. There are times when the data lends itself to open-end class intervals (100 or more, less than 10, etc.). In such cases it will not be possible to calculate the arithmetic mean. There is another measure of central location which may be applied — the median. The median is affected by its **position** in an array rather than by the value of each observation of the variable.

The median is defined as that value which divides the distribution into two equal parts: half of the values are smaller than or equal to the median, while the other half are larger than or equal to the median.

To calculate the median, we still differentiate between ungrouped and grouped data.

Ungrouped Data

In working with ungrouped data, the first step in locating the median is to arrange the values of X in either ascending or descending order. Determine the value which divides the array into two equal parts; this value is the median. In the following two examples the median is calculated for both an odd number of observations[11] and an even number of observations [12] of the variable X.

---

(11)   A formula may be used to determine the location of the median for *odd* ungrouped numbers of observations such as:

$$\text{Med} = X_{\frac{n+1}{2}}, \quad n = \text{number of observations.}$$

(12)   A formula may be used to determine the location of the median for *even* ungrouped numbers of observations:

$$\text{Med} = \left(X_{\frac{n}{2}} + X_{\frac{n}{2}+1} \right) / 2$$

Example 2.15 (odd number of observations): Let X be the annual salaries of 7 teachers in an elementary school: $7500, $6900, $7200, $8000, $6750, $7600, $6500. Find the median salary of this group.

Solution: To solve this problem, arrange these values either in ascending or descending order:

```
   X
$6500
 6750
 6900
 7200 ————————Median = 7200
 7500
 7600
 8000
```

Example 2.16 (even number of observations): Let X be the annual salaries of the first 6 teachers shown in Example 2.15: $7500, $6900, $7200, $8000, $6750, $7600. Find the median salary.

Solution: X is arranged in ascending order:

```
$6750
 6900
 7200
—————————Median = 7200 + 7500 = 14700 = 7350
 7500                  ——————    —————
 7600                     2        2
 8000
```

Grouped Data

Presentation of a mass of data is simplified by classifying such data into a frequency distribution. To find the median for a frequency distribution (or grouped data) the following formula is applied:

$$Med = L_{med} + \frac{\frac{\Sigma f}{2} - F_{Lmed}}{f_{med}} \ i_{med}$$

where
Med= Median

L_{med} = Real lower limit (or the boundary) of the class in which the median falls.

Σf = Sum of frequencies or the number of observations contained in the variable.

F_{Lmed} = Cumulative frequencies less than the lower limit of the median class.

f_{med} = Frequency of the median class.

i_{med} = Class interval of the median class.

Example 2.17: The following is a frequency distribution of the weight of 100 females. Calculate the median weight.

Weight(lbs.)	Frequency	Cumulative Frequencies(F)
110-119	5	5
120-129	18	23
130-139	12	35
140-149	27	62 Median class
150-159	15	77
160-169	15	92
170-179	8	100

$$\Sigma f = 100$$

Solution: Before applying the median formula for grouped data, we must first determine the median class, the class in which the median falls.

We know that the median is a value which divides the frequency distribution into two equal parts. Therefore, if we divide the sum of the observations by two $\frac{\Sigma f}{2}$ we know in which class interval the median will be located. In our example, $\frac{\Sigma f}{2} = 100/2 = 50$. This tells us to examine the cumulative frequencies until we find the class interval which contains the 50th observation.[13] In the example, the 50th observation falls in the class interval 140-149. This, then, is the median class. Given this information, we may now apply the formula:

$$\text{Med} = L_{med} + \frac{\frac{\Sigma f}{2} - F_{Lmed}}{f_{med}} \; i_{med}$$

$L_{med}{}^{[14]} = 139.5$

$\Sigma f/2 = 50$

$F_{Lmed} = 35 \text{ or } (5 + 18 + 12)$

$f_{med} = 27$

$i_{med} = 149.5 - 139.5 = 10$

$$\text{Med} = 139.5 + \frac{50 - 35}{27} \; (10)$$

$$\text{Med} = 139.5 + \frac{15}{27} \; (10)$$

$$= 139.5 + 5.6$$

$$= 145.1$$

Notice that the value of the median (145.1) is contained in the median class interval between 140-149.

---

(13)   It is true that we have an even number of observations (100) and hence an average of the values of the 50th and the 51st observations will be the median. However, in selecting $\Sigma f/2$ to equal $100/2 = 50$ in our example, we simply want to determine the median class. The value of the median will be determined by the formula.

(14)   The lower limit of the median class is 140, the upper limit of the immediately preceding class is 139; hence, the real lower limit of the median class (L_{med}) is 139.5. The one unit difference between 139 and 140 is divided between the two classes to find the boundaries (real limit) or 139.5.

3. MODE

The mode is that value in a frequency distribution which occurs most often. In certain distributions the mode may not exist[15]; or if it exists, it may not be unique such as in the case of a bimodal or trimodal distribution.[16]

Ungrouped Data

To find the mode for ungrouped data, it is helpful but not essential to arrange the values of the variable into ascending or descending order. Example 2.18: Let X be a variable of 18 observations such as 8, 18, 9, 10, 18, 15, 20, 17, 20, 15, 16, 20, 15, 14, 13, 15, 20, 15. Find the mode.

Solution:

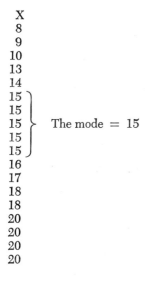

```
X
8
9
10
13
14
15 ⎫
15 ⎪
15 ⎬  The mode = 15
15 ⎪
15 ⎭
16
17
18
18
20
20
20
20
```

---

(15) The mode does not exist if the distribution is rectangular or if the distribution of the variable is as follows:

The mode is any value between X_1 and X_2; it is not unique to the extent that it does not exist.

(16) A bimodal distribution is one that has two identical peaks as shown in the following diagram:

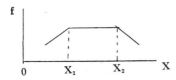

while a trimodal distribution has three peaks.

Grouped Data

The mode of the grouped data falls in the modal class. But what is the modal class? It is the class that has the highest number of frequencies.

Example:

Class	Frequency	
10-14	5	
15-19	22	
20-24	18	
25-29	28	This is the Modal Class.
30-34	16	

The class of (25-29) is the one which has the highest frequencies; therefore, it is the modal class for this distribution.

The mode is contained in the modal class, but to determine its value for grouped data, we have to apply the following formula:

$$Mo = L_{mo} + \frac{f_{mo} - f_1}{2f_{mo} - (f_1 + f_2)} \, i_{mo}$$

where
Mo = the mode
L_{mo} = real lower limit of the modal class
f_{mo} = frequency of the modal class
f_1 = frequency of the class immediately preceding the modal class
f_2 = frequency of the class immediately following the modal class
i_{mo} = class interval of the modal class

Example 2.19: The following is the age distribution of 70 students in a home economics class:

Class	Frequency	
15-19	3	
20-24	10	
25-29	12	
30-34	25	The Modal Class
35-39	15	
40-44	5	

Find the modal age of this group.

Solution: Before applying the formula for grouped data to calculate the mode, first determine modal class, which in the example is the class of (30-34).

Now, apply the formula:

$$Mo = L_{mo} + \frac{f_{mo} - f_1}{2f_{mo} - (f_1 + f_2)} \, i_{mo}$$

$$= 29.5 + \frac{25 - 12}{2(25) - (12 + 15)} \, (5)$$

$$= 29.5 + \frac{13}{23} \, (5)$$

$$= 29.5 + 2.8$$

$$= 32.3$$

Notice that the mode[17] falls within the limits of the modal class (30-34).

Relationship between the mean, the median, and the mode
The mean, the median, and the mode are each single values which tend to be located at the center of the distribution — hence, the name measures of central location. In a symmetrical or bell-shaped distribution, the magnitude of the mean, median, and mode will be equal and will be located at the exact center as demonstrated by the following example.

Example 2.20: The following shows the distribution of grades of 50 students in an economic course. Find the relationship between the mean, the median, and the mode.

Solution

Class (Grade)	f	M	Mf	F	
30 and under 40	2	35	70	2	
40 and under 50	6	45	270	8	
50 and under 60	10	55	550	18	
60 and under 70	14	65	910	32	Median/Modal Class
70 and under 80	10	75	750	42	
80 and under 90	6	85	510	48	
90 and under 100	2	95	190	50	
	$\Sigma f = 50$		$\Sigma fM = 3250$		

$$\overline{X} = \Sigma Mf / \Sigma f = 3250/50 = 65$$

$$Med = L_{med} + \frac{\Sigma f/2 - F_{Lmed}}{f_{med}} \, i_{med}$$

$$= 60 + \frac{25 - 18}{14} \, 10$$

$$= 60 + 70/14 = 65$$

$$Mo = L_{mo} + \frac{f_{mo} - f_1}{2f_{mo} - (f_1 + f_2)} \, i_{mo}$$

$$= 60 + \frac{14 - 10}{28 - 20} \, 10$$

$$= 60 + 40/8 = 65$$

$\overline{X}$ = Median
= Mode
Figure 2-2

---

(17) The value of the mode (32.3) can be interpolated graphically as shown in the diagram, representing the data of the distribution presented in Example 2.19.

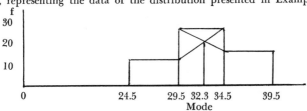

Mode

From this example, we can conclude that if the distribution is symmetrical as in Figure 2-2, then the following relationship exists: $\overline{X}$ = Median = Mode. The magnitude of the three measures of central location divides the frequency distribution into two equal halves.

However, if the distribution is asymmetric, or skewed, the relationship of the three measures of location will depend upon whether the skewness is positive or negative. If the distribution is positively skewed,[18] the relationship becomes:

$$\text{Mode} \; < \; \text{Median} \; < \; \text{Mean}$$

If the distribution is negatively skewed,[19] the relationship becomes:

$$\text{Mean} \; < \; \text{Median} \; < \; \text{Mode}$$

The following two examples will serve to illustrate:

Assume that the grades of 50 students in an economic course are distributed as follows:

Solution

Class	f	M	Mf	F	
30 and less than 40	4	35	140	4	
40 and less than 50	8	45	360	12	
50 and less than 60	15	55	825	27	Median/Modal Class
60 and less than 70	13	65	845	40	
70 and less than 80	5	75	375	45	
80 and less than 90	3	85	255	48	
90 and less than 100	2	95	190	50	
	$\Sigma f = 50$		$\Sigma Mf = 2990$		

$$\overline{X} = \frac{\Sigma Mf}{\Sigma f} = \frac{2990}{50} = 59.8$$

$$\text{Med} = L_{med} + \frac{\Sigma f/2 - F_{Lmed}}{f_{med}} \quad i_{med}$$

$$= 50 + \frac{25 - 12}{15} \; 10$$

$$\text{Med} = 50 + 8.7 = 58.7$$

$$\text{Mo} = L_{mo} + \frac{f_{mo} - f_1}{2f_{mo} - (f_1 + f_2)} \quad i_{mo}$$

$$= 50 + \frac{15 - 8}{30 - 21} \; (10)$$

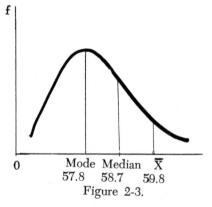

	Mode	Median	$\overline{X}$
	57.8	58.7	59.8

Figure 2-3.

$$\text{Mo} = 50 + 7.8 = 57.8$$

The result of computing the mean, the median, and the mode is summarized in the following double inequality:

$$57.8 \; < \; 58.7 \; < \; 59.8$$

or

$$\text{Mode} \; < \; \text{Median} \; < \; \overline{X}$$

A graphical presentation of the relationship between the mode, median, and mean in a positively skewed distribution is shown in Figure 2-3.

Our next example examines the same relationship in a negatively skewed distribution:

Assume that the grades from the previous example are distributed as follows:

Solution

Class	f	M	Mf	F	
30 and under 40	2	35	70	2	
40 and under 50	3	45	135	5	
50 and under 60	5	55	275	10	
60 and under 70	13	65	845	23	
70 and under 80	15	75	1125	38	Median/Modal Class
80 and under 90	8	85	680	46	
90 and under 100	4	95	380	50	

$$\Sigma f = 50 \qquad \Sigma Mf = 3510$$

$$\overline{X} = \Sigma Mf / \Sigma f = 3510/50 = 70.2$$

$$\text{Med} = L_{med} + \frac{\Sigma f/2 - F_{Lmed}}{f_{med}} \, i_{med}$$

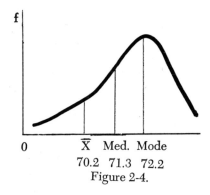

$$= 70 + \frac{25 - 23}{15} \, (10)$$

$$\text{Med} = 70 + 1.3 = 71.3$$

$$\text{Mo} = L_{mo} + \frac{f_{mo} - f_1}{2f_{mo} - (f_1 + f_2)} \, i_{mo}$$

$$= 70 + \frac{15 - 13}{30 - 21} \, (10)$$

$$\text{Mo.} = 70 + 2.2 = 72.2$$

$$\begin{array}{ccc} 0 & \overline{X} & \text{Med.} & \text{Mode} \\ & 70.2 & 71.3 & 72.2 \end{array}$$

Figure 2-4.

Expressing the values of the mean, median and mode in a negatively skewed distribution yields the following inequality:

$$70.2 < 71.3 < 72.2$$
$$\overline{X} < \text{Median} < \text{Mode}$$

This relationship is graphically presented in Figure 2-4.

On the other hand, the relationship among the mean, the median, and the mode can be expressed by the following equation:

$$\text{Mode} = \text{Mean} - 3(\text{Mean} - \text{Median})$$

This equation will help us to estimate the mean, or the median, or the mode provided that the value of the other two measures are available. Most importantly, this equation is very useful to estimate the mode if it does not exist or if it is not unique.

II. Measures of Dispersion (or variation)

The mean, the median, and the mode, presented in the previous section are constants calculated to represent the values of observed data. Observations may differ from any of these constants (e.g. observed data differ from its mean); such differences are called deviations or variations[20]. Measures of central location provide no information concerning the variability of the data. Therefore, another measure which describes the variability or scatter of observations from their mean is called a measure of dispersion (or variation).

Measures of dispersion are of many types; three of them, namely, the range, the mean or median deviation, and the standard deviation, are presented in this section. Each measure is defined and calculated for ungrouped as well as grouped data.

1. Range
The range is very simple to calculate, but it is less reliable than other measures of variation because it depends on two extreme values: the highest and the lowest. As a matter of fact, the range is the difference between the highest and the lowest values.

For **ungrouped** data, the range is defined as:
Range = Highest value — Lowest value
Example 2.21:
Let X be the annual income of 10 families: 17,000; 10,000; 20,000; 5,000; 6,000; 9,500; 15,000; 4,000; 16,000; 25,000.
Range = 25,000 — 4,000 = $21,000
or: The range is between $4,000 and $25,000
For **grouped** data, the range is the difference between the lower limit of the first class and the upper limit of the last class.
Example 2.22:   Assume that the income of 50 families in Example 2.21 are distributed as follows:

Class	Frequency
3,000 - 7,999	10
8,000 - 12,999	4
13,000 - 17,999	18
18,000 - 22,999	11
23,000 - 27,999	7

Range = 27,999 — 3,000 = $24,999
or: The range is between $3,000 and $27,999

2. Mean (and Median) Deviation
Deviations have been defined before as the differences between observed data and its mean or median; for example:
X — $\overline{X}$ = deviation of X from its mean
X — Median = deviation of X from its median
For every observation there exists a deviation that can be positive, negative, or zero. A measure of dispersion is a single value that represents these deviations. In other words, a measure of dispersion is an average of these deviations and can be calculated by the following formula:

$$\frac{\text{Total deviations}}{\text{Number of observations (or deviations)}}$$

---

[20] Deviation or variation of the variable X from its mean ($\overline{X}$) is defined as: X — $\overline{X}$ or x.

$$\text{Mean Deviation}^{(21)} = \frac{\Sigma(X - \overline{X})}{n}$$

$$\text{Median Deviation} = \frac{\Sigma(X - \text{Median})}{n}$$

These two formulas may be used to calculate the mean and the median deviation except that total deviations equal zero. Both $\Sigma(X - \overline{X})$ and $\Sigma(X - \text{Median})$ equal zero. Therefore, summation of the **absolute** values of the deviations is used to calculate the mean and median deviations for **ungrouped** data:

$$\text{Mean Deviation} = \frac{\Sigma|X - \overline{X}|}{n}$$

$$\text{Median Deviation} = \frac{\Sigma |X - \text{Median}|}{n}$$

Example 2.23:
Let X be the time in minutes it takes 15 secretaries to type a particular letter:
X: 13, 12, 5, 10, 6, 8, 14, 6, 12, 10, 11, 11, 12, 9, 11.
Calculate the mean and median deviation.

Solution: 1. Find the mean: $\overline{X} = \dfrac{\Sigma X}{n}$

$$= \frac{150}{15} = 10$$

2. Find the median: Arrange the data in ascending or descending order and locate the median $= 11$.

3. Find $| X - \overline{X} |$ and $| X - \text{Median} |$ as shown below:

X	$\lvert X - \overline{X} \rvert$	$\lvert X - \text{Med} \rvert$	
5	5	6	
6	4	5	
6	4	5	
8	2	3	
9	1	2	
10	0	1	Mean Deviation $= \frac{32}{15} = 2.133$
10	0	1	
11	1	0	Median $=$
11	1	0	
11	1	0	Median Deviation $= \frac{31}{15} = 2.067$
12	2	1	
12	2	1	
12	2	1	
13	3	2	
14	4	3	
150	32	31	

(21) $\dfrac{\Sigma (X - \overline{X})}{n}$ is called the first moment measured about the mean and its value is always zero.

For **grouped** data:

Mean and median deviation can be calculated for grouped data (frequency distributions) by applying the following formulas:

$$\text{Mean Deviation} = \frac{\Sigma \, |M - \overline{X}| \; f}{\Sigma f} \qquad ; M = \text{class midpoint}$$

$$\text{Median Deviation} = \frac{\Sigma \, |M - \text{Median}| \; f}{\Sigma f} \qquad ; M = \text{class midpoint}$$

Example 2.24:

The following is a distribution of weights for 100 females. Calculate mean and median deviation.

Weight (lbs)	Frequency	M	Mf
110 - 119	5	114.5	572.5
120 - 129	18	124.5	2241.0
130 - 139	12	134.5	1614.0
140 - 149	27	144.5	3901.5
150 - 159	15	154.5	2317.5
160 - 169	16	164.5	2632.0
170 - 179	7	174.5	1221.5
	$\Sigma f = \overline{100}$		$\Sigma Mf = \overline{14500.0}$

Solution:

1. Calculate the mean of X: $\overline{X} = \dfrac{\Sigma Mf}{\Sigma f} = \dfrac{14500}{100} = 145.0$

2. Calculate the median of X: Median = 145.1 (Example 2.17)

3. Find $\Sigma \, |M - \overline{X}| \, f$ and $\Sigma \, |M - \text{Med}| \, f$ as follows:

Class	f	M	$|M - \overline{X}|$	$|M - \overline{X}| \, f$	$|M - \text{Med.}|$	$|M - \text{Med.}| \, f$
110 - 119	5	114.5	30.5	152.5	30.6	153.0
120 - 129	18	124.5	20.5	369.0	20.6	370.8
130 - 139	12	134.5	10.5	126.0	10.6	127.2
140 - 149	27	144.5	.5	13.5	.6	16.2
150 - 159	15	154.5	9.5	142.5	9.4	141.0
160 - 169	16	164.5	19.5	312.0	19.4	310.4
170 - 179	7	174.5	29.5	206.5	29.4	205.8
	$\overline{100}$			$\overline{1322.0}$		$\overline{1324.4}$

$$\text{Mean Deviation} = \frac{1322.0}{100} = 13.220$$

$$\text{Median Deviation} = \frac{1324.4}{100} = 13.244$$

3. Standard Deviation

The standard deviation is the most important measure of dispersion. It is similar to the mean deviation where deviations are measured from the mean. Standard deviation is an average of these deviations. As mentioned before, the summation of these deviations, $\Sigma(X - \overline{X})$, is equal to zero; that is why, in the calculation of the mean deviation, the absolute values of the deviations are used. In the case of standard deviation, deviations of the variable X from its mean $(X - \overline{X})$ are squared $(X - \overline{X})^2$, and the average squared deviations[22], $\dfrac{\Sigma(X - \overline{X})^2}{n}$, is called the variance.

The standard deviation is the non-negative root of the variance: $\sqrt{\dfrac{\Sigma(X - \overline{X})^2}{n}}$

The standard deviation for a population is denoted by the lower case of the Greek letter sigma (σ), while the standard deviation of a sample is denoted by small s. Accordingly, the standard deviation formulas are as follows:

For the Population: $\quad \sigma = \sqrt{\dfrac{\Sigma(X - \overline{X})^2}{N}}$

And for the Sample: $\quad s = \sqrt{\dfrac{\Sigma(X - \overline{X})^2}{n}}$

Ungrouped data:

To calculate the standard deviation for ungrouped data, the following formulas can be used:

1. General Formula:

$$s = \sqrt{\dfrac{\Sigma X^2}{n} - \left(\dfrac{\Sigma X}{n}\right)^2}$$

2. Simplified Formulas[23]:

a. $\quad s = \sqrt{\dfrac{\Sigma X'^2}{n} - \left(\dfrac{\Sigma X'}{n}\right)^2} \qquad : X' = X - C; C \text{ is a constant}$

b. $\quad s = K\sqrt{\dfrac{\Sigma X''^2}{n} - \left(\dfrac{\Sigma X''}{n}\right)^2} \; ; X'' = \dfrac{X - C}{n}$

$\quad ; C \text{ and } K \text{ are constants}$

The general formula of the standard deviation has been derived from the original formulas: $s = \sqrt{\dfrac{\Sigma(X - \overline{X})^2}{n}}$ as follows:

$$\Sigma(X - \overline{X})^2 = \Sigma(X^2 - 2\overline{X}X + \overline{X}^2)$$
$$= \Sigma X^2 - 2\overline{X}\Sigma X + n\overline{X}^2$$
$$= \Sigma X^2 - 2\overline{X}\Sigma X + n\dfrac{\Sigma X}{n}(\overline{X})$$

---

(22) $\dfrac{\Sigma(X - \overline{X})^2}{n}$ is called the second moment about the mean which is the variance.

(23) Rules to use simplified formulas for the standard deviation are similar to those stated for the shortcut method to calculate the mean (page 17). The only difference is that subtraction (or addition) of a constant from each value of X will not affect the variability of X; therefore, there is no need to compensate for that in the formulas as shown in:

$s = \sqrt{\dfrac{\Sigma X'^2}{n} - \left(\dfrac{\Sigma X'}{n}\right)^2} \quad ; X' = X - C; C \text{ is a constant.}$

$$= \Sigma X^2 - 2\overline{X}\Sigma X + \overline{X}\Sigma X$$
$$= \Sigma X^2 - \overline{X}\Sigma X$$

$$= \Sigma X^2 - \frac{\Sigma X}{n}(\Sigma X)$$

$$= \Sigma X^2 - \frac{(\Sigma X)^2}{n}$$

hence, $s = \sqrt{\dfrac{\Sigma(X - \overline{X})^2}{n}}$

$$= \sqrt{\frac{\Sigma X^2}{n} - \frac{(\Sigma X)^2}{n^2}}$$

$$= \sqrt{\frac{\Sigma X^2}{n} - \left(\frac{\Sigma X}{n}\right)^2}$$

Example 2.25:

Let X be the bi-weekly salaries (in dollars) of ten teachers in a high school.

X: 250, 230, 300, 410, 260, 250, 300, 300, 410, 300.

Calculate the mean and standard deviation for this group.

Solution: 1. Calculate the mean: $\overline{X} = \dfrac{\Sigma X}{n} = \dfrac{3010}{10} = \$301.00$

2. Calculate the standard deviation:

(1) by using the general formula:

X	X²
250	62500
230	52900
300	90000
410	168100
260	67600
250	62500
300	90000
300	90000
410	168100
300	90000
3010	941700

$$s = \sqrt{\frac{\Sigma X^2}{n} - \left(\frac{\Sigma X}{n}\right)^2}$$

$$= \sqrt{\frac{941700}{10} - \left(\frac{3010}{10}\right)^2}$$

$$= \sqrt{94170 - (301)^2}$$
$$= \sqrt{3569}$$
$$= \$59.75$$

(2) by using the simplified formulas: (C = 300, K = 10)

a. $s = \sqrt{\dfrac{\Sigma X'^2}{n} - \left(\dfrac{\Sigma X'}{n}\right)^2}$

X	X – C	X'	X'²
250	250 - 300 =	−50	2500
230	230 - 300 =	−70	4900
300	300 - 300 =	0	0
410	410 - 300 =	110	12100
260	260 - 300 =	−40	1600
250	250 - 300 =	−50	2500
300	300 - 300 =	0	0
300	300 - 300 =	0	0
410	410 - 300 =	110	12100
300	300 - 300 =	0	0
3010		10	35700

$$s = \sqrt{\frac{35700}{10} - \left(\frac{10}{10}\right)^2}$$
$$= \sqrt{3570 - 1}$$
$$= \sqrt{3569}$$
$$= \$59.75$$

b. $\quad s = K \sqrt{\frac{\Sigma X''^2}{n} - \left(\frac{\Sigma X''}{n}\right)^2}$

X	$\dfrac{X-C}{K}$	X''	X''²
230	(230-300) ÷ 10 =	−7	49
250	(250-300) ÷ 10 =	−5	25
300	(300-300) ÷ 10 =	0	0
410	(410-300) ÷ 10 =	11	121
260	(260-300) ÷ 10 =	−4	16
250	(250-300) ÷ 10 =	−5	25
300	(300-300) ÷ 10 =	0	0
300	(300-300) ÷ 10 =	0	0
410	(410-300) ÷ 10 =	11	121
300	(300-300) ÷ 10 =	0	0
		1	357

$$s = 10 \sqrt{\frac{357}{10} - \left(\frac{1}{10}\right)^2}$$
$$= 10 \sqrt{35.70 - .01}$$
$$= 10 \sqrt{35.69}$$
$$= 10 \ (5.975)$$
$$= 59.75$$

Interpretation of the standard deviation:

The results of the previous problem are:

$$\text{Mean} = \overline{X} = \$301.00$$
$$\text{Standard Deviation} = s = \$59.75$$

The question is what these results mean. The magnitude of X shows that the average bi-weekly salaries for this group is $301.00. Some salaries are higher while others are lower than that average. The average variation of these salaries from its mean is $59.75, the magnitude of the standard deviation. If we deviate one standard deviation from the mean in both directions, an interval AB is constructed as shown in Figure 2-4.

A		B
241.25	301.00	360.75
$\overline{X} - s$	$\overline{X}$	$\overline{X} + s$
301.00 − 59.75		301.00 + 59.75

Figure 2-4: The relationship between X and s.

If the distribution of the salaries is normal, then this interval $\overline{X} \pm 1s$ should contain about 68.26% of the observations, and AB can be described as a 68.26 confidence interval.[24] In our example the interval AB contains 70% of the observations because between the two limits of the interval, \$241.25 and \$360.75, the following seven values of the ten fall: 250, 300, 260, 250, 300, 300, 300.

Grouped data:

For grouped data, the standard deviation can be calculated by using one of the following formulas:

1. General Formula:

$$s = \sqrt{\frac{\Sigma M^2 f}{\Sigma f} - \left(\frac{\Sigma M f}{\Sigma f}\right)^2} \qquad ; M = \text{class midpoint}$$

2. Simplified Formulas:

a. $\quad s = \sqrt{\dfrac{\Sigma M'^2 f}{\Sigma f} - \left(\dfrac{\Sigma M'f}{\Sigma f}\right)^2} \qquad ; M' = M - C, \ C \text{ is a constant.}$

b. $\quad s = K\sqrt{\dfrac{\Sigma M''^2 f}{\Sigma f} - \left(\dfrac{\Sigma M''f}{\Sigma f}\right)^2} \qquad ; M'' = \dfrac{M - C}{K}$

$; C \text{ and } K \text{ are constants.}$

Example 2.26:

The following is a frequency distribution of the monthly salaries in dollars of 125 instructors at a state college:

Salaries (\$)	No. of Instructors
800 and under 1000	10
1000 and under 1200	20
1200 and under 1400	40
1400 and under 1600	22
1600 and under 1800	18
1800 and under 2000	5
2000 and under 2200	5
2200 and under 2400	3
2400 and under 2600	2
	125

Calculate the mean and the standard deviation.

Solution:

1. The mean is a part of the general formula: $\quad \overline{X} = \dfrac{\Sigma M f}{\Sigma f}$

2. Calculate the standard deviation by applying the general formula:

---

(24) Normal distribution and confidence intervals are presented in later chapters in this book.

Class	f	M	Mf	$M^2f = M \times Mf$
800 - 1000	10	900	9000	8100000
1000 - 1200	20	1100	22000	24200000
1200 - 1400	40	1300	52000	67600000
1400 - 1600	22	1500	33000	49500000
1600 - 1800	18	1700	30600	52020000
1800 - 2000	5	1900	9500	18050000
2000 - 2200	5	2100	10500	22050000
2200 - 2400	3	2300	6900	15870000
2400 - 2600	2	2500	5000	12500000
	125		178500	269890000

$$\overline{X} = \frac{\Sigma Mf}{\Sigma f} = \frac{178500}{125} = 1428.00$$

$$s = \sqrt{\frac{269890000}{125} - \left(\frac{178500}{125}\right)^2}$$

$$= \sqrt{2159120 - 2039184}$$
$$= \sqrt{119936}$$
$$= \$346.32$$

3. Calculate the standard deviation by the simplified formulas:

a. $\quad s = \sqrt{\dfrac{\Sigma M'^2 f}{\Sigma f} - \left(\dfrac{\Sigma M'f}{\Sigma f}\right)^2}$ $\qquad ; C = 1300$

Class	f	M	M — C =	M'	M'f	$M'^2f = M' \times M'f$
800 - 1000	10	900	900 - 1300 =	—400	—4000	1600000
1000 - 1200	20	1100	1100 - 1300 =	—200	—4000	800000
1200 - 1400	40	1300	1300 - 1300 =	0	0	0
1400 - 1600	22	1500	1500 - 1300 =	200	4400	880000
1600 - 1800	18	1700	1700 - 1300 =	400	7200	2880000
1800 - 2000	5	1900	1900 - 1300 =	600	3000	1800000
2000 - 2200	5	2100	2100 - 1300 =	800	4000	3200000
2200 - 2400	3	2300	2300 - 1300 =	1000	3000	3000000
2400 - 2600	2	2500	2500 - 1300 =	1200	2400	2880000
	125				16000	17040000

$$\overline{X} = C + \frac{\Sigma M'f}{\Sigma f} = 1300 + \frac{16000}{125}$$

$$= 1300 + 128$$
$$= 1428$$

$$s = \sqrt{\frac{17040000}{125} - \left(\frac{16000}{125}\right)^2}$$

$$= \sqrt{136320 - 16384}$$
$$= \sqrt{119936}$$
$$= \$346.32$$

42

b. $s = K \sqrt{\dfrac{\Sigma M''^2 f}{\Sigma f} - \left(\dfrac{\Sigma M'' f}{\Sigma f}\right)^2}$; $C = 1300$, $K = 100$

Class	f	M	$\dfrac{M-C}{K}$		$= M''$	$M''f$	$M''f \times M''$ $= M''^2 f$
800 - 1000	10	900	(900 - 1300) $\div$ 100	=	−4	−40	160
1000 - 1200	20	1100	(1100 - 1300) $\div$ 100	=	−2	−40	80
1200 - 1400	40	1300	(1300 - 1300) $\div$ 100	=	0	0	0
1400 - 1600	22	1500	(1500 - 1300) $\div$ 100	=	2	44	88
1600 - 1800	18	1700	(1700 - 1300) $\div$ 100	=	4	72	288
1800 - 2000	5	1900	(1900 - 1300) $\div$ 100	=	6	30	180
2000 - 2200	5	2100	(2100 - 1300) $\div$ 100	=	8	40	320
2200 - 2400	3	2300	(2300 - 1300) $\div$ 100	=	10	30	300
2400 - 2600	2	2500	(2500 - 1300) $\div$ 100	=	12	24	288
	125					160	1704

$\overline{X} = C + K \dfrac{\Sigma Mf}{\Sigma f}$

$= 1300 + 100$

$= 1300 + 100(1.28)$

$= 1300 + 128$

$= 1428$

$s = 100 \sqrt{\dfrac{1704}{125} - \left(\dfrac{160}{125}\right)^2}$

$= 100 \sqrt{13.632 - 1.638}$

$= 100 \sqrt{11.9936}$

$= 100\ (3.4632)$

$= \$346.32$

Measures of Relative Dispersion

Standard deviation, as well as other measures of dispersion, provide information concerning the variability or the scatter of the data in an absolute sense. There exist situations where it is useful to compare the scatter of two frequency distributions that have different units of measurement (e.g. dollars and hours). For such comparisons, a relative rather than absolute measure of variation is used. The most important measure of relative dispersion or variation is the V-coefficient.

$V = \dfrac{\sigma}{\mu}$ or $V = \dfrac{s}{\overline{X}}$

Example 2.27:
The following is a frequency distribution for all salaried employees of two companies:

Weekly Wage ($)	Company A	Company B
80 and under 100	5	20
100 and under 120	20	36
120 and under 140	18	34
140 and under 160	7	10
	50	100

Find out which company has the greater scatter.
Solution:
To compare the variability of these two frequency distributions, V_a and V_b are needed.

$$V_a = \frac{s_a}{\overline{X}_a} \qquad\qquad V_b = \frac{s_b}{\overline{X}_b}$$

| | Company A | | | | Company B | | |
Class	f	M	Mf	M²f	f	M	Mf	M²f
80 - 100	5	90	450	40500	20	90	1800	162000
100 - 120	20	110	2200	242000	36	110	3960	435600
120 - 140	18	130	2340	304200	34	130	4420	574600
140 - 160	7	150	1050	157500	10	150	1500	225000
	50		6040	744200	100		11680	1397200

Company A   **Company B**

$$\overline{X}_a = \frac{6040}{50} \doteq 120.80 \qquad\qquad \overline{X}_b = \frac{11680}{100} = 116.80$$

$$s_a = \sqrt{\frac{744200}{50} - (120.80)^2} \qquad s_b = \sqrt{\frac{1397200}{100} - (116.80)^2}$$

$$= \sqrt{14884 - 14592.64} \qquad\qquad = \sqrt{13972 - 13642.24}$$
$$= \sqrt{291.36} \qquad\qquad\qquad = \sqrt{329.76}$$
$$= 17.07 \qquad\qquad\qquad\qquad = 18.16$$

$$V_a = \frac{17.07}{120.80} = .1413 \qquad\qquad V_b = \frac{18.16}{116.80} = .1555$$

The magnitude of V_b is greater than that of V_a, which indicates that the frequency distribution of Company B has a greater variation in wage than that of Company A.

Example 2.28:
   In this example two frequency distributions with different units of measurement will be compared. Suppose that the mean and standard deviation of the age distribution for the employees of Company A are: $X = 40$ years and $s = 15$ years. Would you say that there is more dispersion in weekly wages or in age?
Solution:
   We need to compare the coefficient of variation of weekly wages with that of the age distribution.
   1. Variability of weekly wages distribution for employees of Company A has been calculated in the previous example:
$$V_a = .1413$$
   2. Variability of age distribution for the same company is:

$$V_{age} = \frac{s}{\overline{X}} = \frac{15}{40} = .375$$

Comparing V_a and V_{age}, it is obvious that the employees of Company A exhibit more variation in age than in weekly wages.

III.   Measures of Skewness and Kurtosis:

Measures of central location and of dispersion provide information concerning the average value of a distribution and the variability of the data about the mean, but nothing about the skewness or the peakedness of that frequency distribution.

a.   Measures of Skewness:

It is often important to know whether a frequency distribution is symmetrical (normal) or non-symmetrical (skewed). This can be determined by calculating the coefficient of skewness. The popular formula of skewness[25] developed by the famous statistician, Karl Pearson is:

$$Sk_P = \frac{Mean - Mode}{Standard\ Deviation} = \frac{\overline{X} - Mode}{s}$$

However, if the mode does not exist or is not unique the following formula may be used:[26]

$$Sk_P = \frac{3(Mean - Median)}{Standard\ Deviation} = \frac{3(\overline{X} - Med)}{s}$$

The magnitude of the skewness coefficient indicates the degree of skewness. If the coefficient is zero, then the frequency distribution is symmetrical; if it is different than zero, then it is skewed. The sign associated with the magnitude of the skewness coefficient refers to the type of skewness. The positive sign indicates that the distribution is positively skewed, or it has a tail to the right; the negative sign indicates a negatively skewed distribution with a tail to the left.

b.   Measures of Kurtosis:

Measures of kurtosis provide information concerning the peakedness of a frequency distribution. The most important coefficient of kurtosis is Beta two (β_2) or sometimes called Alpha four (α_4). The magnitude of β_2 determines one of three types of distribution with different degrees of peakedness. If $\beta_2 = 3$, then we have a Mesokurtic distribution; if $\beta_2 > 3$, the distribution is Leptokurtic; and if $\beta_2 < 3$, the distribution becomes Platykurtic as shown in Figure 2-5.

---

(25)   The third moment, $\dfrac{\Sigma (X - \overline{X})^3}{n}$, may be used as an absolute skewness measure. A more valuable skewness measure is the relative skewness measure, which is the ratio of the 3rd moment squared to the 2nd moment cubed; it is called Beta one.

$$\beta_1 = \frac{[\Sigma (X - \overline{X})^3/n]^2}{[\Sigma (X - \overline{X})^2/n]^3} \quad \text{or} \quad \sqrt{\beta_1}, \text{ which is called } \alpha_3.$$

Nonetheless, the sign of the third moment indicates the type of skewness.
(26) Notice the $3(\overline{X} - Med)$, the numerator of the formula, has been derived from the equation expressing the relationship of the mean, the median, and the mode: Mode $= \overline{X} - 3(\overline{X} - Med)$.

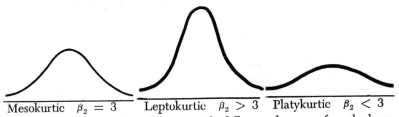

Mesokurtic $\beta_2 = 3$ Leptokurtic $\beta_2 > 3$ Platykurtic $\beta_2 < 3$

Figure 2-5:   Three distributions with different degrees of peakedness.

The formula of β_2 or α_4 is as follows:[27]

Ungrouped Data

$$\beta_2 = \frac{\Sigma(X - X)^4/n}{[\Sigma(X - \overline{X})^2/n]^2}$$

Grouped Data

$$\beta_2 = \frac{\Sigma f(M - X)^4/\Sigma f}{[\Sigma f(M - \overline{X})^2/\Sigma f]^2}$$

(27) The coefficient of peakedness, β_2 or α_4, is based on the Fourth Moment: $\frac{\Sigma (X - \overline{X})^4}{n}$. As a matter of fact, β_2 is the ratio of the fourth moment to the second moment squared.

EXERCISES

2.1 Differentiate among the measures of descriptive statistics: measures of location, measures of dispersion, and measures of skewness.

2.2 a. Define:
The artihmetic mean
The geometric mean
The weighted mean
The harmonic mean
b. State the relationship existing among the arithmetic, the geometric, and the harmonic means.

2.3 What are the main characteristics of:
1. The arithmetic mean
2. The geometric mean
3. The harmonic mean

2.4 a. Define:
The median
The mode
b. Describe the relationship existing among the mean, the median, and the mode.

2.5 a. Define:
The range
The variance
The standard deviation
b. What is the interpretation of the standard deviation?

2.6 The following table shows the acreage of 26 private camp grounds in Indiana:

48	80	136	65	100
50	80	160	258	70
54	80	160	114	71
55	83	161	120	74
60	96	180	75	121
125				

Calculate:
1. The arithmetic mean
2. The median
3. The mode
4. The standard deviation

2.7 a. Construct a frequency distribution for the data in Exercise 2.6. Compute the mean, the median, the mode, and the standard deviation.
b. Compare the results of Exercise 2.6 and 2.7 and state the reason for discrepancies if they exist.

only arith.

2.8 Calculate the mean, the median, the mean deviation, the median deviation and the standard deviation for the following distribution:

Average Hourly Wage of Production Workers
in 100 Metropolitan Areas
(in Dollars)

Class	Frequency (f)
2.00 and less than 2.25	1
2.25 and less than 2.50	6
2.50 and less than 2.75	5
2.75 and less than 3.00	11
3.00 and less than 3.25	21
3.25 and less than 3.50	22
3.50 and less than 3.75	15
3.75 and less than 4.00	11
4.00 and less than 4.25	6
4.25 and less than 4.50	2
	100

2.9 The following are two frequency distributions of the weight (in pounds) and the height (in inches) of 110 football players:

Weight (in pounds)		Height (in inches)	
Class	f	Class	f
166 - 175	9	68 - 69	5
176 - 185	19	70 - 71	17
186 - 195	14	72 - 73	30
196 - 205	9	74 - 75	37
206 - 215	13	76 - 77	17
216 - 225	12	78 - 79	4
226 - 235	11		110
236 - 245	8		
246 - 255	7		
256 - 265	8		
	110		

Compare the two frequency distributions.

2.10 The following frequency distribution represents the number of home runs hit in both National and American Leagues that occurred during a fifty-year period:

Class	Frequency
10 - 19	1
20 - 29	10
30 - 39	31
40 - 49	45
50 - 59	11
60 - 69	2
	100

As a consultant, what do you recommend as bases to rate a new player?

48

2.11 The following data shows the time spent in a packaging process (minute per unit):

12.6   11.5   10.9   17.1   12.9   8.7   9.9   8.8   11.1
18.0

Compute the harmonic mean, the arithmetic mean, and the geometric mean, and compare the results.

2.12 Calculate the geometric mean for the percentage change in the yields of U. S. Treasury bonds for 1961 to 1966: (1960 = 100)

1961	.9726
1962	.9850
1963	.9975
1964	1.0349
1965	1.0499
1966	1.1621

Interpret the results.

2.13 Production for 1970 was 250,000 units and for 1961 was 100,000 units. Calculate the average annual percentage change in production from 1961 to 1970.

2.14 For the data of Exercise 2.6, calculate:
    a. The skewness coefficient
    b. The kurtosis coefficient (β_2)
    c. Interpret the results of parts a, and b.

2.15 Test the skewness and peakedness of the frequency distribution in Exercise 2.8.

Chapter III

PROBABILITY

Traditionally, statistics has been looked upon as the science dealing with the collection, organization, analysis, and interpretation of quantitative data. This phase of statistics has been covered in the previous chapter.

Today, statistics is concerned with decision making. The role of statistics in decision making is to help the businessman to draw conclusions about the unknown future. Uncertainty is a fact of life that businessmen face in making their decisions. Decisions concerning inventory, production, and sales are just few of many decisions to be made for the uncertain future. Probability theory lends itself to the statistical methods used to analyze the uncertain phenomena. Such analysis will guide the decision maker to implement the right course of action. On one hand, a businessman can use his past experience to express his judgment by assigning probabilities to each possible event that might affect the outcome of his decision. Moreover, the decision maker can use these probabilities together with other economic information to improve his decision-making process.

On the other hand, many of the business phenomena are of repetitive nature. Probability theory can provide an appropriate mathematical model, or probability distribution, to describe and interpret such observed phenomena. These mathematical models are constructed to simulate actual situations. Conclusions drawn can be reliable to the extent that the model is a good approximation to the real phenomenon.

Even though probability theory is an important branch of pure mathematics, it has its vital role in statistical methods used for decision making. The roots of probability lie in a simple mathematical theory of games of chance. In such games, the outcome of any trial cannot be accurately predicted. For example, if a coin is tossed many times under the same conditions, one cannot predict with accuracy the outcome of any toss. It is true that the possible outcomes of tossing a coin is known in advance, it is either Head or Tail. Nonetheless, this information will not change the fact that if the experiment is repeated under the same conditions, it is not possible to tell whether the outcome of the next trial is a Head or a Tail. These experiments are called random phenomena. The outcome of a random phenomenon is called the random event.

Probability theory has many notations from the set theory. Set theory is the main subject of any finite mathematical course, but a review of some of the set theory concepts will pave the road to understand the theory of probability.

50

Review of Set Theory:
A Set: is a collection of objects.

For example: Let A be a set of the outcomes of tossing a coin, then the elements contained in the set A are: Head, and Tail, and the set A is listed as follows:

A = {H, T}   where[1]   HεA,   TεA

Another example: if B is a set, elements of this set are the outcome of rolling a die, then the set B is:

B = {1, 2, 3, 4, 5, 6}

A Subset: (or event) is a part of a set.
For example: if B and B_1 are two sets:

B = {1, 2, 3, 4, 5, 6}
and B_1 = {2, 5}

B_1 is called a subset of B and can be written in the following form:

B_1 ⊂ B or B ⊃ B_1

B_1 is a subset of B if every element in B_1 is an element in B but not vice versa. (Figure 3-1)

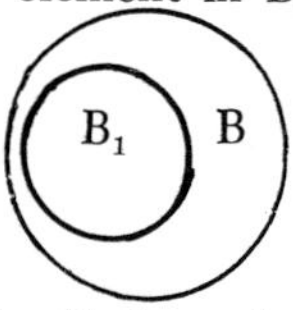

Figure 3-1: B_1 is a subset of B.

Two sets, A and C, are said to be equal if and only if every element in A is also an element in C and vice versa, or if A is a subset of C, and C is a subset of A:

A = C   if A ⊂ C and C ⊂ A.
For example: if A = {2, 4, 6, 8}   and C = {8, 6, 2, 4}
      then A = C

Union and intersection:
The union and intersection are two notations associated with sets. ∪ is the symbol to denote the union of two or more sets, e.g., A ∪ B (A union B), A ∪ B ∪ C (A union B union C) and so on. ∩ is used to denote the intersection of two or more sets.
Example 3.1:   Let A and B be two sets:

A = {a, b, c, d, f}
and B = {1, 2, a, b, c}

then A ∪ B is a new set, say C, that contains all the elements in A OR B:

C = {1, 2, a, b, c, d, f}; C = A ∪ B
The A ∪ B is shown graphically in Figure 3-2a.

Figure 3-2a.   The shaded area is A ∪ B

(1) ε is a symbol used to denote "the element of" or the member contained in the set.

On the other hand, the $A \cap B$, is a set, say D, that contains the elements that are in A AND B:

$$D = \{a, b, c\}; \quad D = A \cap B$$

Figure 3-2b.   Shows the intersection of the two sets

Figure 3-2b.   The shaded area is $A \cap B$

Example 3.2:   Let E and F to be two sets:

$$E = \{1, 2, 3\}$$
and $F = \{a, b, c, d\}$
then $E \cup F = \{1, 2, 3, a, b, c, d\}$
and $E \cap F = \phi$, ϕ is the null set[2]

Joint and disjoint sets:

In the first example, A and B are said to be joint or partially overlapping sets, while in the second example, E and F are disjoint or mutually exclusive sets. As a general rule, if the intersection of two or more sets is the empty set, then these sets are mutually exclusive, mathematically:

if $A_i \cap A_j = \phi$ for $i \neq j$

then A's are mutually exclusive sets.

Complement set:

For every set there is a complement, e.g., if A is a set then A^c (or A') is the complement of A that contains all the elements in the space or universe which are **not** in A.

Example 3.3:   If S, a sample space, has these elements:

$$S = \{a, b, c, d, e, f, g\}$$
and let $A = \{b, e, d\}$
then $A^c = \{a, c, f, g\}$

This is shown graphically in Figure 3-3.

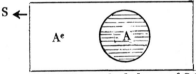

Figure 3-3:   The unshaded area of S is A^c

In this example:

$$A \cup A^c = S$$
and $A \cap A^c = \phi$

Also, de Morgan's laws show the connection between complement sets and the two notations of $\cup$ and $\cap$ as follows:

$$(A \cup B)^c = A^c \cap B^c$$
$$\text{and } (A \cap B)^c = A^c \cup B^c$$

The de Morgan's laws can be expanded to n sets or events.

---

(2) ϕ, 0, or —⌒—   are symbols used to denote the null, void, or empty set. A null set is one that has no elements.

The three important algebraic laws: commutative, associative, and distributive, are applicable to the union and the intersection of the events A, B, and C as follows:

Commutative law:

$$A \cup B = B \cup A \qquad \text{and} \qquad AB = BA$$

Associative law:

$$A \cup (B \cup C) = (A \cup B) \cup C \qquad A(BC) = (AB)C$$

Distributive law:

$$A(B \cup C) = AB \cup AC \qquad A \cup (BC) = (A \cup B)(A \cup C)$$

This brief review of the set theory and its concepts will help to better understand the probability theory.

Probability

Probability of an event is a value between zero and one assigned to measure the degree of uncertainty of the occurrence of the event. If it is certain that the event will occur, then the probability of this event equals one. This means that we are sure 100% that this event will occur. On the contrary, if the event never occurs, then its probability equals zero. For example, the probability that it snows in July in the Midwest is zero, while the probability it snows in January in that region is one. On the other hand, the event that it snows on a particular day in January in the Midwest cannot be predicted with certainty; however, the event is more likely to occur, therefore its probability falls between one and zero. Also, the event that it rains in January in the Midwest is unlikely to occur, but it can occur; therefore the probability of this event falls between zero and one. To assign one or zero as the probability of an event is easier than to assign values in between.

There are three approaches that help to assess the probability of any event between the two extreme values: one and zero. The three approaches or concepts of probability assessments are:

1. Theoretical   2. Experimental   3. Subjective

1. Theoretical assessments of probability:

This approach is also called the classical, equiprobable, or the equally likely outcome approach. This approach is useful in assigning probabilities of events involving games of chance. Probabilities determined by this method are based on a prior concept. For example, if a fair coin is tossed under the same conditions, the possible outcomes are either Head or Tail; the chances of a Head occurring are equally likely to those of a Tail. Therefore, one may assign ½ as a probability value for a Head or a Tail, or: $P(H) = P(T) = ½$. Another example, the possible outcomes of rolling a die are: 1, 2, 3, 4, 5, 6. If the die is fair and the process of rolling this die is uniform, then there is no reason to favor one outcome over the other. Therefore, the probability of each event occurring is equal to 1/6.

If the condition of equally likely outcomes does not apply for any reason, then the experimental approach to assess probabilities will be more appropriate to use.

2. Experimental assessment of probabilities:

The theoretical approach to assess probabilities is limited to events that can assume symmetrical probabilities, such as tossing a fair coin or rolling a fair die under the same conditions. Neither of these two criteria can exist, e.g., one cannot be sure that the die or the coin is well balanced or fair or that uniform or consistent tossing will be performed. Difficulties encountered in the selection of a criterion for the symmetry or equal possibility of outcomes led to the foundation of the experimental method.

The experimental approach is very useful to assess probabilities for the outcome of business and economic phenomena. Business and economic phenomena are not symmetrical and in order to analyze any business event we need to gather data from an experiment that deals with this event. For example, to determine the percentage of defectives in the production of a particular machine, an experiment or series of experiments should take place before arriving at any decision about this problem. The more observations (trials) to be included in the experiment the closer the decision to reality. In this example, the ratio of the number of defectives to the number of items produced included in the experiment, indicates the relative frequency of the occurrence of the event.

In general, if a random experiment is repeated n times, then the experimental assessment of the probability of an event A (denoted by P(A)) is the limiting value of relative frequency of A as to the number of trials, such as:

$$P(A) = \lim_{n \to \infty} \frac{f}{n}; \quad f = \text{frequency of the event A}$$

and n = number of observations or trials.

As the number of trials n gets larger and larger, the relative frequency $\frac{f}{n}$ reaches a stable limit which is used to assess the probability of A.

3. Subjective assessment of probabilities:

Subjective or personalistic probability is an approach used frequently in assigning probabilities for business events where experiments are either very costly or cannot be conducted. For example, the probabilities assigned to selling a new product can be determined by the decision maker (say the head of Marketing Research Division) based on his own judgment. Such assessment of probabilities reflect the experience, the attitude, and the values of the decision maker and the information available to him. These factors can differ from one decision maker to another, and even for the same decision maker probabilities assigned can differ from one time to another time depending on the availability of more information.

Subjective approach of assigning probabilities is very useful and it is frequently applied in business and economic decision making.

Axioms of Probability

Given a random phenomenon whose possible outcomes are the events or the points on a sampling description space, S, a non-negative value between zero and one inclusive is the probability of any of these events. The property of the probabilities can be described by the following axioms:

Axiom 1.　　$0 \leq P(A_i) \leq 1$

This axiom is stating that the probability assigned to any event of A_i is a non-negative value that falls between zero and one inclusive.

Axiom 2.　　　$P(S) = 1$,　$S =$ sample space

The second axiom of probability is concerned with the summation of probabilities assigned to all the elements or events contained in the sample space (or the set). If $A_i \in S$,　then $\Sigma P(A_i) = P(S) = 1$.

Axiom 3.　$P(A_1 \cup A_2 \cup A_3 \ldots \cup A_n) = P(A_1) + P(A_2) + P(A_3) + \ldots + P(A_n)$ provided that the subsets A_i are mutually exclusive events or that $A_i \cap A_j = \phi$; for $i \neq j$

This axiom is considered the basis for the addition theorem of probability which will be presented later in this chapter.

The three axioms of probability are illustrated in the following example:

Example 3.4:　Let S be the sample space that contains all the possible outcomes of rolling two fair dice for 36 times under the same conditions. The 36 possible outcomes are:

1,1	1,2	1,3	1,4	1,5	1,6
2,1	2,2	2,3	2,4	2,5	2,6
3,1	3,2	3,3	3,4	3,5	3,6
4,1	4,2	4,3	4,4	4,5	4,6
5,1	5,2	5,3	5,4	5,5	5,6
6,1	6,2	6,3	6,4	6,5	6,6

The same space, S, contains 36 events:

$S = \{(1,1),(2,1),(3,1), \ldots ,(5,6),(6,6)\}$

or　$S = \{A_1, A_2, A_3, \ldots , A_{35}, A_{36}\}$

The probability of each event of A_i equals 1/36, a non-negative value between 0 and 1 inclusive, which satisfies Axiom 1.

The probability of all the 36 elements of S, is one, or $\Sigma P(A_i) = P(S) = 1$ which is consistent with Axiom 2.

On the other hand, events $A_1, A_2, \ldots, A_{36}$ are mutually exclusive and:

$P(A_1 \cup A_2 \cup A_3 \cup \ldots \cup A_{36}) = 1/36 + 1/36 + 1/36 + \ldots + 1/36$

$$= P(A_1) + P(A_2) + P(A_3) + \ldots + P(A_{36})$$

The probability of the union of A_i events is an obvious illustration of Axiom 3.

Theorems of Probability:

There are many probability theorems based on the three axioms presented above. Some of these theorems will be stated without proof to be a good exercise for the reader to apply the 3 axioms in proving them.

Theorem 1.　$P(A) + P(A^c) = 1$

Theorem 2.　$P(\phi) = 0$

Theorem 3.　$P(A_1) \leq P(A_2)$　, $A_1 \subset A_2$

Theorem 4.　$P(A_1) \leq 1$　, $A \subset S$

Theorem 5.　The addition theorem

Theorem 6.　The multiplication theorem

Theorem 7.　The Bayesian theorem

Theorems 5, 6, and 7 will be presented in detail.

The Addition Theorem

To apply this theorem, one has to differentiate between mutually exclusive and non-mutually exclusive events. Event: A_1 and A_2 are said to be mutually exclusive if the two events cannot occur together, otherwise they are non-mutually exclusive. For example: In tossing a coin, either a Head or a Tail occurs but one cannot expect both of them to occur at the same time. Therefore, the events of the occurrence of a Head or that of a Tail are considered to be mutually exclusive events.

On the other hand, a card being drawn from a deck of 52 cards can be a face card, a spade card, or a face card and a spade card at the same time. Therefore, the events of drawing a face card or a spade card are considered to be non-mutually exclusive events.

Addition of mutually exclusive events:

If A_1 and A_2 are mutually exclusive events, then the probability of A_1 or A_2 is:

$$P(A_1 \cup A_2) = P(A_1) + P(A_2)$$

Example 3.5:

What is the probability of one or five occurring when rolling a fair die?

Solution: let A_1 be the event of one occurring

and A_2 be the event of five occurring

A_1 and A_2 are mutually exclusive events because in one throw of a die either one or five can occur. Therefore,

$$P(A_1 \text{ OR } A_2) = P(A_1) + P(A_2)$$
$$= 1/6 + 1/6 = 1/3$$

Notice that the addition theorem for mutually exclusive events is an application of Axiom 3.

Addition of non-mutually exclusive events:

If B_1 and B_2 are not-mutually exclusive events, then the probability of their union, or $P(B_1 \cup B_2)$ is:

$$P(B_1 \cup B_2) = P(B_1) + P(B_2) - P(B_1 \cap B_2)$$

This is illustrated graphically in Figure 3-4:

$$B_1 \cap B_2$$

Figure 3-4: The shaded area is $P(B_1 \cup B_2)$.

Example 3.6: What is the probability of drawing one card from a deck of 52 cards to be either a face card or a spade card?

Solution: Let B_1 to be the event of drawing a face card

and B_2 to be the event of drawing a spade card

then B_1, B_2 elements and probabilities are:

$B_1 = \{J_S, Q_S, K_S, J_H, Q_H, K_H, J_D, Q_D, K_D, J_C, Q_C, K_C\}$

$P(B_1) = 12/52$

$B_2 = \{J_S, Q_S, K_S, 1_S, 2_S, 3_S, 4_S, 5_S, 6_S, 7_S, 8_S, 9_S, 10_S\}$

$P(B_2) = 13/52$

B_1 and B_2 are not mutually exclusive events then $P(B_1 \cup B_2) = P(B_1) + P(B_2) - P(B_1 B_2)$. Values of $P(B_1)$ and $P(B_2)$ have been calculated and we need to find $P(B_1B_2)$. B_1B_2 consists of the elements that are in B_1 and B_2; J_S, Q_S, K_S. Hence the $P(B_1B_2) = 3/52$.

Accordingly,
$$P(B_1 \cup B_2) = P(B_1) + P(B_2) - P(B_1B_2)$$
$$= 12/52 + 13/52 - 3/52$$
$$= 22/52$$

The Multiplication Theorem:

This theorem differentiates between independent and dependent events. Two or more events are said to be independent if neither affects the occurrence of the other. In other words, events A_1 and A_2 are considered to be independent events if and only if the occurrence of A_1 does not depend on the occurrence of A_2 or vice versa, the occurrence of event A_2 does not depend on the occurrence of A_1.

Multiplication of independent events:

If A_1 and A_2 are independent events, then the joint probability of A_1 AND A_2, or the $P(A_1 \cap A_2)$ is:
$$P(A_1 \cap A_2) = P(A_1) \bullet P(A_2)$$
or $$P(A_2 \cap A_1) = P(A_2) \bullet P(A_1)$$

Example 3.7:

An urn contains 6 white balls, and two black balls; two balls are drawn simultaneously from this urn with replacement. Find the probability that the two balls will be white.

Solution:

Drawing the balls with replacement means that the event of drawing the first ball in no way affects the event of drawing the second ball, or that the two events are independent.

Let W_1 be the event of drawing the first ball to be white
and W_2 be the event of drawing the second ball to be white
$P(W_1) = 6/8$, the probability of drawing a white ball
and $P(W_2) = 6/8$, is the same as $P(A_1)$ because the first ball has been replaced in the urn before drawing the second ball
then
$$P(W_1W_2) = P(W_1) \bullet P(W_2)$$
$$= 6/8 \bullet 6/8$$
$$= 36/64 = 9/16$$

A tree diagram showing the different values of joint probabilities for the independent events in the previous example is shown in Figure 3-5.

57

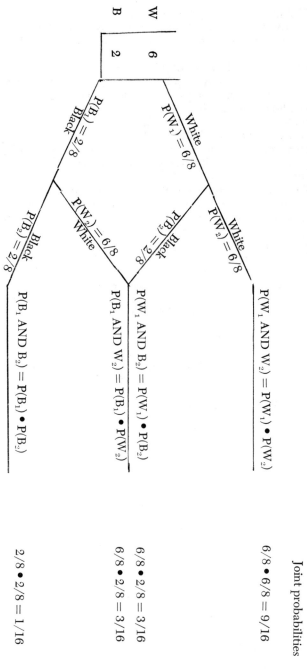

Figure 3-5: A tree diagram for joint probabilities of independent events.

Multiplication of dependent events:

Event A_2 is said to depend on event A_1 if the occurrence of A_1 affects the occurrence of A_2. The joint probability of the two dependent events A_1 AND A_2 is:

$P(A_1 \cap A_2) = P(A_1) \bullet P(A_2/A_1)$

or the joint probability equals the probability of the second event given (denoted by/) or knowing the outcome of event A_1. $P(A_2/A_1)$ is known as the conditional probability.

Example 3.8:

An urn contains 8 balls, 6 white and 2 black. Two balls are drawn simultaneously **without** replacement from the urn. Find the probability of drawing the first ball to be white and the second ball to be black.

Solution:

Drawing two balls without replacement indicates that the probability of drawing the second ball depends on the outcome of the first draw. If the first ball drawn is white, then 7 balls are left in the urn: 5 white and 2 black, while drawing a black ball in the first draw will leave 7 balls: 6 white and one black.

In the example: the assumption is that a white ball has been drawn in the first draw, event W_1, then the $P(W_1) = 6/8$. The second ball drawn is assumed to be black, event B_2. The probability of drawing the second ball, given that the first ball is white, $P(B_2/W_1)$, equals $2/7$. The joint probability, $P(W_1 \cap B_2)$, is:

$$P(W_1 B_2) = P(W_1) \bullet P(B_2/W_1)$$
$$= 6/8 \bullet 2/7$$
$$= 3/14$$

The $P(B_2/W_1)$ is called the conditional probability which can be derived from this formula as:

$$P(B_2/W_1) = \frac{P(W_1 B_2)}{P(W_1)}$$

A tree diagram to show the different joint probabilities for different assumptions of drawing the balls is shown in Figure 3-6.

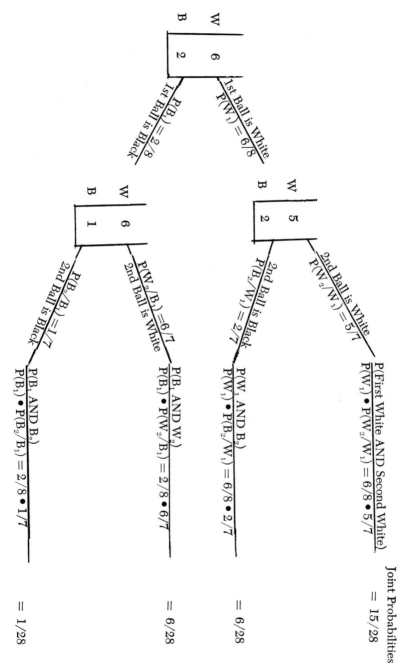

Figure 3-6: A tree diagram to calculate the joint probabilities for dependent events.

The addition theorem looks upon the events as mutually exclusive and non-mutually exclusive, while the multiplication theorem is concerned with independent and dependent events. It is not necessarily true that mutually exclusive events are independent or that non-mutually exclusive events are dependent. The following illustration is presented to show the relationship that exists between mutually exclusive and independent events:

Let A_1 be the event that Mr. X, a chess player, wins.

and A_2 be the event that Mr. Y, another chess player, wins.

(a) If Mr. X is playing Mr. Y

then A_1 and A_2 are mutually exclusive but **not** independent events

(b) If Mr. X is playing Mrs. Y

and Mr. Y is playing Mrs. X

then A_1 and A_2 may be considered as independent events but **not** mutually exclusive events.

The Bayesian Theorem:

The theorem has been developed by the Reverend Thomas Bayes, an English minister who was interested in making inductive inferences about the hypothesis given the occurrence of an event based on this hypothesis. The theorem is a systematic method to revise subjective probabilities assigned to the outcome of the hypothesis by the decision maker. Such revision is based on the availability of more relevant empirical data about an event which is part of the hypothesis.

Bayesian theorem is a direct application of the conditional probability and can be derived as follows:

Let H_1, H_2, H_3, . . . , H_n be n mutually exclusive and exhaustive events in the sample space, S, and let E be an event; that is $E \subset S$.

Probabilities of H_1, H_2, . . . , H_n are assigned by the subjective approach and called the prior probabilities.

An experiment is conducted to gather data about the event E, and the conditional probabilities of E given H_i, or $P(E/H_i)$, are referred to as the likelihood probabilities.

The main goal of the Bayesian theorem is to revise the subjective (or prior probabilities) by providing the posterior probabilities, $P(H_i/E)$ which in turn can be revised as more relevant empirical data becomes available.

A graphical presentation of the Bayesian theorem in Figure 3-7, where S, the same space is partitioned into H_1, H_2, . . ., H_n. The event E is shown as a subset of S.

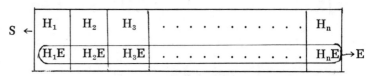

Figure 3-7:   Event E is a subset of the partitioned sample space S.

The assumptions stated before are: $P(H_i)$, and $P(E/H_i)$ are known. Also, the joint events of H_i and E, $(H_i \cap E)$, are mutually exclusive. Having these assumptions in mind, the posterior probabilities, $P(H_i/E)$, can be derived as follows:

$$E = (H_1 \cap E) \cup (H_2 \cap E) \cup (H_3 \cap E) \cup \ldots \cup (H_n \cap E)$$
$$P(E) = P(H_1 \cap E) + P(H_2 \cap E) + P(H_3 \cap E) + \ldots + P(H_n \cap E);$$

$H_i \cap E$ are mutually exclusive

$$P(E/H_1) = \frac{P(E \cap H_1)}{P(H_1)} = \frac{P(H_1 \cap E)}{P(H_1)} \; ; \; H_1 \cap E = E \cap H_1$$

$$P(H_1 \cap E) = P(H_1) \bullet P(E/H_1)$$
$$P(E) = P(H_1) \bullet P(E/H_1) + P(H_2) \bullet P(E/H_2) + \ldots + P(H_n) \bullet P(E/H_n)$$
$$= \Sigma P(H_i) \bullet P(E/H_i)$$

The posterior probability to be figured out is:

$$P(H_1/E) = \frac{P(H_1 \cap E)}{P(E)}$$

$$= \frac{P(H_1) \bullet P(E/H_1)}{\Sigma P(H_i) \bullet P(E/H_i)}$$

In general, $P(H_i/E) = \dfrac{P(H_i) \bullet P(E/H_i)}{\Sigma P(H_i) \bullet P(E/H_i)}$ $i = 1, 2, \ldots, n$

Example 3.9:

Let H_1, H_2, H_3 be the output produced by Machine I, II, and III. Machine I produces 35%, Machine II produces 20%, and Machine III produces 45% of the output. Percentage of defectives produced by Machine I, II, III is 2%, 1.5%, 1% respectively.

An item has been selected randomly for inspection and found to be defective. What is the probability that this item has been produced by Machines I, II, or III?

Solution:

1. Prior Probabilities: $P(H_1) = .35$, $P(H_2) = .20$, $P(H_3) = .45$, indicate the probabilities of producing defective as well as non-defective items by Machine I, II, and III.

2. The event of selecting an item for the purpose of inspection, is the event E. The item was found to be defective.

3. Conditional probabilities (or likelihood) $P(E/H_i)$ refer to the probability of a defective item being produced by Machine I, II, or III:
$$P(E/H_1) = 2\%, P(E/H_2) = 1.5\%, P(E/H_3) = 1\%$$

4. From the information we have the posterior probability for each machine, $P(H_i/E)$, indicates the probability that the defective item has been produced by Machine I, II, or III.

The following table shows the calculations of the posterior probabilities:

Event	Prior Prob. $P(H_i)$	Likelihood × Prob. $P(E/H_i)$	Joint = Prob. $P(H_i \cap E)$	Posterior Prob. $P(H_i/E)$
H_1: Output of Machine I	.35	.020	.0070	$\frac{.0070}{.0145} = .48$
H_2: Output of Machine II	.20	.015	.0030	$\frac{.0030}{.0145} = .21$
H_3: Output of Machine III	.45	.010	.0045	$\frac{.0045}{.0145} = .31$
	1.00		$P(E) = .0145$	1.00

The probability of an item (defective or nondefective) to be produced by Machine I, II, III is shown by the prior probabilities: .35, .20, .45 respectively. If an item is selected randomly and found to be defective, then the probability that this defective item belongs to Machine I, II, or III is shown by the posterior probabilities: .48, .21, .31 respectively.

Machine III, producing 45% of the total output, has the lowest percentage of defective output (1%), which explains why the probability that an item selected randomly and found to be defective belongs to Machine III is lower (.31) than that of Machine I (.48).

Bayesian Theorem is very helpful as a decision making tool especially when dealing with small sample size. More of the Bayesian theorem application to decision theory is introduced later in this book.

Counting Methods

To assign probabilities, one needs to know the possible outcomes of the event. In some cases, it is very easy to enumerate the possible outcomes of the event such as tossing a coin, or rolling a die. If the event has few stage experiments then the tree diagram method can be used to determine the probability of the possible outcomes as shown in Figure 3-5, and Figure 3-6. In these two Figures, the tree diagram method has been used to calculate the joint probabilities for independent and dependent events.

The more stages of an experiment and the more possibilities for each stage, the more difficult to use the tree diagram method to enumerate the possible outcomes of the complex event. In these cases other counting methods based on algebraic formulas are applied. The most popular algebraic methods used for counting the possible outcomes of an experiment or event are as follows:

1. If an event E_1 can result in n_1 outcomes, and event E_2 can result in n_2 outcomes, then the joint events (E_1 and E_2) can result in $n_1 n_2$ outcomes.

   This can be extended to more than two events. For example, a woman has 15 dresses, 10 shoes, 6 hats: How many combinations of attire can she wear?

   E_1 = event of having a dress, its outcome n_1 = 15
   E_2 = event of having a shoe, its outcome n_2 = 10
   E_3 = event of having a hat, its outcome n_3 = 6

   The number of combinations of attire she can wear or the outcome of the joint events (E_1, E_2, and E_3) = $n_1 \bullet n_2 \bullet n_3$
   $$= 15 \bullet 10 \bullet 6 = 900.$$

2. Permutations:

   Permutation is arrangement of n different elements of a set. Let S be a finite set with distinct elements:
   $$S = \{e_1, e_2, e_3, \ldots, e_n\}$$
   The number of distinct **arrangements** that can be formed from the n elements contained in S, using X of them at a time, X≤n, is called "the number of permutations of n objects taken X at a time." Using the notation of permutation, the number of arrangements can be calculated by:
   $$_nP_x \text{ or } (n)x$$

where[3] $_nP_x = \dfrac{n!}{(n - x)!}$

Example 3.10: if S = { a,b,c,d,e,f}, then the number of permutations of the 6 letters of S taken 2 at a time is:

$$_6P_2 = \frac{6!}{(6 - 2)!} = \frac{6!}{4!} = 6 \bullet 5 = 30$$

The 30 permutations are:
```
ab  ba  bc  cb  cd  dc  de  ed  ef  fe
ac  ca  bd  db  ce  ec  df  fd
ad  da  be  eb  cf  fc
ae  ea  bf  fb
af  fa
```
In the previous example if we are interested to find the number of permutations of the 6 letters taken 6 at a time, then:

$$_6P_6 = \frac{6!}{(6 - 6)!} = \frac{6!}{0!} = 6!$$

In general, the number of permutations of the n elements of set S, taken all of them at a time, $_nP_n$, equals n!

If the set S contains of n_1 elements that are alike, n_2 elements that are alike but different kind, and so on, or simply the set S is partitioned into r subgroups that are alike, then the number of permutations of the n elements of this partitioned set is:

$$\frac{n!}{n_1!n_2! \ldots n_r!} \qquad , n = n_1 + n_2 + \ldots + n_r$$

This permutation is called the multinomial coefficient. For example, the number of permutations of a bridge deck be partitioned in four hands each of size 13 is:
$$n = n_1 + n_2 + n_3 + n_4$$
$$52 = 13 + 13 + 13 + 13$$
Then the number of permutations $= \dfrac{52!}{13!13!13!13!}$

3. Combinations:
The calculation of permutations or arrangements is concerned with the order of the different elements or objects, the arrangement ab is different than the arrangement ba. If the order does not matter, then ab is not different than ba, and that ab and ba are considered to be a subset that contained the two elements of a and b. The number of subsets of size x to be formed from the n elements of S is called the number of combinations and is denoted by:

$$\binom{n}{x} \qquad \text{or } _nC_x \qquad \text{or } C_x^n$$

(3)   ! is the symbol used for factorial.

where $_nC_x$ is the number of combinations of n different elements of S, taken X at a time, is

$$\binom{n}{x} = \frac{n!}{x!(n-x)!}$$

The number of combinations $_nC_x$ is known as the binomial coefficient. In example 3.10 where S is a set of 6 elements:

S = {a,b,c,d,e,f}

the number of combinations of the 6 letters contained in S taken 2 letters at a time is:

$$\binom{6}{2} = \frac{6!}{2!(6-2)!} = \frac{6!}{2!4!} = 15 \qquad \frac{6 \cdot 5 = 30 = 15}{2}$$

The 15 subsets of combinations are:

ab bc cd de ef
ac bd ce df
ad be cf
ae bf
af

Comparing the formulas used to find the number of permutations and the number of combinations, one can express one formula in terms of the other:

$$_nP_x = x! \, _nC_x$$

and $_nC_x = \dfrac{1}{x!} \; _nP_x$

In example 3.10 of the 6 letters taken 2 at a time, the number of permutations can be figured out by using the number of combinations time x! (= 2!):

$_6C_2 = 15$, then $_6P_2 = 2!(15) = 30$. Also, the number of combinations can be calculated from the number of permutations:

$$_6P_2 = 30 \text{ and } x! = 2!, \text{ then } _6C_2 = \frac{1}{2!} 30 = 15.$$

EXERCISES

3.1 a. What is the role of the probability theory in statistics?
    b. Differentiate among the following probability assessments:
       Theoretical
       Experimental
       Subjective

3.2 Define:
    A set
    A subset
    Equal sets
    Union of two or more sets
    Intersection of two or more sets
    Empty set
    Mutually exclusive sets
    Independent sets

3.3 Prove the following probability theorems:
    a. $P(A) + P(A^c) = 1$
    b. $P(\phi) = 0$
    c. $P(A_1) \leq P(A_2)$, $A_1 \subset A_2$
    d. $P(A_1) \leq 1$, $A_1 \subset S$

3.4 a. Three balls are drawn with replacement from a box containing 10 balls, of which 6 are white and 4 are red.
    Find the probability:
      1. P (all the three balls will be white)
      2. P (all the three balls will be the same color)
      3. P (at least one is red)
    b. Solve part a assuming that the balls are drawn without replacement.
      1. P (all the three balls will be white)
      2. P (all the three balls will be the same color)
      3. P (at least one is red)

3.5 a. If one card is drawn from a regular deck of 52 cards, what is the probability it will be a heart or a face card?
    b. What is the probability of an odd number appearing in a single toss of a die?
    c. Toss two fair coins. What is the probability of:
      1. P(2 heads)
      2. P (at least one head)
    d. Two fair dice are tossed. What is the probability that the sum of the dice will be either 6 or 12?

3.6 X and Y are members of a football team of 25 players. After a winning game, all of the 25 players throw their helmets in the air. Each player starts to pick up randomly one of the helmets. What is the probability that:
    a. X will get his own helmet.
    b. X and Y will get their own helmets.
    c. At least one, either X or Y, will get his own helmet.

3.7 a. An instructor grades each student as follows: A die is cast; if one occurs, the student receives A grade. If two or three occur, the student receives B grade; otherwise the student receives C grade.

   If 15 students are graded according to the above scheme, what is the probability of 4 A's, 5 B's, and 6 C's?

   b. The student body of a certain college is composed of 55% men and 45% women. 80% of the men and 58% of the women are democrats.

   1. What is the probability that a student who is a democrat is a man?

   2. What is the probability that a student who is a democrat is a woman?

3.8 a. A man tosses 2 fair coins; what is the probability that he has tossed 2 tails, given that he has tossed at least one tail?

   b. A man tosses 2 fair dice. What is the probability that the sum of the two dice will be 5 given that the sum is odd?

3.9 a. Find $\frac{4}{36} = \frac{1}{2}$ *list all possibilities for 5*
                                              14,

   $(5)_2$ $P_{5,2}$

   $(5)^2$ *-25*

   5!

   $\binom{5}{2}$ $C_{5,2}$

Order doesn't matter
Order does matter

$5 \cdot 9 \cdot 6 \cdot 4 = 1080$

   b. 1. Four politicians met at a party. How many hand shakes are exchanged if each politician shakes hands with every other politician once? $C_{4,2}$

   2. A restaurant menu lists 5 soups, 9 meat dishes, 6 desserts and 4 beverages. An ordered meal consists of all these components. How many customers can order different meals?

   3. Five of 12 girls are to be selected to form a discussion team. In how many ways can the team be made? $C_{12,5}$

3.10 What is the practical significance of the Bayesian theorem?

3.11 Urn I contains 7 white and 4 red balls, while urn II contains 5 white and 3 red balls. An urn is selected at random, and a ball is drawn from it. Given that the ball drawn is white, what is the probability that urn II was selected?

3.12 Mr. X, Mr. Y, and Mr. Z are the only production workers in a small workshop. Mr. X produces 30% and Mr. Y produces 25% of the total production. The previous records showed that the percentage of defective units produced by X, Y, and Z is 2%, 4%, 1.5% respectively. A customer received a defective unit. What is the probability that it has been produced by Z?

Chapter IV

PROBABILITY FUNCTIONS OF RANDOM VARIABLES

Probability theory provides mathematical models to describe the observed numerical values of a random variable that assumes the set of outcomes of a random phenomenon. Random variables are either discrete or continuous. A discrete random variable may assume a finite number or infinite sequence of distinct values, while a random variable that may assume values exist in an interval or intervals is considered to be continuous.

Probability functions or probability distributions are those mathematical models formulated to describe the random variable. One may expect two classifications of the probability function: discrete and continuous, depending on the type of the random variable they are supposed to describe. On the other hand probability functions may be formulated to describe one random variable or more than one. Discrete and continuous probability functions for one variable will be presented and followed by discrete and continuous joint probability functions.

Random variable: (X)

As mentioned above, a random variable, based on the outcome of a random experiment, is a numerical valued variable defined on a sample space. For example: the random experiment of rolling two dice: if X denotes the sum of the points of the two dice, then X is considered to be a random variable that can assume integral values from 2 to 12.

Probability Function: (f(X))

A function f(X) that yields the probabilities of the random variable X within any value in the range of X is called the probability function or frequency function of the random variable.

Cumulative Probibility Function: (F(X))

A function closely related to the probability function f(X) is the cumulative probability function F(X) that provides the probibility of those values of the random variable less or equal to the specific value of X.

The random variable X, its probability function f(X), and its cumulative function F(X) as defined above will be considered in the presentation of the one variable probability functions and the joint probability functions for discrete as well as continuous random variables.

1. **Probability Functions for One random variable:**
   A. Discrete Variable:
       In the experiment of rolling two dice where X denotes the sum of points occurred, X is considered a random variable that assumes integral values from 2 to 12. X is a discrete random variable defined on the sample space that consists of the following 36 possible outcomes:

						X_i (the sum of points)	f
1,1							
1,2	2,1					2	1
1,3	2,2	3,1				3	2
1,4	2,3	3,2	4,1			4	3
1,5	2,4	3,3	4,2	5,1		5	4
1,6	2,5	3,4	4,3	5,2	6,1	6	5
	2,6	3,5	4,4	5,3	6,2	7	6
		3,6	4,5	5,4	6,3	8	5
			4,6	5,5	6,4	9	4
				5,6	6,5	10	3
					6,6	11	2
						12	1
							36

X_i is a discrete random variable and f is the frequency of occurrence of the events of X_i.

Probability Function: f(X)

From the frequency table, X_i and f, we can formulate a function f(X), a probability function that can be used to derive the probabilities for the values that X_i assume. A probability function for the example of rolling the two dice is derived as follows:

X_i	f	$f(X_i)$
2	1	1/36
3	2	2/36
4	3	3/36
5	4	4/36
6	5	5/36
7	6	6/36
8	5	5/36
9	4	4/36
10	3	3/36
11	2	2/36
12	1	1/36
	36	

$$f(X) = \frac{X-1}{36} \quad X = 2,3,4,5,6,7$$

$$= \frac{13-X}{36} \quad X = 7,8,9,10,11,12$$

$$= 0 \quad \text{elsewhere}$$

f(X) is a discrete probability function that must satisfy two properties:

1. $0 \le f(X) \le 1$ for all X

This property implies that the probability of the different values of X are non-negative and falls between 0 and 1 inclusive. This is consistent with axiom I of the probability theory.

2. $\sum_{\text{all X}} f(X) = 1$

This implies that the summation of all probabilities of X_i equals to one. This property agrees with the second axiom of probability: $P(S) = 1$, since $P(S) = \sum P(X_i) = \sum_{\text{all X}} f(X)$

From the probability function f(X), and its two properties, one can find out the probability of any value that X assumes. For example:

$$P(X = 6) = f(X = 6) = \frac{6-1}{36} = 5/36$$

and $P(X = 10) = f(X = 10) = \frac{13-10}{36} = 3/36$ ·

and $P(6 \leq X \leq 8) = \sum_{x=6}^{8} f(X) = f(X = 6) + f(X = 7) + f(X = 8)$

$$= \frac{6-1}{36} + \frac{7-1}{36} + \frac{13-8}{36}$$

$$= \frac{5+6+5}{36}$$

$$= 16/36 = 4/9$$

In general, if the probability function is discrete, then the $P(a \leq X \leq a)$ $= P(X = a) = f(X = a)$, while the $P(a \leq X \leq b) = \sum_{x=a}^{b} P(X) =$ $f(X = a) + f(X = a + 1) + \ldots + f(X = b - 1) + f(X = b)$

Cumulative Probability Function: $F(X)$:

The discrete cumulative probability function can be defined as:

$F(X) = \sum_{t \leq x} f(t)$

where the summation occurs overall the values of the random variable X that are less than or equal to a particular value of X, referred to by t. For example: the cumulative probability function $F(X)$ for the random experiment of rolling two dice is:

X_i	$f(X_i)$	$F(X_i)$
2	1/36	1/36
3	2/36	3/36
4	3/36	6/36
5	4/36	10/36
6	5/36	15/36
7	6/36	21/36
8	5/36	26/36
9	4/36	30/36
10	3/36	33/36
11	2/36	35/36
12	1/36	36/36

From the cumulative probability function of rolling the two dice, cumulative probabilities can be calculated with no difficulty at all, for example, the cumulative probability of $X \leq 6$ is:

$P(X \leq 6) = F(X = 6) = 15/36$

70

A graphical presentation of the Probability Function f(X), and the Cumulative Probability Function F(X) is shown in Figure 4-1.

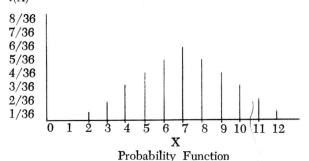

Probability Function

Cumulative Probability Function
Figure 4-1:   Discrete Random variable

B.   Continuous Variable:

As mentioned before, a random variable is a function of a random phenomenon. If the random phenomenon is of a continuous nature, then the random variable representing it will be continuous. For example the phenomenon of waiting for a bus or at the counter of a supermarket can be considered to be continuous and the random variable, X, representing the continuous phenomenon is also a continuous random variable.

Probability Density Function (p.d.f.)

The probability function formulated for the continuous random variable is a continuous function and is called the probability density function. The probability density function must satisfy two properties:

1. $0 \leq f(X) \leq 1$ for all X's
2. $\int f(X)dx = 1$
    all X

These two properties are similar to those of the discrete probability function except that in the continuous case differential calculus has to be used to find the probability of X between any two values in the domain of X.

Example 4.1:

Let X be a continuous random variable, its probability density function is:

$$f(X) = 0 \qquad\qquad \text{for } X < 0$$
$$= 0.1(X + 1) \qquad 0 \le X \le 1$$
$$= 0.4(X - \tfrac{1}{2}) \qquad 1 \le X \le 2$$
$$= 0.3(3 - X) \qquad 2 \le X \le 3$$
$$= 0.2(4 - X) \qquad 3 \le X \le 4$$
$$= 0.1 \qquad\qquad 4 \le X \le 6$$
$$= 0 \qquad\qquad \text{elsewhere}$$

Let us examine f(X) and prove that it is a p.d.f. This means that the function should satisfy the previous two properties:

1. $0 \le f(X) \le 1$ f(X)

f(X)= 0   X < 0   P(X < 0)   = 0.0

$$= 0.1(X + 1) \quad 0 \le X \le 1 \quad P(0 \le X \le 1) = \int_0^1 0.1(X + 1)dx = 0.15$$

$$= 0.4(X - \tfrac{1}{2}) \quad 1 \le X \le 2 \quad P(1 \le X \le 2) = \int_1^2 0.4(X - \tfrac{1}{2})dx = 0.40$$

$$= 0.3(3 - X) \quad 2 \le X \le 3 \quad P(2 \le X \le 3) = \int_2^3 0.3(3 - X)dx = 0.15$$

$$= 0.2(4 - X) \quad 3 \le X \le 4 \quad P(3 \le X \le 4) = \int_3^4 0.2(4 - X)dx = 0.10$$

$$= 0.1 \quad\quad 4 \le X \le 6 \quad P(4 \le X \le 6) = \int_4^6 0.1dx \quad = 0.20$$

$$= 0 \quad\quad \text{elsewhere} \quad P(X > 6) \quad\quad\quad\quad = 0$$

The first property of a probability density function has been satisfied because the f(X) for any interval within its domain is non-negative.

2. $\int_{\text{all X}} f(X)dx = 1$

For this f(X), the second property can be proved by:

$$\int_0^6 f(X)dx = \int_0^1 0.1(X + 1)dx + \int_1^2 0.4(X - \tfrac{1}{2})dx + \int_2^3 0.3(3 - X)dx$$

$$+ \int_3^4 0.2(4 - X)dx + \int_4^6 0.1dx$$

$$= 0.15 + 0.40 + 0.15 + 0.10 + 0.20 = 1.00$$

In the case of the continuous functions, the value of the probability function for any interval may be obtained by evaluating the integral of the p.d.f. over the desired interval, for example:

$$P(0 \leq X \leq 1) = \int_0^1 f(X)dx = \int_0^1 0.1(X+1)dx = 0.1\left(\frac{X^2}{2}+X+C\right)\Big|_0^1$$

$$= 0.1(\tfrac{1}{2}+1+C) - 0.1(0/2+0+C) = 0.15$$

$$P(0 \leq X \leq \tfrac{1}{2}) = \int_0^{1/2} f(X)dx = \int_0^{1/2} 0.1(X+1)dx = 0.1\left(\frac{X^2}{2}+X+C\right)\Big|_0^{1/2}$$

$$= 0.1(1/8+\tfrac{1}{2}+C) - (0+C) = 0.0625$$

$$P(1.5 \leq X \leq 1.5) = \int_{1.5}^{1.5} f(X)dx = \int_{1.5}^{1.5} 0.4(X-\tfrac{1}{2})dx$$

$$= 0.4\left(\frac{X^2}{2} - \frac{X}{2} + C\right)\Big|_{1.5}^{1.5} = 0$$

The last example, $P(1.5 \leq X \leq 1.5)$, shows that the probability of any point on a continuous probability function is equal to zero. Mathematically,

$$P(a \leq X \leq a) = \int_a^a f(X)dx = 0, \text{ if the probability function is continuous.}$$

Cumulative Probability Function: F(X)

The cumulative probability function is related to the p.d.f. and is defined as:

$$F(X) = \int_{t \leq x} f(t)dt$$

The cumulative function $F(X)$ for Example 4.1 is:

$$f(X) = 0 \qquad X < 0 \qquad 0.0 \quad \int_{-\alpha}^0 f(X)dx = P(X < 0) \quad = 0.0$$

$$= 0.1(X+1) \quad 0 \leq X \leq 1 \quad 0.15 \quad \int_0^1 f(X)dx = P(X \leq 1) \quad = 0.15$$

$$= 0.4(X-\tfrac{1}{2}) \quad 1 \leq X \leq 2 \quad 0.40 \quad \int_0^2 f(X)dx = P(X \leq 2) \quad = 0.55$$

$$= 0.3(3-X) \quad 2 \leq X \leq 3 \quad 0.15 \quad \int_0^3 f(X)dx = P(X \leq 3) \quad = 0.70$$

$$= 0.2(4-X) \quad 3 \leq X \leq 4 \quad 0.10 \quad \int_0^4 f(X)dx = P(X \leq 4) \quad = 0.80$$

$$= 0.1 \qquad 4 \leq X \leq 6 \quad 0.20 \quad \int_0^6 f(X)dx = P(X \leq 6) \quad = 1.00$$

$$= 0 \qquad \text{elsewhere}$$

A graphical presentation of $f(X)$ and $F(X)$ is shown in figure 4-2:

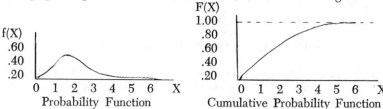

Figure 4-2: Continuous Random Variable

2. Probability Functions for more than One Random Variable:

Probability functions formulated to describe more than one random variable are called Joint Probability functions. If X and Y are two random variables defined as functions on the same sample space, then their joint probability function f(X,Y) describes the simultaneous probability of the two variables. Joint probability functions are either discrete or continuous.

A. Discrete Joint Probability Functions:

The joint probability function that describes two or more discrete random variables is a discrete function. Let X and Y be two random variables representing drawing 2 balls with replacement (and without replacement) from a box that contains 10 balls: 4 white and 6 red. Denote the first draw by X and the second draw by Y. Let X and Y assume 0 or 1, depending on the color of the ball drawn from the box: 0 if the ball is Red, and 1 if the ball is White.

The sample space that describes the joint probability f(X,Y) is shown in table 4-1(a), and 4-1(b):

With Replacement

X / Y	Red = 0	White = 1	f(Y)
Red = 0	(.6) (.6) .36	(.4) (.6) .24	.60
White = 1	(.4) (.6) .24	(.4) (.4) .16	.40
f(X)	.60	.40	1

Table 4-1(a): $f(X,Y); X = 0,1$
$Y = 0,1$

Without Replacement

X / Y	Red = 0	White = 1	f(Y)
Red = 0	6/10 • 5/9 30/90	4/10 • 6/9 24/90	54/90
White = 1	6/10 • 4/9 24/90	4/10 • 3/9 12/90	36/90
f(X)	54/90	36/90	1

Table 4-1(b): $f(X,Y); X = 0,1$
$Y = 0,1$

The joint probability f(X,Y) can be expressed in an equation form, for example, if we assume a sample probability space as follows:

Example 4.2: $f(X,Y) = \dfrac{X + Y + 1}{42}$; $\begin{array}{l} X = 0,1,2,3 \\ Y = 0,1,2 \end{array}$

Then the joint probabilities, $P(X \cap Y)$, are calculated in table 4-2:

X / Y	0	1	2	3	f(Y)
0	1/42	2/42	3/42	4/42	10/42
1	2/42	3/42	4/42	5/42	14/42
2	3/42	4/42	5/42	6/42	18/42
f(X)	6/42	9/42	12/42	15/42	1

Table 4-2: $f(X,Y); \quad X = 0,1,2,3$
$Y = 0,1,2$

As any probability function, the f(X,Y) must satisfy the following two criteria:

(1) $0 \leq f(X,Y) \leq 1$ for all ordered pairs of X and Y

(2) $\sum_X \sum_Y f(X,Y) = 1$

Marginal Probability Function: (Discrete)

Marginal probability function is simply the function that describes the probabilities of a single random variable. Accordingly, f(X), and f(Y) are the two marginal probability functions involved in the joint probability function f(X,Y).

The marginal probability function, f(X) or f(Y), can be derived from the joint probability function f(X,Y) as follows:

$$f(X) = \sum_{all\ Y} f(X,Y)$$

and

$$f(Y) = \sum_{all\ X} f(X,Y)$$

Example 4.3: From Example 4.2:

(A) $f(X) = \displaystyle\sum_{Y=0}^{2} \frac{X+Y+1}{42}$

$\qquad = \dfrac{X+0+1}{42} + \dfrac{X+1+1}{42} + \dfrac{X+2+1}{42}$

$\qquad = \dfrac{X+1+X+2+X+3}{42}$

$f(X) = \dfrac{3X+6}{42} \qquad X = 0,1,2,3$

$f(X=0) = \dfrac{0+6}{42} = 6/42$

$f(X=1) = \dfrac{3+6}{42} = 9/42$

$f(X=2) = \dfrac{6+6}{42} = 12/42$

$f(X=3) = \dfrac{9+6}{42} = 15/42$

All these values are the sum of the columns of the joint probability function in Table 4-2.

(B) $f(Y) = \displaystyle\sum_{X=0}^{3} \frac{X+Y+1}{42}$

$\qquad = \dfrac{0+Y+1}{42} + \dfrac{1+Y+1}{42} + \dfrac{2+Y+1}{42} + \dfrac{3+Y+1}{42}$

$\qquad = \dfrac{Y+1+Y+2+Y+3+Y+4}{42}$

$f(Y) = \dfrac{4Y+10}{42} \qquad Y = 0,1,2$

then $\quad f(Y=0) = \dfrac{0 + 10}{42} = \dfrac{10}{42}$

$f(Y=1) = \dfrac{4 + 10}{42} = \dfrac{14}{42}$

$f(Y=2) = \dfrac{8 + 10}{42} = \dfrac{18}{42}$

These values are the sum of the rows of the joint probabilities in Table 4-2.

Conditional Probability Functions:

$$\text{Conditional probability} = \dfrac{\text{Joint Probability}}{\text{Marginal Probability}}$$

If **A** and **B** are two dependent[1] events such that the outcome of B depends on the outcome of A, or vice versa, then the P(A/B) or P(B/A) is called the conditional probability and is defined as:

$$P(A/B) = \dfrac{P(A \cap B)}{P(B)} \quad ; \; P(B) > 0$$

In Example 4.3:

$$P(X/Y) = \dfrac{P(X \cap Y)}{P(Y)}$$

in probability functional terms:

$$P(X/Y) = \dfrac{f(X,Y)}{f(Y)}$$

likewise $\quad P(Y/X) = \dfrac{f(X,Y)}{f(X)}$

For example: $\quad P(Y=0/X=3) = \dfrac{f(3,0)}{f(X=3)} = 4/42 \div 15/42 = 4/15$

$$P(X=1/Y=2) = \dfrac{f(1,2)}{f(Y=2)} = 4/42 \div 18/42 = 4/18$$

B. Continuous Joint Probability Functions:

If the random variables are continuous, then the joint probability function for two or more variables is continuous and is defined as:

$$\int_x \int_Y f(X,Y) dy \, dx$$

Let X and Y be two continuous random variables, their joint probability function is:

---

(1) If the two events are independent then $P(A/B) = P(A)$, and $P(A \cap B) = P(A) \bullet P(B)$.

Example 4.4:

$$\int_1^4 \int_0^3 1/18(X+Y-2)dy \ dx \qquad \begin{cases} 1 < X < 4; \\ 0 < Y < 3 \end{cases}$$

The different values of the joint probabilities can be calculated by the evaluation of the double integer of $f(X,Y)$ over the intervals of the domain of the function as shown in table 4-3:

Y \ X	$\int_1^2$	$\int_2^3$	$\int_3^4$	f(Y)
$\int_0^1$	0	1/18	2/18	3/18
$\int_1^2$	1/18	2/18	3/18	6/18
$\int_2^3$	2/18	3/18	4/18	9/18
f(X)	3/18	6/18	9/18	1

Table 4-3:   Continuous Joint Probability Function

Two examples to evaluate the joint probability for the two intervals:

(a) $1 < X < 2$ and $0 < Y < 1$
(b) $2 < X < 3$ and $1 < Y < 2$
are presented below:

(a) For $1 < X < 2$ and $0 < Y < 1$, the joint probability is:

$$\int_1^2 \int_0^1 1/18(X+Y-2)dy \ dx = 0 \ \text{(from Table 4-3)}$$

$$\int_1^2 \int_0^1 1/18(X+Y-2)dy \ dx = \int_1^2 [\int_0^1 1/18(X+Y-2)dy]dx$$

$$= \int_1^2 [1/18(XY + \frac{Y^2}{2} - 2Y) \ |_0^1] \ dx$$

$$= \int_1^2 [1/18\{X(1) + \tfrac{1}{2} - 2(1)\} - 0]dx$$

$$= \int_1^2 [1/18(X - 3/2)]dx$$

$$= 1/18(\tfrac{1}{2}X^2 - 3/2X) \ |_1^2$$

$$= 1/18[(4/2 - 3/2(2)) - (\tfrac{1}{2} - 3/2)]$$
$$= 1/18(-1 + 1)$$
$$= 0$$

(b) For $2 < X < 3$ and $1 < Y < 2$, the joint probability is:

$$\int_2^3 \int_1^2 1/18(X+Y-2)dy \ dx = 2/18 \quad \text{(from Table 4-3)}$$

$$\int_2^3 \int_1^2 1/18(X + Y - 2)dy \ dx = \int_2^3 [\int_1^2 1/18(X + Y - 2)dy]dx$$

$$= \int_2^3 [1/18(XY + \frac{Y^2}{2} - 2Y \ \Big|_1^2 \ ]dx$$

$$= \int_2^3 1/18\{(2X + \frac{4}{2} - 4) - (X + \frac{1}{2} - 2)\}dx$$

$$= \int_2^3 1/18(X - \frac{1}{2})dx$$

$$= 1/18(\frac{1}{2}X^2 - \frac{1}{2}X) \ \Big|_2^3$$

$$= 1/18\{(9/2 - 3/2) - (4/2 - 1)\}$$
$$= 1/18(3 - 1)$$
$$= 2/18$$

The continuous joint probability function must satisfy two criterion:
(1) $f(X,Y) \geq 0$
(2) $\int_X \int_Y f(X,Y) \ dy \ dx = 1$

Marginal Probability Function: (continuous)

The marginal probability function $f(X)$, or $f(Y)$ can be derived from the joint probability function in the same way as in the discrete case.

$$f(X) = \int_Y f(X,Y) \ dy \qquad 1 < X < 4$$
$$\text{and } f(Y) = \int_X f(X,Y) \ dx \qquad 0 < Y < 3$$

$f(X)$ and $f(Y)$ the marginal probability of X and Y respectively are already calculated in Table 4-3, where the sums of the columns refer to $f(X)$, and the sums of the rows refer to $f(Y)$. .

Conditional Probability:

In the case of continuous dependent random variables, the conditional probability can be calculated by dividing the continuous joint probability by the continuous marginal probability.

$$P(Y/X) = \frac{f(X,Y)}{f(X)} \qquad \text{or } P(X/Y) = \frac{f(X,Y)}{f(Y)}$$

For example:
$$P(1 < Y < 2 \ / \ 1 < X < 2) = \frac{\int_1^2 \int_1^2 1/18(X+Y-2)dy \ dx}{\int_1^2 f(X)dx} = \frac{1/18}{3/18}$$

$$= \frac{1}{3}$$

(Table 4-3)

EXERCISES

4.1 Define:
A random variable
Probability density function
Cumulative probability function
Joint probability function
Conditional probability function

4.2 a. What are the two properties that a probability function must possess?
b. Differentiate between discrete and continuous random variables. Sustain your answer graphically.

4.3 The following is a probability function:

$$f(X) = \frac{3 - X}{6} \qquad \text{for } X = 0,1,2$$

$$= 0 \qquad \text{elsewhere}$$

a. Find $P(X = 2), P(X = 1)$
b. Construct the cumulative probability function $F(X)$.
c. Graph $f(X)$ and $F(X)$.

4.4 Graph the following probability function:
$f(X) = 1/40 \ (X^2 + X) \qquad \text{for } X = 1,2,3,4$
$= 0 \qquad \text{elsewhere}$
a. Find $P(X=3)$, $P(X=4)$
b. Find $P(X \geq 2)$, $P(X>4)$, $P(X \leq 3)$

4.5 Given the following probability function:

$$f(X) = \binom{5}{x}(¼)^x \ (¾)^{5-x} \qquad X = 0,1,2,3,4,5$$

$$= 0 \qquad \text{elsewhere}$$

a. Find $P(X=3), P(X \leq 2), P(X \geq 4)$
b. Graph the function.
c. Calculate $F(X)$ and graph the function.

4.6 The following is a probability function of X:

$$f(X) = \frac{\binom{7}{x} \binom{3}{4-x}}{\binom{10}{4}} \qquad X = 0,1,2,3,4$$

$$= 0 \qquad \text{elsewhere}$$

Calculate:
a. $P(X=2), P(X=3)$
b. $P(X \leq 1)$, $P(X>3)$
c. $P(X>4)$

4.7 Given the following probability distribution of X:

$$f(X) = e^{-3} \frac{3^x}{x!} \qquad\qquad X = 0,1,2,3, \ldots$$

$$= 0 \qquad\qquad\qquad \text{elsewhere}$$

a. Find $P(X=4)$, $P(X \geqslant 5)$
b. Find $P(X=0)$, $P(X \geqslant 1)$, $P(X=2)$, $P(2 \leqslant X \leqslant 4)$

4.8 The following is a probability distribution:

$$f(X) = \tfrac{1}{8} (\tfrac{7}{8})^{x-1} \qquad\qquad X = 1,2, \ldots$$

$$= 0 \qquad\qquad\qquad \text{elsewhere}$$

Find: $P(X=1)$, $P(X \geqslant 2)$, $P(1 \leqslant X \leqslant 2)$, $P(X=0)$

4.9 The following is a probability density function:

$$f(X) = \tfrac{1}{2} X^2 \qquad\qquad \text{for } 0 \leqslant X \leqslant 1$$

$$= \tfrac{1}{2}(6X - 2X^2 - 3) \qquad 1 \leqslant X \leqslant 2$$

$$= \tfrac{1}{2}(X^2 - 6X + 9) \qquad 2 \leqslant X \leqslant 3$$

$$= 0 \qquad\qquad\qquad \text{elsewhere}$$

Calculate: $P(1.5 \leqslant X \leqslant 2.5)$, $P(2.5 \leqslant X)$, $P(X=2)$
Graph the function.

4.10 The following is a p.d.f. of X:

$$f(X) = 2/3(X-2) \qquad\qquad 1 \leqslant X \leqslant 4$$

$$= 0 \qquad\qquad\qquad \text{elsewhere}$$

Find: $P(X \leqslant 1.5)$, $P(2 \leqslant X \leqslant 3)$, $P(X \geqslant 2.5)$, $P(0 \leqslant X < 1)$

4.11 Graph the following p.d.f. of X:

$$f(X) = 1/18 (\tfrac{1}{2}X + 1) \qquad\qquad 0 \leqslant X \leqslant 2$$

$$= 2/24 (2X - 1) \qquad\qquad 2 \leqslant X \leqslant 4$$

$$= 0 \qquad\qquad\qquad \text{elsewhere}$$

Find:
a. $P(X=3)$, $P(X \leqslant 1)$, $P(X \geqslant 2.5)$, $P(1 \leqslant X \leqslant 3)$
b. Construct and graph the $F(X)$.

4.12 Prove that the following function is a p.d.f.:

$$f(X) = 1/11 (X^2 - X + 2) \qquad\qquad 0 \leqslant X \leqslant 1$$

$$= 2 - X \qquad\qquad\qquad 1 \leqslant X \leqslant 2$$

$$= 1/50 (X^2 - 1) \qquad\qquad 2 \leqslant X \leqslant 4$$

$$= 0 \qquad\qquad\qquad\qquad \text{elsewhere}$$

4.13 Prove that the following is a p.d.f.:

$$f(X) = 3/2 (X^2 - 3X + 2) \qquad\qquad 0 \leqslant X \leqslant 2$$

$$= 0 \qquad\qquad\qquad\qquad \text{elsewhere}$$

and if it is a p.d.f., calculate:
$P(X \leqslant 1)$, $P(1.5 \leqslant X \leqslant 2.5)$

4.14 The following is a joint probability function for X and Y:

$$f(X,Y) = \frac{X - Y + 3}{30} \qquad\qquad \begin{array}{l} \text{for } X=0,1,2 \\ \text{and } Y=0,1,2,3 \end{array}$$

   a. Construct a table to show the different probabilities of each pair of values of X and Y.
   b. Derive $f(X)$ and $f(Y)$
   c. Calculate: $P(Y=1/X=2)$, $P(X=1/Y=0)$

4.15 Prove that the following is a joint probability function:

$$f(X,Y) = \frac{4Y - X^2}{57} \qquad \text{for } X=0,1,2 \\ \text{and } Y=0,1,2,3$$

If this function proved to be a joint probability function, calculate:
   a. $P(X=2)$, $P(X=1)$
   b. $P(Y=1)$, $P(Y \geq 2)$
   c. $P(X=0/Y=3)$, $P(Y=2/X=2)$

4.16 Prove that the following function is a joint probability distribution function for X and Y:

$$f(X,Y) = 1/36\ (X + Y) \qquad 0 \leq X \leq 3 \\ \text{and } 1 \leq Y \leq 4$$

If it is proved that it is a joint probability distribution function, find:
   a. $f(X)$
   b. $f(Y)$
   c. $P(1 \leq X \leq 2)$ and $(1 \leq Y \leq 3)$
   d. $P(0 \leq X \leq 1)/(2 \leq Y \leq 3)$
   e. $P(3 \leq Y \leq 4)/(0 \leq X \leq 1)$

Chapter V

EXPECTED VALUE AND VARIANCE
OF
RANDOM VARIABLES

In Chapter II, it is found that the mean, as a measure of central location, and the variance as a measure of dispersion, together can provide enough information to describe the data of a deterministic frequency distribution.

In a probabilistic situation, where the outcome of the event is uncertain, the expected value (or the mathematical expectation) and the variance of a probability model are corresponding to the mean and the variance in a deterministic situation. The expected value, or the mean, of a random variable indicates the value of the variable that occurs "on the average," while the variance of a random variable shows the spread of the values of the variable about its mean.

The expected value concept is used extensively in making decisions. The expected pay off, and the expected opportunity loss are a few to mention the application of the expected value concept in making decisions.

Properties of the expected value and the variance of random variables are presented in this chapter and followed by the different methods to calculate these two concepts for discrete as well as continuous random variables.

Properties of the expected value of a random variable:

a. $E(C) = C$
b. $E(X+C) = E(X) + C$ \quad $C = \text{constant}$
c. $E(CX) = CE(X)$
d. $E(X+Y+Z) = E(X) + E(Y) + E(Z)$
e. $E(X \bullet Y) = \sum_X \sum_Y (X \bullet Y)\ f(X,Y)$

$$= E(X)E(Y) + E\ [(X-E(X))\ (Y-E(Y))]$$

Properties of the variance of a random variable:

a. $Var(C) = 0$
b. $Var(X+C) = Var(X)$ \quad $C = \text{constant}$
c. $Var(CX) = C^2\ Var(X)$
d. $Var(X+Y) = Var(X) + 2\ Cov(X,Y) + Var(Y)$

$$= Var(X) + 2E\ [(X-E(X))\ (Y-E(Y))] + Var(Y)$$

e. If $X_1, X_2, \ldots X_n$ are independent random variables, then
$$Var(X_1 + X_2 + \ldots + X_n) = Var(X_1) + Var(X_2) + \ldots + Var(X_n)$$

Expected value and variance of discrete random variables:

Let X be a discrete random variable, the expected value of X is:

$$E(X) = \sum_{i=1}^{n} X_i f(X_i)$$

and the variance of X is:

$$\begin{aligned} \text{Var } (X) &= E[(X - E(X)]^2 \\ &= \sum_{x} [X - E(X)]^2 \; f(X) \\ &= E(X^2) - [E(X)]^2 \end{aligned}$$

where $E(X^2) = \sum X^2 f(X)$

The expected value of X is the sum of the variable X weighted by its probabilities, and the variance of X is equal to the mean square of X, $E(X^2)$, minus its square mean, $[E(X)]^2$. The standard deviation of X is the square root of the variance.

Example 5.1:

Find the $E(X)$, $Var(X)$, and the standard deviation of X, where X is a discrete random variable of the possible outcomes of rolling two dice 36 times; X and $f(X)$ are as follows:

Solution

X	f(X)	Xf(X)	X^2	$X^2f(X)$	$[X-E(X)]^2f(X)$
2	1/36	2/36	4	4/36	$(2-7)^2(1/36) = 25/36$
3	2/36	6/36	9	18/36	$(3-7)^2(2/36) = 32/36$
4	3/36	12/36	16	48/36	$(4-7)^2(3/36) = 27/36$
5	4/36	20/36	25	100/36	$= 16/36$
6	5/36	30/26	36	180/36	$= 5/36$
7	6/36	42/36	49	294/36	$= 0$
8	5/36	40/36	64	320/36	$= 5/36$
9	4/36	36/36	81	324/36	$= 16/36$
10	3/36	30/36	100	300/36	$= 27/36$
11	2/36	22/36	121	242/36	$= 32/36$
12	1/36	12/36	144	144/36	$= 25/36$
		252/36		1974/36	210/36
		$\sum Xf(X)$		$\sum X^2f(X)$	Var(X)
		E(X)=7		$E(X^2)=54.83$	

$$\begin{aligned} \text{Var}(X) &= E(X)^2 - [E(X)]^2 \\ &= 54.83 - 7^2 \\ &= 54.83 - 49 = 5.83 \end{aligned}$$

standard deviation $(X) = \sqrt{5.83} = 2.41$

In the case of having two probability distributions, X and Y, the expected value of the joint probability distribution, XY, is:

$$E(XY) = E(X)E(Y) + E[(X-E(X))(Y-E(Y))]$$

Example 5.2:

This example is based on the joint probability function defined in Example 4.2, and its two marginal probability functions derived in Example 4.3(A), and 4.3(B):

$$f(X,Y) = \frac{X+Y+1}{42} \qquad\qquad ; \quad \begin{matrix} X = 0,1,2,3 \\ Y = 0,1,2 \end{matrix}$$

$$f(X) = \frac{3X+6}{42} \qquad\qquad ; \quad X = 0,1,2,3$$

$$f(Y) = \frac{4Y+10}{42} \qquad\qquad ; \quad Y = 0,1,2$$

Find the $E(XY)$.

Solution:

To solve for $E(XY)$, one needs to calculate $E(X)$, $E(Y)$, and $E[(X - E(X))(Y - E(Y))]$

$$E(X) = \Sigma X f(X) = \sum_{x=0}^{3} X \left(\frac{3X+6}{42} \right)$$

$$= 0 + 1 \left(\frac{3+6}{42} \right) + 2 \left(\frac{6+6}{42} \right) + 3 \left(\frac{9+6}{42} \right)$$

$$= 0 + 9/42 + 24/42 + 45/42$$

$$= 78/42 = 1.8571$$

$$E(Y) = \Sigma Y f(Y) = \sum_{Y=0}^{2} Y \left(\frac{4Y+10}{42} \right)$$

$$= 0 + 1 \left(\frac{4+10}{42} \right) + 2 \left(\frac{8+10}{42} \right)$$

$$= 0 + 14/42 + 36/42$$

$$= 50/42 = 1.1905$$

$E[(X - E(X))(Y - E(Y))] = -0.0681$ as calculated in Table 5-1.

Table 5-1

(1) X − E(X)	(2) Y − E(Y)	(3) f(X,Y)	(4)=(1)×(2)×(3) (X−E(X))(Y−E(Y)) • f(X,Y)
0 − 1.8571 = −1.8571	0 − 1.1905 = −1.1905	1/42 = .0238	(−1.8571)(−1.1905)(.0238) = .0526
1 − 1.8571 = −.8571	0 − 1.1905 = −1.1905	2/42 = .0476	= .0486
2 = .1429	0 = −1.1905	3/42 = .0714	= −.0122
3 = 1.1429	0 = −1.1905	4/42 = .0952	= −.1296
0 = −1.8571	1 = −.1905	2/42 = .0476	= .0168
1 = −.8571	1 = −.1905	3/42 = .0714	= .0117
2 = .1429	1 = −.1905	4/42 = .0952	= −.0026
3 = 1.1429	1 = −.1905	5/42 = .1190	= −.0259
0 = −1.8571	2 = .8095	3/42 = .0714	= −.1074
1 = −.8571	2 = .8095	4/42 = .0952	= −.0661
2 = .1429	2 = .8095	5/42 = .1190	= .0138
3 = 1.1429	2 = .8095	6/42 = .1429	= .1322
			−0.0681

$$E(XY) = (1.8571)(1.1905) + (-0.0681)$$
$$= 2.2109 - 0.0681$$
$$= 2.1428$$

The E(XY) can be calculated from f(X,Y) shown in Table 4-2. The formula to be used is:

$$E(XY) = \sum_x \sum_y (XY)f(X,Y)$$

Table 5-2 shows the steps to find E(XY).

Table 5-2

X Y	0	1	2	3	X Y	0	1	2	3	
0	1/42	2/42	3/42	4/42	0	0	0	0	0	
1	2/42	3/42	4/42	5/42	1	0	3/42	8/42	15/42	26/42
2	3/42	4/42	5/42	6/42	2	0	8/42	20/42	36/42	64/42
						0	11/42	28/42	51/42	90/42

$$\sum_x \sum_y (XY)f(X,Y)$$

E(XY) = 90/42 = 2.1429

The variance of the sum of the two random variables X and Y can be calculated by the following formula:

Var(X+Y) = Var(X) + Var(Y) + 2Cov(X,Y)

The variance of (X+Y) of Example 5.2 is calculated from the functions defined the two random vaiiables:

$$f(X) = \frac{3X + 6}{42} \qquad\qquad X = 0,1,2,3$$

$$\text{and } f(Y) = \frac{4Y + 10}{42} \qquad\qquad Y = 0,1,2$$

The Var(X) = $E(X^2) - [E(X)]^2$, and the
   Var(Y) = $E(Y^2) - [E(Y)]^2$.
The values of E(X), and E(Y) are already available in the solution

of Example 5.2.

Var(X) = $E(X^2) - [E(X)]^2$	Var(Y) = $E(Y^2) - [E(Y)]^2$
= $4.5714 - (1.8571)^2$	= $2.0476 - (1.1905)^2$
= $4.5714 - 3.4488$	= $2.0476 - 1.4173$
= 1.1226	= 0.6303

$$E(X^2) = \Sigma X^2 f(X)$$

$$= \sum_{x=0}^{3} X^2 \left(\frac{3X + 6}{42}\right)$$

$$= 0+1(9/42)+4(12/42)+9(15/42)$$

$$= 4.5714$$

$$E(Y^2) = \Sigma\ Y^2 f(X)$$

$$= \sum_{y=0}^{2} Y^2 \left(\frac{4Y + 10}{42}\right)$$

$$= 0+1(14/42)+4(18/42)$$

$$= 2.0476$$

$$Cov(X,Y) = E[(X-E(X))(Y-E(Y))]$$
$$= -0.0681 \qquad \text{(From Table 5-1)}$$
$$Var(X+Y) = Var(X) + Var(Y) + 2Cov(X,Y)$$
$$= 1.1226 + 0.6303 + 2(-0.0681)$$
$$= 1.6167$$

Expected value and variance of continuous random variables:

Let X be a continuous random variable; the expected value of X is:
$$E(X) = \int_{\text{all x}} Xf(X)\,dx$$

and the variance of X is:
$$Var(X) = \int [X - E(X)]^2 f(X)dx$$
$$= \int X^2 f(X)dx - [\int Xf(X)dx]^2$$
$$= E(X^2) - [E(X)]^2$$

Example 5.3:

Find the $E(X)$, and the $Var(X)$ of the following probability function:

$$f(X) = 0.1\ (X+1) \qquad\qquad 0 \leq X \leq 1$$
$$= 0.4\ (X-1/2) \qquad\qquad 1 \leq X \leq 2$$
$$= 0.3\ (3-X) \qquad\qquad 2 \leq X \leq 3$$
$$= 0.2\ (4-X) \qquad\qquad 3 \leq X \leq 4$$
$$= 0.1 \qquad\qquad\qquad 4 \leq X \leq 6$$

Solution:

$$E(X) = \int Xf(X)dx$$

$$= \int_0^1 X\,[0.1(X+1)]dx + \int_1^2 X\,[0.4(X-\tfrac{1}{2})]dx + \int_2^3 X\,[0.3(3-X)]dx +$$

$$\int_3^4 X\,[0.2(4-X)]dx + \int_4^6 X\,(0.1)dx$$

$$= \int_0^1 0.1(X^2+X)dx + \int_1^2 0.4(X^2-\tfrac{1}{2}X)dx + \int_2^3 0.3(3X-X^2)dx +$$

$$\int_3^4 0.2(4X-X^2)dx + \int_4^6 (0.1X)dx$$

$$= 0.083 + 0.633 + 0.351 + 0.333 + 1.0$$
$$= 2.40$$

$$\int_0^1 0.1(X^2+X)dx = 0.1\left(\frac{X^3}{3} + \frac{X^2}{2}\right)\Big|_0^1 = 0.1(1/3 + \tfrac{1}{2}) = 0.083$$

$$\int_1^2 0.4(X^2-\tfrac{1}{2}X)dx = 0.4\left(\frac{X^3}{3} - \frac{X^2}{4}\right)\Big|_1^2$$
$$= 0.4[(8/3 - 4/4)-(1/3-1/4)] = 0.633$$

$$\int_2^3 0.3(3X-X^2)dx = 0.3\left(\frac{3X^2}{2} - \frac{X^3}{3}\right)\Big|_2^3$$
$$= 0.3[(27/2 - 27/3)-(12/2-8/3)] = 0.351$$

$$\int_{3}^{4} 0.2(4X-X^2)dx = 0.2\left(\frac{4X^2}{2} - \frac{X^3}{3}\right)\Big|_{3}^{4}$$

$$= 0.2[(64/2-64/3)-(36/2-27/3)] = 0.333$$

$$\int_{4}^{6}(0.1X)dx = \frac{0.1X^2}{2}\Big|_{4}^{6} = (1.8 - 0.8) = 1.0$$

$$Var(X) = E(X^2) - [E(X)]^2$$

To use this formula to calculate the variance of X, one needs to find the value of $E(X^2)$ because the value of $E(X)$ is already calculated and equals 2.40.

$$E(X^2) = \int X^2 f(X)dx$$

$$= \int_{0}^{1} X^2[0.1(X+1)]dx + \int_{1}^{2} X^2[0.4(X-\frac{1}{2})]dx + \int_{2}^{3} X^2[0.3(3-X)]dx +$$

$$\int_{3}^{4} X^2[0.2(4-X)dx] + \int_{4}^{6} X^2(0.1)dx$$

$$= \int_{0}^{1} 0.1(X^3+X^2)dx + \int_{1}^{2} 0.4(X^3-\frac{1}{2}X^2)dx + \int_{2}^{3} 0.3(3X^2-X^3)dx +$$

$$\int_{3}^{4} 0.2(4X^2-X^3)dx + \int_{4}^{6} 0.1(X^2)dx$$

$$= 0.058 + 1.034 + 0.825 + 1.117 + 5.066$$

$$= 8.10$$

$$Var(X) = 8.10 - (2.4)^2$$

$$= 8.10 - 5.76 = 2.34$$

$$\int_{0}^{1} 0.1(X^3+X^2)dx = 0.1\left(\frac{X^4}{4} + \frac{X^3}{3}\right)\Big|_{0}^{1} = 0.1(\frac{1}{4} + 1/3) = .058$$

$$\int_{1}^{2} 0.4(X^3-\frac{1}{2}X^2)dx = 0.4\left(\frac{X^4}{4} - \frac{X^3}{6}\right)\Big|_{1}^{2}$$

$$= 0.4[(4 - 4/3)-(\frac{1}{4} - 1/6)] = 1.034$$

$$\int_{2}^{3} 0.3(3X^2-X^3)dx = 0.3\left(X^3 - \frac{X^4}{4}\right)\Big|_{2}^{3} = 0.3[(27-81/4)-(8-4)] = 0.825$$

$$\int_{3}^{4} 0.2(4X^2-X^3)dx = 0.2\left(\frac{4X^3}{3} - \frac{X^4}{4}\right)\Big|_{3}^{4}$$

$$= 0.2[(256/3-64)-(36-81/4)] = 1.117$$

$$\int_{4}^{6} 0.1(X^2)dx = 0.1\left(\frac{X^3}{3}\right)\Big|_{4}^{6} = 0.1\left(\frac{216-64}{3}\right) = 5.066$$

The expected value of a continuous joint probability of X and Y is:

$$E(XY) = \int_X \int_Y XY\, f(X,Y)dy\, dx$$

Example 5.4:

From Example 4.4, X and Y are continuous random variables; their joint probability function is:

$$\int_1^4 \int_0^3 1/18(X + Y - 2)dy\, dx$$

Calculate the E(XY).

Solution:

$$E(XY) = \int_1^4 \int_0^3 1/18[XY(X + Y - 2)]dy\, dx$$

$$= \int_1^4 \int_0^3 1/18(X^2Y + XY^2 - 2XY)dy\, dx$$

$$= \int_1^4 [1/18(\tfrac{1}{2}X^2Y^2 + 1/3XY^3 - XY^2)\,\big|_0^3]dx$$

$$= \int_1^4 [1/18(9/2X^2 + 9X - 9X) - 0]dx$$

$$= \int_1^4 (1/18 \bullet 9/2X^2)dx$$

$$= \int_1^4 1/4X^2 dx$$

$$= 1/12X^3 \,\big|_1^4$$

$$= 1/12(64 - 1) = 63/12 = 5.25$$

The expected value concept is vital to decision theory. The course of action that yields the highest expected pay off or the lowest expected opportunity loss will be followed. The expected pay off values as well as the opportunity loss values are different terms for the expected value of random variables. Decision theory will be examined in later chapters in this book.

EXERCISES

5.1 a. For the probability function of Exercise 4.3, calculate:
          E(X), Var(X), and σ(X).
     b. Find out the expected value, the variance, and the standard devia-
         tion for the probability function in Exercise 4.4.

5.2 For the p.d.f. in Exercise 4.9 calculate: E(X), Var(X), and σ(X).

5.3 Calculate the E(X), Var(X), and σ(X) for the p.d.f. in Exercise 4.11.

5.4 For the joint probability in Exercise 4.14 calculate: E(XY), Var
     (X + Y).

5.5 For the joint probability in Exercise 4.16 calculate: E(XY).

Chapter VI

PROBABILITY DISTRIBUTIONS

A probability distribution (or model) is a specific probability function that describes the observed numerical valued random variable; the outcome of a random phenomenon. A probability distribution is a probability law which the outcome of a random phenomenon may obey and it is used to find out the probability of any event that is a part of the random phenomenon. Tossing a fair coin, where $p(H) = p(T) = \frac{1}{2}$, probability law (Binomial distribution) is devised to calculate the probabilities of the outcome of the n trials, e.g. probability of 0, 1, 2, . . ., or n heads to occur.

Probability distributions are either discrete or continuous depending on the type of random variables they describe. Discrete probability distributions and continuous probability distributions are presented in this chapter.

A. Discrete Probability Distributions:

Five probability distributions representing discrete random variables are considered. These distributions are:

1. Binomial
2. Hypergeometric
3. Poisson
4. Negative Binomial (Pascal)
5. Geometric

Probability function, expected value, and variance of these probability distributions are presented below.

1. Binomial Probability Distribution:

A random phenomenon that has only *two* outcomes such as: True or False, Success or Failure, Heads or Tails, . . ., etc., can be described by a binomial probability distribution.

The binomial probability distribution is based on the Bernoulli probability law:

$$P(x) = p \qquad \text{for } x = 1 \qquad \text{(refers to the success of the outcome)}$$
$$= 1-p=q \qquad x = 0 \qquad \text{(refers to the failure of the outcome)}$$
$$= 0 \qquad \text{elsewhere}$$

where p is the probability of success and q stands for the probability of failure. Also, it is assumed that the trials are independent.

If the independent trials are repeated n times, the number of successes x are described to be independent; therefore, the probability of success p remains constant from trial to trial. Such random phenomenon obeys a binomial probability function:

90

$$f(x) = {}_nC_x p^x(1-p)^{n-x}$$
$$\text{or } f(x) = {}_nC_x p^x q^{n-x} \qquad\qquad x = 0,1,2,\ldots,n$$
$$= 0 \qquad\qquad\qquad \text{elsewhere}$$

where n = number of trials
  x = number of successes
  p = probability of success
  q = probability of failure

Example 6.1:
  Toss a fair coin twice. Find the probability of 0,1, and 2 heads to occur.

Solution: $n = 2$ $x = 0,1,2$ $p = q = \frac{1}{2}$

  The possible outcomes of tossing a fair coin twice are:
  TT, TH, HT, and HH.

Possible outcome	x		P(x)		
TT	0	$q \bullet q = q^2$ or $\frac{1}{2} \bullet \frac{1}{2}$	$= \frac{1}{4}$	$P(x=0)$
TH	1	$\begin{matrix} q \bullet p = \\ p \bullet q = \end{matrix}$ $2pq = 2(\frac{1}{2} \bullet \frac{1}{2}) = \frac{1}{2}$	$P(x=1)$
HH	2	$p \bullet p = p^2 = \frac{1}{2} \bullet \frac{1}{2} = \frac{1}{4}$	$P(x=2)$

$$q^2 + 2pq + p^2 = (q+p)^2 = (\tfrac{1}{2}+\tfrac{1}{2})^2 = 1$$

The same results can be found by applying the binomial distribution formula:

$$f(x) = {}_nC_x\, p^x q^{n-x} \qquad\qquad x = 0,1,2$$
$$P(x=0) = {}_2C_0 \quad (\tfrac{1}{2})^0(\tfrac{1}{2})^{2-0} \qquad = \tfrac{1}{4}$$
$$P(x=1) = {}_2C_1 \quad (\tfrac{1}{2})^1(\tfrac{1}{2})^{2-1} \qquad = \tfrac{1}{2}$$
$$P(x=2) = {}_2C_2 \quad (\tfrac{1}{2})^2(\tfrac{1}{2})^{2-2} \qquad = \tfrac{1}{4}$$
$$\Sigma_n C_x p^x q^{n-x} \qquad\qquad = 1 = (p+q)^n$$

Expected Value of the Binomial Distribution:

$$E(X) = \sum_{x=0}^{n} Xf(X)$$

$$= \sum_{x=0}^{n} X\binom{n}{x}p^x q^{n-x}$$

$$= \sum_{x=0}^{n} X\ \frac{n!}{x!(n-x)!}\ p^x q^{n-x}$$

$$= \sum_{x=1}^{n} \frac{n(n-1)!}{(x-1)!(n-x)!}\ p(p^{x-1}q^{n-x})$$

$$= \sum_{x=1}^{n} np\frac{(n-1)!}{(x-1)!(n-x)!}\ p^{x-1}q^{n-x}$$

$$= np \sum_{x=1}^{n} \binom{n-1}{x-1}p^{x-1}q^{n-x}$$

$$= np(p+q)^{n-1}$$
$$= np(1)^{n-1}$$
$$= np$$

Variance of the Binomial Distribution:

$$\sigma^2(X) = E(X^2) - [E(X)]^2$$

$$E(X^2) = \sum_{x=0}^{n} X^2 f(X)$$

$$= \sum_{x=0}^{n} X^2 \frac{n!}{x!(n-x)!} p^x q^{n-x}$$

Let $X^2 = x(x-1) + x$

Then $E(X^2) = \sum_{x=2}^{n} X(x-1) \frac{n!}{x!(n-x)!} p^x q^{n-x} + \sum_{x=0}^{n} X\,_nC_x p^x q^{n-x}$

$= n(n-1)p^2 \Sigma \binom{n-2}{x-2} p^{x-2} q^{n-x} + E(X)$

$= n(n-1)p^2(p+q)^{n-2} + np$

$= n(n-1)p^2 + np$

$= n^2p^2 - np^2 + np$

$= n^2p^2 + np(1-p)$

$= n^2p^2 + npq$

Then $\sigma^2(X) = E(X^2) - [E(X)]^2$

$= n^2p^2 + npq - (np)^2$

$= n^2p^2 + npq - n^2p^2$

$= npq$

Example 6.2:

From past experience it is known that machine A produces units that are consistently 5% defective. A sample of size 20 is inspected. What is the probability that:

- a) None to be defective
- b) at least one to be defective
- c) not more than two to be defective.

Solution:

$n = 20$ $p =$ the probability of success to find defectives $= .05$

a) P(none defectives) = $P(X=0) = {}_{20}C_0(.05)^0 (.95)^{20}$

b) P(at least one defective) = $P(X \geqq 1)$

$= P(X=1) + P(X=2) + \ldots + P(X=20)$

or $= 1 - P(X=0)$

$= 1 - {}_{20}C_0 (.05)^0 (.95)^{20}$

c) P(not more than two defectives) = $P(X \leqq 2)$

$= P(X=0) + P(X=1) + P(X=2)$

$= {}_{20}C_0(.05)^0(.95)^{20} + {}_{20}C_1(.05)^1(.95)^{19} + {}_{20}C_2(.05)^2(.95)^{18}$

Example 6.3:

Find the expected value, the variance, and the standard deviation for the data presented in Example 6.2.

Solution:

Expected value of a binomial variable $= np$

Variance of a binomial variable $= npq$

Standard deviation of a binomial variable $= \sqrt{npq}$

$E(X) = np = (20)(.05) = 1$

$Var(X) = npq = (20)(.05)(.95) = .95$

$\sigma(X) = \sqrt{npq} = \sqrt{.95} = .975$

    The expected value $(E(X) = 1)$ indicates that samples of size 20 selected from the production of machine A yields on the average one defective item.

2. Hypergeometric Probability Distribution:

    In the binomial distribution, the drawings are with replacement. This is consistent with the assumption of independent trials and having infinite population or sample space.

    If the sample space is finite, and drawings are without replacement, then the trials are *not* independent. Accordingly, the probability of success (p) will change from one trial to another.

Example 6.4:

    A box contains 10 balls, 6 white and 4 blue. Two balls are selected from the box simultaneously. What is the probability that:

    a) the two balls are white.

    b) the two balls are different colors.

Solution:

  A. With Replacement:

    a) P(two white balls) = $(0.6)(0.6)$

                    = $_2C_2(0.6)^2(0.4)^0$

    b) P(one white and one blue) = $(0.6)(0.4)$

                    = $_2C_2(0.6)^1(0.4)^1$

    Notice that the probability of success to draw a white ball (p) did not change in the 2 trials.

  B. Without Replacement:

    a) P(two white balls) = $(6/10 \bullet 5/9) = 30/90$

        P(the 1st ball to be white) = 6/10

        And it is white.

        P(the 2nd ball to be white) = 5/9

    Notice that the probability of success to obtain a white ball has changed from $(6/10)$ in the first trial to $(5/9)$ in the second trial.

b) P(1 white and 1 blue) = $(6/10)(4/9)+(4/10)(6/9) = \dfrac{48}{90}$

    These results can be calculated by using the following hypergeometric probability distribution:

$$f(x) = \frac{\binom{Np}{x}\binom{Nq}{n-x}}{\binom{N}{n}} \qquad \text{for } x = 0,1,2,\ldots,n$$

$$= 0 \qquad \text{elsewhere}$$

where $Np + Nq = N$

Example 6.5:
Solve Example 6.4 by using the hypergeometric probability distribution formula.

Solution: (without Replacement)

N = 10   n = 2   Np = number of white balls = 6
                     Nq = number of non-white balls = 4

a) P(two balls to be white) $= \dfrac{\binom{6}{2}\binom{4}{0}}{\binom{10}{2}} = \dfrac{15}{45}$

b) P(one white and one blue) $= \dfrac{\binom{6}{1}\binom{4}{1}}{\binom{10}{2}} = \dfrac{24}{45}$

Expected Value of the Hypergeometric Distribution:

$$E(X) = \sum_{x=0}^{n} Xf(X)$$

$$= \sum_{x=0}^{n} X \frac{\binom{Np}{x}\binom{Nq}{n-x}}{\binom{N}{n}}$$

$$= \frac{1}{\binom{N}{n}} \sum_{x=1}^{n} X \binom{Np}{x}\binom{Nq}{n-x}$$

$$= np$$

Variance of the Hypergeometric Distribution:

$\sigma^2 = E(X^2) - [E(X)]^2$
$= E[X(X-1)] + E(X) - [E(X)]^2$

$$= npq \frac{N-n}{N-1}$$

The expected value of the hypergeometric distribution is the same as the expected value of the binomial distribution ($\mu = np$), while the variance differs:

σ^2 (binomial) $= npq$
σ^2 (hypergeometric) $= npq \dfrac{N-n}{N-1}$

$\dfrac{N-n}{N-1}$ is called the correction factor for finite population, if N, the number of observations in the population, is very large, or as $N \to \infty$, the limit $\dfrac{N-n}{N-1} \to 1$. This means that the variance of the hypergeometric distribution of a very large population sampled without replacement, is very close to the variance of the same population sampled with replacement. In general, a binomial distribution can be used as a good approximation to a hypergeometric distribution of a very large population.

3. Poisson Probability Distribution:

The binomial probability distribution is very useful. However, it has its limitation. If $n \to \infty$, and p is small, then the calculation of the $P(X)$ becomes more complicated. For example, if $n = 100$, and $p = 0.05$, then:

$$P(X) = {}_{100}C_x(.05)^x(.95)^{100-x} \qquad x = 0,1,2, \ldots ,100$$

Poisson probability distribution is used to approximate a binomial distribution of a large number of trials (large n). The Poisson probability distribution is derived from the binomial probability distribution as follows:

$$f(X) = \lim_{n \to \infty} {}_nC_x p^x (1-p)^{n-x}$$

$$\text{if } np = \lambda \text{ or } p = \frac{\lambda}{n}$$

$$\text{then } f(X) = \lim_{n \to \infty} {}_nC_x \left(\frac{\lambda}{n} \right)^x \left(1 - \frac{\lambda}{n} \right)^{n-x}$$

$$= e^{-\lambda} \frac{\lambda^x}{x!}$$

Poisson Probability function:

$$f(X) = e^{-\lambda} \frac{\lambda^x}{x!} \qquad x = 0,1,2, \ldots$$

$$= 0 \qquad \text{elsewhere}$$

This function is a probability function and satisfies its conditions:

(1) $f(X) \geqq 0$ (probabilities of X are non-negative)

(2) $\sum\limits_{\text{all } x} f(X) = 1$

$$\sum_{\text{all } x} f(X) = \sum_{x=0}^{\infty} e^{-\lambda} \frac{\lambda^x}{x!} = e^{-\lambda} \sum_{x=0}^{\infty} \frac{\lambda^x}{x!}$$

$\sum\limits_{x=0}^{\infty} \dfrac{\lambda^x}{x!}$ a Maclaurin series which is a special case of Taylor series.

$$= \left[1 + \frac{\lambda}{1!} + \frac{\lambda^2}{2!} + \frac{\lambda^3}{3!} + \ldots + \frac{\lambda^n}{n!} \right]$$

$$= e^{\lambda}$$

then, $\sum\limits_{\text{all } x} f(X) = e^{-\lambda} \; e^{\lambda}$

$$= e^{-\lambda+\lambda}$$

$$= e^0$$

$$= 1$$

Expected value of the Poisson Distribution:

$$E(X) = X\Sigma f(X) = \sum_{x=0}^{\infty} X e^{-\lambda} \frac{\lambda^x}{x!}$$

$$= \sum_{x=1}^{\infty} X e^{-\lambda} \ \frac{\lambda \ \lambda^{x-1}}{x(x-1)!}$$

$$= \lambda e^{-\lambda} \sum_{x=1}^{\infty} \frac{\lambda^{x-1}}{(x-1)!}$$

let $n = x-1$

$$= \lambda e^{-\lambda} \sum_{n=0}^{\infty} \frac{\lambda^{n}}{n!}$$

$$= \lambda e^{-\lambda} \ e^{\lambda}$$

$$= \lambda$$

Variance of the Poisson distribution:

$\sigma^2(X) = E(X^2) - [E(X)]^2$
$ = \lambda^2 + \lambda - \lambda^2$
$ = \lambda$

Expected value of the Poisson distribution = variance $= \lambda = np$

The standard deviation of the Poisson distribution $= \sqrt{\lambda}$

Example 6.6:

Past experience showed the number of defectives produced by Machine A to follow a Poisson Probability Distribution. The percentage of defectives is 2.5%. In a particular shift, the machine produced 200 parts.

(a) What is the probability of these conditions?
  1. all produced parts non-defective.
  2. at least one defective.
  3. not more than two defectives.

(b) Find the E(X), Var(X), and $\sigma(X)$.

Solution:

$n = 200 \qquad p = 0.025 \qquad \lambda = (200)(0.025) = 5$

x = number of defectives

(a) 1. $P(X=0) = e^{-5} \dfrac{5^0}{0!} = e^{-5}$

  2. $P(X \geqslant 1) = 1 - P(x=0) = 1-e^{-5}$

  3. $P(X \leqslant 2) = P(x=0)+P(x=1)+P(x=2)$

$$= e^{-5} + e^{-5} \ \frac{5^1}{1!} + e^{-5} \ \frac{5^2}{2!}$$

(b) $E(X) = Var(X) = \lambda = 5$
  $\sigma(X) = \sqrt{5}$

4. Negative Binomial Distribution (Pascal Probability):

The negative binomial distribution is the reverse of the binomial distribution. In the binomial distribution, the probability of successes is to be found, given a specific number of trials, while in the negative binomial distribution, the number of trials required to get a specific number of successes is to be found.

Negative Binomial Probability Function:

$$f(n) = \left[\left(\begin{matrix} n-1 \\ x-1 \end{matrix} \right) p^{x-1} \ q^{n-x} \right] p \qquad n = x, x+1, x+2, \ \ldots$$

$$= \binom{n-1}{x-1} p^x q^{n-x}$$

$$= 0 \qquad\qquad \text{elsewhere}$$

Expected Value and Variance:

$$E(n) = \frac{X}{p}$$

$$Var(n) = \frac{Xq}{p^2}$$

$$\sigma(n) = \sqrt{\frac{Xq}{p^2}}$$

Example 6.7:

A production manager planned to produce 100 non-defective units every day. Past experience showed 80% of the production to be non-defective.

(a) What is the probability that 120 units produced will be enough to produce the 100 non-defective units.

(b) What average number of units must be produced to satisfy the plan? Also, find the variance and the standard deviation.

Solution:

$$n = 120 \qquad x = 100 \qquad p = 0.80$$

a) $P(n=120) = \left[\binom{120-1}{100-1}(.80)^{100-1} \quad (.20)^{120-100}\right](.80)$

$$= \left[\binom{119}{99}\ (.80)^{99} \quad (.20)^{20}\right](.80)$$

$$= [P(x=99) \text{ out of } 119 \text{ trials}]\ [P(x=1) \text{ out of } 1 \text{ trial}]$$

or $P(n=120) = \binom{120-1}{100-1}(.80)^{100} \quad (.20)^{120-100}$

$$= \binom{119}{99}(.80)^{100} \quad (.20)^{20}$$

b) Average units to be produced = E(n)

$$E(n) = \frac{X}{p}$$

$$= \frac{100}{.80} = 125$$

$$\text{Var(n)} = \frac{Xq}{p^2}$$

$$= \frac{(100)\,(.20)}{(.80)^2} = \frac{20}{.64} = 31.25$$

$$\sigma(n) = \sqrt{31.25} = 5.59$$

5. Geometric Probability Distribution:

A random variable that represents the number of trials required to obtain the first success in a sequence of independent trials (n), where the probability of success (p) is the same for each trial, is said to obey a geometric probability distribution. The geometric probability function with parameter p is:

$$f(x) = p\,q^{x-1} \qquad\qquad x = 1,2,\dots$$
$$= 0 \qquad\qquad\qquad \text{elsewhere}$$

Expected value, and variance:

$$E(X) = \frac{1}{p}$$

$$\text{Var}(X) = q/p^2$$
$$\sigma(X) = \sqrt{q/p^2}$$

Example 6.8:

A man has 4 similar keys. One fits the door which he wants to open. What is the probability that:

a) the 1st key will open the door?
b) the 2nd key will open the door?
c) the Kth key will open the door?

Solution:

a) $P(x=1) = (\frac{1}{4})\,(3/4)^{1-1} = \frac{1}{4}$
b) $P(x=2) = (\frac{1}{4})\,(3/4)^{2-1} = \frac{1}{4} \bullet 3/4 = 3/16$
c) $P(x=k) = (\frac{1}{4})\,(3/4)^{k-1}$ $\qquad\qquad k = 1,2,3,4$

B. Continuous Probability Distributions:

There are many continuous probability distributions. However, only the following are considered:

1. Uniform probability distribution
2. Gamma probability distribution
3. Exponential probability distribution
4. Normal probability distribution
5. Sampling probability distribution

1. Uniform Probability Distribution:

A random variable whose values lie only in a certain interval, from a to b, such that the probability of each value in the interval is constant, is said to be following a uniform probability distribution, or a rectangular distribution.

Probability Density Function:

$$f(x) = \frac{1}{b-a} \qquad\qquad a \leq x \leq b$$

$$= 0 \qquad\qquad \text{elsewhere}$$

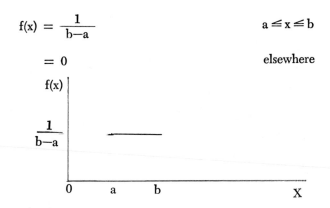

Expected value and variance:

$$E(X) = \frac{a+b}{2}$$

$$Var(X) = \frac{(b-a)^2}{12}$$

$$\sigma(X) = \sqrt{Var(X)}$$

2. Gamma Probability Distribution:

As mentioned before, the geometric and negative binomial probability distributions are constructed to find the number of trials needed to obtain the Xth success in a sequence of n independent Bernoulli trials where each trial has a constant probability of success (p).

In the continuous probability functions, the gamma probability distribution is constructed to find how long one has to wait to observe the Xth occurrence of an event that follows a Poisson distribution at the rate of r events per unit of time (t).

Probability Density Function:

$$f(x) = c\ x^{a-1}\ e^{-x/\beta} \qquad \text{for } x > 0$$
$$= 0 \qquad\qquad\qquad \text{for } x \leq 0$$

where $a > 0$, $\beta > 0$
and C is a constant equal to the value that makes the $\displaystyle\int_{-\infty}^{\infty} f(x)dx = 1$

C is defined as $\dfrac{1}{\Gamma(a)\beta^a}$ for $0 < x < \infty$

therefore $f(x) = \dfrac{1}{\Gamma(a)\beta^a}\ x^{a-1}e^{-x/\beta} \qquad 0 < x < \infty$

$$= 0 \qquad\qquad\qquad\qquad \text{elsewhere}$$

and $\Gamma(a) = (a-1)!$

100

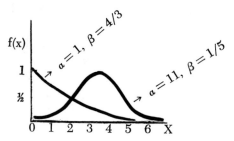

Expected value and variance:

$$E(X) = \alpha\beta$$
$$Var(X) = \alpha\beta^2$$
$$\sigma(X) = \sqrt{\alpha\beta^2}$$

From the Gamma distribution we can derive important probability distributions such as the exponential and Chi-square (χ^2) distributions as follows:

if $\alpha = 1$ then we obtain the exponential probability distribution.

if $\alpha = \dfrac{r}{2}$ (where r refers to the degrees of freedom)

and $\beta = 2$ then we obtain the Chi-square probability distribution with r degrees of freedom.

3.   Exponential Probability Distribution:

The exponential probability distribution has an important role in business. It can be used to describe random phenomena that are spread over intervals of time; e.g., the time intervals between accidents. Also, it describes the lengths of waiting time. These components of the waiting theory are used by management and operation researchers to make decisions about the maximum number of beds in a hospital, number of barbers in a barbershop, number of telephone operators or lines in a particular area, and so on.

The exponential probability distribution is a special case of the gamma probability distribution with $\alpha = 1$. The exponential distribution, sometimes called the negative exponential distribution, can be derived from the Poisson probability distribution.

Probability Density Function:

$$f(x) = \frac{1}{\beta}e^{-x/\beta} \qquad 0 < x < \infty$$

$$= 0 \qquad\qquad\qquad \text{elsewhere}$$

where $1/\beta$ is the average number of successes per interval, or $1/\beta$ is λ, the mean of the Poisson distribution.

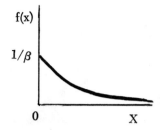

Expected value and variance:
$$E(X) = \beta$$
$$\text{Var}(X) = \beta^2$$
$$\sigma(X) = \sqrt{\beta^2} = \beta$$

Example 6.9:

In an emergency room of a large hospital the operators receive an average of two phone calls per minute. From past experience, it has been established that the number of phone calls per minute follows a Poisson distribution.

Find the probability of these.

a)   No calls within the next two minutes following the previous call.
b)   No calls within the next one minute.
c)   The length of time until the first call received is one-half minute.

Solution:

We are dealing with a continuous variable X, the length of time. So the Poisson distribution should be approximated by a continuous function, the Exponential distribution:

$$f(x) = 1/\beta e^{-x/\beta} \qquad\qquad 0 < x < \infty$$
$$= 0 \qquad\qquad\qquad \text{elsewhere}$$
$$1/\beta = \lambda = 2 \qquad \text{(average of 2 calls/minute)}$$

a)   P(no calls within the next 2 minutes) = P(2 < X < ∞)

$$P(2 < X < \infty) = 1 - P(0 < X < 2)$$

which represents the shaded area
in the diagram

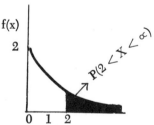

$$P(0 < X < 2) = \int_0^2 2e^{-2x}\,dx$$

$$= -e^{-4} \Big|_0^2$$

$$= 1 - e^{-4} = .9817$$
$$P(2 < X < \infty) = 1 - .9817 = .0183$$

b)　P(no calls within one minute) $= P(1 < X < \infty)$
$P(1 < X < \infty) = 1 - P(0 < X < 1)$

$$P(0 < X < 1) = \int_0^1 2e^{-2x} \, dx$$

$$= -e^{-2x} \Big|_0^1$$

$$= 1 - e^{-2} = .8647$$

$P(1 < X < \infty) = 1 - .8647 = .1353$

c)　$P(0 < X < \tfrac{1}{2}) = \int_0^{\tfrac{1}{2}} 2e^{-2x} \, dx$

$$= -e^{-2x} \Big|_0^{\tfrac{1}{2}}$$

$$= 1 - e^{-1}$$

$$= .6321$$

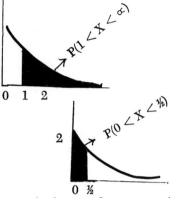

4.　Normal Probability Distribution:

The normal probability distribution plays a vital role in modern statistical theory. The distribution is a bell-shaped curve where the mean divides it into two symmetrical halves.

Probability Density Function:

$$f(x) = \frac{1}{\sigma\sqrt{2\pi}} \, e^{-\tfrac{1}{2}\left(\frac{x-\mu}{\sigma}\right)^2} \qquad -\infty < x < \infty$$

where μ and σ are constants and $\sigma > 0$

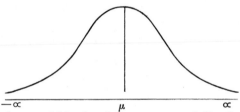

If X is a random variable that follows a normal distribution, then one needs to know the mean and the standard deviation (or the variance) of X to draw the normal curve that represents the variable X and to find the probability of any interval or area of the function. The normal probability distribution of X is denoted as follows:

$$n(x; \mu, \sigma^2)$$

If X has a mean $= 10$, and variance $= 4$, then: $n(X;10,4)$ means that X is normally distributed or a normal distribution with $\mu = 10$ and $\sigma^2 = 4$ and can be represented by the following curve:

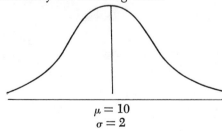

$\mu = 10$
$\sigma = 2$

Expected value and variance:

$E(X) = \mu$

$Var(X) = \sigma^2$

Standard deviation$(X) = \sigma$

The mean of the normal distribution, μ, determines the location of the curve while the standard deviation, σ, shows the degree of dispersion or variation of the distribution around the mean μ.

The total area under the normal curve which represents the probability of all the elements of the normal variable equals one, or the cumulative probability function :

$$F(X) = \int_{-\infty}^{\infty} f(x)\ dx = 1 = \Phi\left(\frac{X-\mu}{\sigma}\right)$$

where $\dfrac{X-\mu}{\sigma}$ is a standard normal distribution Z with $\mu = 0$ and $\sigma^2 = 1$,

or $n(Z;0,1)$

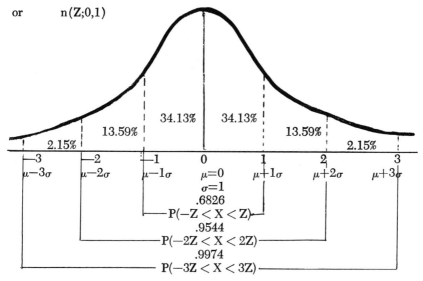

There are tables to provide the probability of any value of Z, where

$$Z = \frac{X-\mu}{\sigma}$$

If X is a normal distribution with mean $= \mu$ and variance $= \sigma^2$, then to find the probability of X for an interval ab or

$$P(a < x < b) = \int_{-\infty}^{b} f(x)dx - \int_{-\infty}^{a} f(x)dx$$

$$= \Phi\left(\frac{b-\mu}{\sigma}\right) - \Phi\left(\frac{a-\mu}{\sigma}\right)$$

$$= P\left(\frac{a - \mu}{\sigma} < Z < \frac{b - \mu}{\sigma} \right)$$

or find the $P(Z_b)$ and the $P(Z_a)$ and subtract $P(Z_a)$ from $P(Z_b)$ as follows:

$Z_a = \frac{a - \mu}{\sigma}$ then from the table find $P(Z_a)$

$Z_b = \frac{b - \mu}{\sigma}$ then from the table find $P(Z_b)$

$P(a < X < b) = P(Z_b) - P(Z_a)$ which represents the shaded area in the diagram.

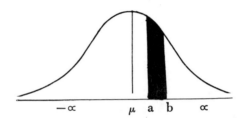

$$-\propto \qquad \mu \quad a \quad b \qquad \propto$$

Example 6.10:

The grades of 400 students in a statistics course is normally distributed with $\mu = 65$ and variance $= 100$, or if we let X represent these grades, then $n(X; 65, 100)$. Find the probability that a student selected randomly from this group would score within any interval given below:

a)   a grade between 60 and 65
b)   a grade between 70 and 65
c)   a grade between 52 and 68
d)   a grade that is greater than 85
e)   a grade that is less than 72
f)   a grade between 70 and 78

Solutions:

X is a normal distribution with $\mu = 65$ and $\sigma^2 = 100$. This information helps to draw the normal curve which is essential to find the above mentioned probabilities.

(a) P(a grade between 60 and 65) $= P(60 \leq X \leq 65) = \int_{60}^{65} f(x)\, dx$

$P(60 \leq X \leq 65)$ is P(Z) between 65 and 60

$Z = \frac{X - \mu}{\sigma}$

$= \frac{60 - 65}{10} = -0.5$

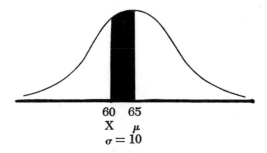

60 65
X μ
σ = 10

The minus sign has no significance other than indicating that the shaded area is located within the left part of the normal curve.

$P(60 \leq X \leq 65) = P(Z) = .1915$

This result also means that 19.15% of the class scored a grade between 60 and 65.

(b)   P(a grade between 70 and 65) $= P(65 \leq X \leq 70) = \int\limits_{65}^{70} f(x)\, dx$

$$Z = \frac{X - \mu}{\sigma}$$

$$Z = \frac{70 - 65}{10} = 0.5$$

$$P(Z) = .1915$$

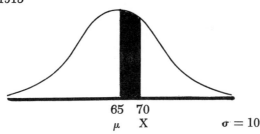

65 70
μ X   σ = 10

Then $P(65 \leq X \leq 70) = .1915$, or 19.15% of the class scored a grade between 65 and 70. '

(c)   P(a grade between 52 and 68) $= P(52 \leq X \leq 68) = \int\limits_{52}^{68} f(x)\, dx$

$$P(52 \leq X \leq 68) = P(Z_1) + P(Z_2)$$

$$Z_1 = \frac{X_1 - \mu}{\sigma}$$

$$= \frac{52 - 65}{10} = -1.3$$

$$P(Z_1) = .4032$$

$$Z_2 = \frac{X_2 - \mu}{\sigma}$$

$$= \frac{68-65}{10} = .3$$

$P(Z_2) = .1179$
$P(52 \leq X \leq 68) = .4032 + .1179 = .5211$, or 52.11% of the class scored
a grade between 52 and 68.

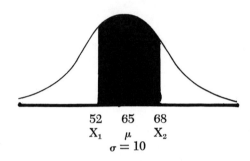

$$52 \qquad 65 \qquad 68$$
$$X_1 \qquad \mu \qquad X_2$$
$$\sigma = 10$$

(d)   P(a grade that is greater than 85) $= P(X \geq 85) = \int\limits_{85}^{\infty} f(x) \, dx$

$P(65 \leq X \leq \infty) = .5$
$P(X \geq 85) = P(65 \leq X \leq \infty) - P(65 \leq X \leq 85)$
$P(65 \leq X \leq 85) = P(Z)$

$$Z = \frac{X - \mu}{\sigma} = \frac{85 - 65}{10} = 2$$

$P(Z) = .4772$
$P(X \geq 85) = .5 - .4772$
$\qquad\qquad = .0228$
or 2.28% of the class scored a grade greater than 85.

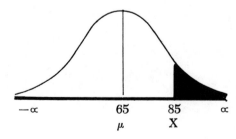

$$-\infty \qquad\qquad 65 \qquad\qquad 85 \qquad\qquad \infty$$
$$\mu \qquad\qquad X$$

(e)   P(a grade less than 72) $= P(X \leq 72) = \int\limits_{-\infty}^{72} f(x) \, dx$

$P(-\infty \leq X \leq 65) = .5$

$P(X \leq 72) = P(-\infty \leq X \leq 65) + P(65 \leq X \leq 72)$

$P(65 \leq X \leq 72) = P(Z)$

$Z = \dfrac{X - \mu}{\sigma}$

$\quad = \dfrac{72 - 65}{10} = .7$

$P(Z) = .2508$

$P(X \leq 72) = .5 + .2508 = .7508$ or 75.08% of this class scored a grade less than 72.

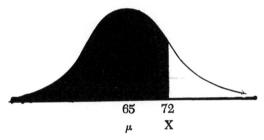

65   72

μ X

(f)   P(a grade between 70 and 78) $= P(70 \leq X \leq 78) = \int_{70}^{78} f(x)\ dx$

$P(70 \leq X \leq 78) = P(-\infty \leq X \leq 78) - P(-\infty \leq X \leq 70)$

or $= P(\mu \leq X \leq 78) - P(\mu \leq X \leq 70)$

$\quad = P(Z_1) - P(Z_2)$

$Z_2 = \dfrac{X_1 - \mu}{\sigma}$

$\quad = \dfrac{78 - 65}{10} = 1.3$

$P(Z_1) = .4032$

$Z_2 = \dfrac{X_2 - \mu}{\sigma}$

$\quad = \dfrac{70 - 65}{10} = .5$

65   70   78

μ X_2 X_1

$P(Z_2) = .1915$

$P(70 \leq X \leq 78) = .4032 - .1915$

$\qquad\qquad\qquad = .2117$ or 21.17% of the class scored a grade between 70 and 78.

Normal Distribution to approximate Binomial Distribution

Most of the populations, including the binomial populations, can be described by a normal probability distribution. A binomial probability distribution can be approximated by a Poisson distribution if $n \to \infty$ and p is small; n refers to the number of trials and p is the probability of success. The binomial distribution of populations that follow a binomial probability distribution can be approximated by a normal probability function, if $n \to \infty$ and p is large.

A binomial variable X approximated by a normal distribution is denoted as n(X;np,npq), or X is normally distributed with mean = np and variance = npq. The Z standardized normal variable to be used to calculate the probabilities is:

$$Z = \frac{X-np}{\sqrt{npq}}$$

where $\sqrt{npq}$ is the standard deviation of the binomial variable.

Example 6.11:

Let X be a binomial variable with n = 20 and p = .5. Find the probability of success = 15.

Solution:

1. Using the binomial distribution:
   $P(x=15) = {}_{20}C_{15}(15)^{15}(15)^5 = .0148$

2. Using the normal distribution:

$$P(x=15) = \int_{15}^{15} f(x)\, dx = 0 \qquad \text{because the normal distri-}$$

bution is a continuous function.

Therefore, one has to make up for moving from the discrete function (binomial) to the continuous function (normal). This can be done by moving a half unit to the left and a half unit to the right, so $P(X = 15)$ becomes $P(14.5 \le X \le 15.5)$. Such probability can be evaluated by a normal probability distribution with mean = np = $(20)(\frac{1}{2})$ = 10 and variance = npq = $(20)(\frac{1}{2})(\frac{1}{2})$ = 5.

$$\begin{array}{c|c|c|c} & 14.5 & 15.5 & \\ \hline 14 & 15 & 16 \end{array}$$

$$P(14.5 \le X \le 15.5) = \int_{14.5}^{15.5} f(x)\, dx$$

$$= P\left(\frac{15.5 - 10}{2.236}\right) - P\left(\frac{14.5 - 10}{2.236}\right)$$

$$= P(2.45) - P(2.01)$$

$P(2.45) = .4929$ (From the table)
$P(2.01) = .4778$ (From the table)
$P(14.5 \le X \le 15.5) = .4929 - .4778 = .0151$

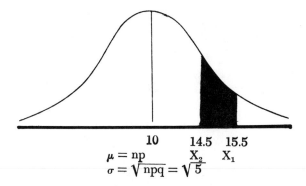

$$\mu = np$$
$$\sigma = \sqrt{npq} = \sqrt{5}$$

(with X_2 at 14.5 and X_1 at 15.5, and 10 marked at μ)

Compare the results using the binomial (.0148) and using the normal to approximate the binomial (.0151), the difference is very small.

5. Sampling Probability Distribution:

Characteristics of populations such as the mean and the proportion are of great interest to business decision makers. To find these parameters by using every element of the population is sometimes prohibitive (e.g., with infinite populations) and most of the time is costly and time consuming. For example, to find the mean annual income per family in the United States, it would be impossible to collect data from each household in the fifty states. On one hand it is very costly, and on the other hand the data will be obsolete at the end of the research. Therefore, selection of samples (or a sample) from such populations is very important because it enables the decision makers to know the characteristics of the population based on information derived from samples selected randomly from these populations.

Under sampling probability distribution, one can differentiate between these two important distributions:

A. Sampling distribution of the Mean (or distribution of $\overline{X}$)
B. Proportion Sampling distribution (or distribution of p)

A. Sampling distribution of the Mean:

The means of selected random samples of size n from the N element of a population, such that $n \leq N$, and the probabilities assigned to these means are called sampling probability distribution of the mean, or simply sampling distribution (or distribution of $\overline{X}$).

Theoretically, if samples of size n are selected randomly from the N elements of a population, then the distribution of $\overline{X}$ will have the following characteristics:

The mean of the sampling distribution, or the mean of the means, denoted by $\mu_{\overline{x}}$, $\overline{X}_{\overline{x}}$, or $E(\overline{X})$ equals the mean of the population

$$E(\overline{X}) = \mu$$

and the variance of the sampling distribution of the mean denoted by $\sigma_{\overline{x}}^2$ or Var($\overline{X}$) equals the variance of the population σ^2 divided by the size of the sample n:

$$\text{Var}(\overline{X}) = \frac{\sigma^2}{n}$$

this indicates the greater the size of the sample (n), the smaller the variance or the dispersion of the sampling distribution of the mean around the mean of the population. This also shows that the greater the sample size, the smaller the standard error of the sampling distribution $\sigma_{\bar{x}}$:

$$\sigma_{\bar{x}} = \frac{\sigma}{\sqrt{n}}$$

For small populations, the variance and the standard error will be multiplied by a correction factor: $\sqrt{\dfrac{N-n}{N-1}}$, so the variance and the standard error become:

$$\text{Var}(\bar{X}) = \frac{\sigma^2}{n} \sqrt{\frac{N-n}{N-1}} \quad \text{and} \quad \sigma_{\bar{x}} = \frac{\sigma}{n} \sqrt{\frac{N-n}{N-1}}$$

The $\lim\limits_{N \to \infty} \sqrt{\dfrac{N-n}{N-1}}$ is one. This means as the number of elements or observations contained in the population increases, the correction factor tends to equal unity. In other words, with large populations, there is no need to use this correction factor.

Simulation may be used to construct empirical sampling distribution (the distribution of the mean or the proportion sampling distribution) by applying the Monte Carlo method. Also, a large sample, instead of many smaller samples, may be selected randomly from the population by different methods. Selection of a random sample by using random tables, and the stratified sampling selection are two of many techniques to be used to secure samples from populations.

The distribution of $\bar{X}$ for samples selected randomly from normal population is considered to be normally distributed regardless of the sample size. On the other hand, and according to the central limit theorem, if the sample size is large (or if $n \to \infty$), a random sample of size n selected from a population (not necessarily normal) approaches a normal distribution with

mean $= \mu$ and variance $= \dfrac{\sigma^2}{n}$, or $n(\bar{X}; \mu, \dfrac{\sigma^2}{n})$, and probabilities of

sample mean represented by any area under the normal distribution can be evaluated by:

$$Z = \frac{\bar{X} - \mu}{\sigma_{\bar{x}}} \qquad ; \quad \sigma_{\bar{x}} = \frac{\sigma}{\sqrt{n}}$$

To calculate Z and the P(Z) one needs to know the variance σ^2 or the standard deviation of the population which may not be available in many practical cases. In other words, one may have no information about the population and the only data available concerns the sample selected randomly from this population. Statistics such as the standard deviation s or the variance s^2 can be calculated for selected samples and may be used instead of the standard deviation σ or the variance of the population σ^2. In this case, t-distribution (student's distribution) may be used instead of Z-distribution to evaluate the probabilities of sample means:

$$t = \frac{\overline{X} - \mu}{s_{\overline{x}}} \quad ; \quad s_{\overline{x}} = \frac{s}{\sqrt{n-1}}$$

The probability density function of t-distribution is:

$$f(X) = \frac{1}{\sqrt{r\pi}} \frac{\Gamma[(r+1)/2]}{\Gamma(r/2)} \left(1 + \frac{x^2}{r}\right)^{-(r+1)/2}$$

where r refers to the degree of freedom.

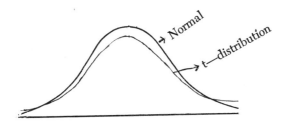

There are tables to find the probability of the t-distribution. It is necessary to determine the degree of freedom for the sample or samples under investigation. For a single sample, the degree of freedom (denoted by r,d.f., or v.) is equal to $n-1$. For example, if we have a sample of size 20, then $v = 20 - 1 = 19$. For two or more samples, find the degree of freedom for each sample $(n_i - 1)$ and simply add them together to find the degree of freedom for the two samples or more. For example, if we have two samples, the first sample of size 10, and the second of size 15, then

$$v = n_1 + n_2 - 2 = 10 + 15 - 2 = 23$$

or $v_1 = 10 - 1$ and $v_2 = 15 - 1$ and $v = v_1 + v_2$
$= 9$ $= 14$ $= 9 + 14 = 23$

If n is large $(n \geqq 31)$, then t-distribution approaches the Z-distribution and one can use either to evaluate the probabilities of the sample means. Example 6.12:

A production process is considered to be under control if the diameter of the parts produced may be looked upon as a normal population with mean $= 6''$ and variance $= .0036''$.

Thirty-six units are selected randomly from each shift production, and the process is considered under control if the mean diameter falls between $5.99''$ and $6.01''$.

What is the probability that a sample will fail to meet this criterion?

Solution:

(a) A sample selected randomly from a normal population is also normally distributed with mean $=\mu$, and variance $= \dfrac{\sigma^2}{n}$ or:

$$n\left(\ \overline{X};\ 6,\ \dfrac{.0036}{36}\ \right)$$

(b) The variance of the population σ^2 is known; then we can use the Z-distribution to evaluate probabilities:

$$Z = \dfrac{\overline{X} - \mu}{\sigma_{\overline{x}}}\quad ;\ \sigma_{\overline{x}} = \dfrac{\sigma}{\sqrt{n}} = \dfrac{\sqrt{.0036}}{\sqrt{36}} = \dfrac{.06}{6} = .01$$

(c) Draw a normal curve to determine the nonshaded area that indicates the process is under control.

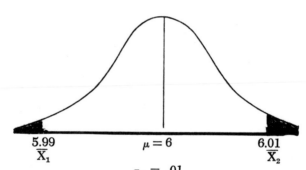

$$\begin{array}{ccc} 5.99 & \mu = 6 & 6.01 \\ \overline{X}_1 & & \overline{X}_2 \end{array}$$

$$\sigma_{\overline{x}} = .01$$

(d) P(a sample mean fails to meet this criterion) $= P(\overline{X}_2 < \overline{X} < \overline{X}_1)$

$$P(6.01 < \overline{X} < 5.99) = \int\limits_{6.01}^{5.99} f(x)\ dx + \int\limits_{-\infty}^{\infty} f(x)\ dx$$

$$= 1 - \left[\ P\left(\dfrac{6.01 - 6.00}{.01}\right) +\ P\left(\dfrac{5.99 - 6.00}{.01}\right)\ \right].$$

$$= 1 - [P(Z = 1)\ +\ P(Z = -1)]$$
$$= 1 - (.3414\ +\ .3414)$$
$$= 1 - .6828$$
$$= .3172\quad\text{the probability of the shaded area.}$$

Example 6.13:
   A sample of size 225 selected randomly from a normal population with $\mu = 100$ and variance $= 400$. What is the probability that the sample mean will be greater than the population mean by 3 or more?

Solution:

(a) Any sample selected randomly from a normal population is also normally distributed with mean = μ

and variance = $\dfrac{\sigma^2}{n}$

(b) The variance of the population is known, thus use the Z-distribution.

(c) Draw a normal curve with μ = 100 and standard error

$$\sigma_{\bar{x}} = \frac{\sigma}{\sqrt{n}} = \sqrt{\frac{400}{225}} = 1.33.$$

(d) Determine the area where the sample mean is greater than by 3 or more (the shaded area).

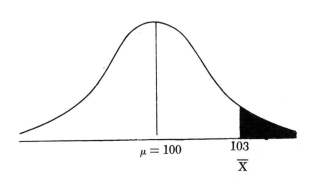

$$P(X > 103) = \int_{103}^{\infty} f(x)\,dx$$

$$= \int_{\mu}^{\infty} f(x)\,dx - \int_{\mu}^{103} f(x)\,dx$$

$$= .5 - P\left(\frac{103 - 100}{1.33}\right)$$

$$= .5 - P(Z = 2.26)$$

$$= .5 - .4881$$

$$= .0119$$

Example 6.14:

A normal population yielded an average of 50. What is the probability that a sample of size 101 selected randomly from this population and yielded a variance of 225 will have a mean less than 47?

Solution:

(a) The variance of the population is unknown; therefore use the t-distribution.

(b) Draw a normal curve with μ = 50, and $s_{\bar{x}} = \dfrac{s}{\sqrt{n-1}}$ or

$$s_{\bar{x}} = \frac{\sqrt{225}}{\sqrt{101-1}} = \frac{15}{10} = 1.5.$$

(c) Determine the area where the sample mean is less than 47 (the shaded area in the diagram).

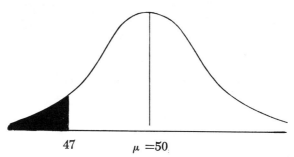

47          $\mu = 50$

(d) $P(\text{a sample mean less than } 47) = \int\limits_{-\infty}^{47} f(x) \, dx$

$$= P\left(\frac{47-50}{1.5}\right)$$

$$= P(t = -2) \qquad\qquad \mu = 50$$

$$= .0225 \quad \text{(from t-distribution table with degree of freedom } = 100)$$

(e) Since n is large, one may use the Z-distribution instead of t-distribution as follows:

$$P(\text{a sample mean less than } 47) = \int\limits_{-\infty}^{47} f(x) \, dx$$

$$= \int\limits_{-\infty}^{\mu} f(x) \, dx - \int\limits_{47}^{\mu} f(x) \, dx$$

$$= .5 - P\left(\frac{47-50}{1.5}\right)$$

$$= .5 - P(Z = -2)$$

$$= .5 - .4772$$

$$= .0228$$

B. Proportion Sampling Distribution:

This probability distribution is similar to the probability distribution of the mean except that the population of the proportion sampling distribution is binomial. Many populations that describe business problems are binomial. For example, the production process can be viewed as binomial populations with two, and only two, outcomes: defectives and non-defectives. Proportioning of defectives of samples selected randomly from these populations either by simulation (Monte Carlo method) or by other techniques can be used to construct the proportion sampling distribution with the following characteristics:

$$E(p) = \pi$$

The expected value of the sampling proportion equals the population proportion. The variance of the sampling proportion is:

$$Var(p) = \frac{\pi(1-\pi)}{n}$$

and the standard error of the sampling distribution is:

$$\sigma_p = \sqrt{\frac{\pi(1-\pi)}{n}}$$

The standard error of the sampling distribution σ_p shows the degree of dispersion of the sampling proportion p from the population or universe proportion π. If π is unknown then the variance and the standard error become:

$$s_p^2 = \frac{p(1-p)}{n-1}$$

and $\qquad s_p = \sqrt{\frac{p(1-p)}{n}} \qquad$ or $\qquad s_p = \sqrt{\frac{p(1-p)}{n-1}}$

Example 6.15:

Machine A produces parts of which 5% are defectives. A sample of size 15 is selected randomly from the output of machine A. What is the expected proportion of defectives and the standard error of the sample proportion?.

Solution:

$$E(p) = \pi = .05$$

$$\sigma_p = \sqrt{\frac{\pi(1-\pi)}{n}} = \sqrt{\frac{(.05)(1-.05)}{15}} = .056$$

Example 6.16:

Of fifty shoes selected randomly from the daily production of shoes five are found to be defective. What is the expected proportion of defectives in the total production of these shoes, and what is the standard error of the sampling proportion?

Solution:

(a) The universe proportion of defectives is not known; therefore, the $E(p) = p$, will be used as an estimate and the expected proportion of defectives in the total production is:

$$E(p) = p = \frac{5}{50} = .10$$

(b) The standard error of the sampling proportion is:

$$s_p = \sqrt{\frac{p(1-p)}{n-1}} = \sqrt{\frac{(.10)(.90)}{50-1}} = .0429$$

116

EXERCISES

6.1 a. A young man, while waiting for a young lady who is late, decided to amuse himself by walking either to the north or to the south 5 yards according to the following scheme: He tosses a fair die. If an odd number occurs he walks 5 yards to the south; if an even number occurs, he walks 5 yards to the north. His young lady was so late that he walked 50 yards. What is the probability of these:
1. he will be back at his starting point?
2. he will be exactly 10 yards either way from his starting point?

b. Given that a binomial variable X has mean = 6 and standard deviation = 2, find:
$$P(X=0), P(X \geq 10), P(X \leq 1), P(2 \leq X \leq 4)$$

6.2 a. An airline company discovered that an average of 3% of the reservations for a particular flight have been cancelled for the last 5 years. Therefore, the company set a policy of selling three more tickets than the 85-seat capacity of the flight. What is the probability that for every passenger who shows up for the flight there will be a seat available?

b. It is known from past experience that machine A produces 2.5% defectives. A sample of size 10 is selected randomly from the output of the machine. Find the probability that the sample will contain:
1. no defectives.
2. at least one defective.
3. not more than three defectives.

6.3 a. Box I contains 4 white and 6 green balls. Box II contains 2 white and 2 green balls. From I two balls are transferred to II. What is the probability that the sample will contain exactly one green ball?

b. Mr. X produces 100 units per day of which 10 are defective. A sample of size 5 is selected from the production of Mr. X without replacement. Find:
1. P(no defectives in the sample)
2. P(exactly two defectives)
3. P(at least one defective)
4. P(not more than two defectives)
5. P(less than three defectives)

6.4 a. Consider a lottery that sells 50 tickets and offers 3 prizes to be selected without replacement from the 50 tickets. If a person buys 4 tickets, what is the probability of winning two prizes, given that he has won at least one prize?

b. Solve part a. assuming that the prizes are awarded by drawing with replacement.

6.5 a. Consider 3 urns: urn I contains 2 white and 4 green balls, urn II contains 8 white and 4 green balls, and urn III contains one white and 3 green balls. Two fair coins are tossed. If two tails occur urn I is selected and 2 balls are drawn; if one head and one tail occur urn II is selected and 2 balls are drawn; if two heads occur, urn III is selected and 2 balls are drawn. Compute the conditional probability of selecting urn III given that 2 green balls are drawn with replacement.

    b. Solve part a. assuming that the balls have been drawn without replacement.

6.6 a. Assume that the number of telephone calls made to a medical clinic during an hour can be viewed as a random phenomenon that follows a Poisson distribution with $\lambda = 10$. What is the probability of:
  1. no phone calls received during an hour.
  2. at least one phone call during an hour.
  3. more than 5 phone calls during an hour.
  4. not less than 8 phone calls during an hour.

    b. Assume that surgical cases arriving in the accident ward of a hospital can be described by a Poisson probability function with $\lambda = 6$ per day. Find the probability of:
  1. no surgical cases in a particular day.
  2. exactly five surgical cases.
  3. at least one surgical case.
  4. more than 8 surgical cases.

6.7 a. The records show that machine A produces 2% defectives, and the number of defectives produced by the machine appears to follow a Poisson distribution. For a sample of 100 units selected randomly from the output of the machine find the probability of:
  1. no defectives.
  2. at least one defective.
  3. exactly 5 defectives.
  4. not less than 2 defectives.

    b. For a liquor store, it has been determined that the number of times a customer gets drunk after 5 drinks is well approximated by a Poisson probability distribution with $\lambda = 3$. Calculate: $P(X = 2)$, $P(2 \le X \le 4)$, $P(X \le 1)$.

6.8 a. Past records show that 15% of the coming orders had been rejected because they did not meet the specifications. What is the probability that 250 units ordered will yield 215 accepted units?

    b. Ignoring multiple births, and assuming that the probability of having a boy is .52, what is the probability that the second baby born will be a boy?

6.9 a. Tossing two fair dice, what is the probability that the first throw will be the first time that the sum of the dice is 12?

b. Tossing two fair dice, what is the probability that the second throw will be the second time the sum of 7 occurs?

c. Tossing two fair dice, what is the probability that the fourth throw will be the second time the sum of 5 occurs?

6.10 a. Assume that the time (in minutes) a newsboy spent from the time he leaves his house and returns back after finishing his route is a random phenomenon obeying a uniform probability distribution over the interval 40 - 50. If the boy leaves his house at 3:30 p.m., what is the probability that he will come back at 4:00 p.m.

b. In a department store customers arrive randomly at a rate of 20 per hour. What is the probability that the time interval between the first two customers will be:
1. more than 2 minutes.
2. less than 4 minutes.
3. between 1 and 3 minutes.

6.11 a. The specifications to produce a certain part are as follows: the length should be $15'' \pm .2''$. A machine has been set up to produce this part. The production of the machine is normally distributed with $\mu = 15.01''$ and $\sigma = .10''$.
What is the percentage of defectives produced by this machine?

b. Assume that the machine in part a. is adjusted so that the production is normally distributed with $\mu = 14.98''$ and $\sigma = .15''$. What is the percentage of defectives produced in this case?

6.12 Assume that the weight of football players is a random variable obeying a normal distribution with mean = 210 pounds and a variance = 625 pounds.
1. What is the percentage of football players whose weight is between 180 and 200 pounds?
2. What is the percentage of those who weigh 195 or less?
3. What is the percentage of those who weigh 240 or more?
4. Find the probability that the weight of one player is 235 pounds or more given that he weighs more than 220 pounds?

6.13 a. The life in hours of a radio tube is normally distributed with mean equals 1000 hours. Find the variance that makes the life of the tube between 750 and 1250 hours, and has a probability of 95%.

b. In part a., what is the probability that the tube will have a life of 1300 hours or more?

6.14 An automatic machine fills cans with coffee. The machine is set for 16 oz. net weight. The process is viewed as normally distributed with $\mu = 16$ and $\sigma = 0.5$.

A sample of 20 cans is selected randomly.   What is the probability
that the mean of this sample:
1. falls between 15.9 and 16.2.
2. is less than 16.
3. is more than 16.

6.15 Past experience showed that the fiber strength of cotton purchased
from a certain company appears to follow a normal probability distribution with mean = 80 and standard deviation of 10. What is the
probability that the mean fiber strength of fifty samples selected
randomly from a lot of cotton differs from the population mean by 13?

6.16 a. The proportion of defectives in the total production of tires in
factory A is found to be 20%. A sample of 100 tires has been
selected randomly from the output of one week.
Calculate the standard error of the sample proportion.

b. In part a. assume that the proportion of defectives in total production is unknown, and out of the 100 tires selected randomly
18 are found to be defectives. Calculate the estimated standard
error of proportion.

Chapter VII

STATISTICAL DECISION MAKING:
STATISTICAL INFERENCE

The main objective of statistical theory is to be applied in decision making. In the area of decision making one has to distinguish between classical and non-classical approaches used to arrive at conclusions and decisions using statistical analysis.

The process of making decisions concerning the paramters of populations based on information contained in a sample or samples selected randomly from these populations is called "statistical in ference," which is considered the classical approach of statistical decision making.

The non-classical approach for statistical decision making includes Decision theory and Econometrics. Decision makers sometimes face a situation where many alternative courses of action exist and they have to choose the one that optimizes their goal. This can be achieved through the application of decision theory. On the other hand, whenever historical data (time series) are readily available, an appropriate mathematical model can be constructed and the parameters of the model can be estimated by statistical techniques to provide the decision maker with a reliable predictive model. This is the econometric approach to statistical decision making.

In this chapter, the classical approach of statistical decision making, namely "Statistical Inference," will be covered, while subsequent chapters will provide the reader with the elements of the non-classical approach. Statistical Inference:

Statistical inference or analytical statistics refers to the process of arriving at decisions about the parameters of the populations by examining a sample or samples drawn from these populations. For example, to find the average diameter of a part produced by 10 machines, the diameter of a sample of n parts selected randomly from the production of the machines to be measured, and the average diameter of the selected sample ($\overline{X}$), is used as an estimate of the average diameter of the total production or of the population (μ). This statistical technique is called "Estimation." In other cases, the mean of the population is known (or predetermined) and the mean of a sample selected from this population may differ from the mean of the population. This difference can be viewed as significant or as due to sampling. Tests designed to arrive at such decisions are called "Test of Hypotheses." Statistical inference can be classified into two categories:

1. Estimation
2. Test of Hypotheses

1. Estimation:

Estimation is a common statistical technique that plays an important role in applied statistics. For example, one may use the mean of the lifetime of 12 batteries to estimate the true average time of this brand of batteries. Estimation is classified into two types:

    A. Point estimation

    B. Interval estimation

A. Point Estimation:

A point estimate is a single value that represents a sample statistic used to describe a population parameter. If a sample is selected randomly from a population, the statistics calculated from this sample such as: $\overline{X}$, p, s^2 and s are point estimates for the population parameters: μ, π, σ^2 and σ respectively. Point estimates should possess the following properties: unbiasedness, consistency, relative efficiency, and sufficiency.

An example of the application of point estimate: the mean height of 10 plants is found to be 10″. With this information one can describe the average height of the population of this plant to be 10″. Another example: if the proportion of defectives in 100 parts selected randomly from the production of machine A is 2%, then based on this information one can conclude that machine A produces 2% defectives.

In the first example, the average height of the plant population could be 10″, less than 10″, or more than 10″. It is true that the average height of the population of this plant is around 10″ but not necessarily exactly 10″. Also machine A produces around 2% defectives. In general, it is most likely that the statistics will not hit the parameters they suppose to estimate "on the nose." Therefore it is advisable to use interval estimation.

B. Interval Estimation:

An interval is a distance between two points or limits, e.g., the interval $4 \le X \le 8$ has a lower limit of 4 and an upper limit of 8, and X assumes any value between the lower and the upper limit. This interval may be written as: $4 < X < 8$.

Interval estimation can be used to describe the average height of the plant population:

$$8″ < \mu < 10″$$

and the proportion of defectives in the total production of machine A:

$$1.5\% < \pi < 2.5\%$$

Interval estimation is more desirable and flexible than point estimation. There are different intervals, or confidence intervals, for the mean and the proportion of the population.

Confidence intervals for the population mean:

Sampling distribution can be approximated by a normal distribution if the sample is large enough or if the sample selected randomly is from a normal population. In both cases the mean of the sample of size n is normally distributed with mean $= \mu$, and variance $= \dfrac{\sigma^2}{n}$ or $n(\overline{X};\mu, \dfrac{\sigma^2}{n})$.

To construct an interval estimation or confidence interval for μ the mean of the population, one has to determine the degree of the confidence interval $(1 - \alpha)$ as shown in the diagram.

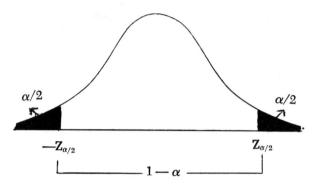

If $\alpha = .05$ then the degree of confidence is 95% or we have a 95% confidence interval. This means that the probability that the mean of the population μ falls between $-Z_{\alpha/2}$ and $Z_{\alpha/2}$ is 0.95, or we are confident 95% that μ falls between the lower limit at $-Z_{\alpha/2}$ and the upper limit at $Z_{\alpha/2}$. The confidence interval $1 - \alpha$ is:

$$\int_{-Z_{\alpha/2}}^{Z_{\alpha/2}} f(x)\, dx = P\left(-Z_{\alpha/2} < \frac{\overline{X} - \mu}{\sigma/\sqrt{n}} < Z_{\alpha/2}\right) = 1 - \alpha$$

The confidence interval $1 - \alpha$ for the population mean μ, where the variance or the standard deviation of the population is known, can be derived from the double inequality:

$$-Z_{\alpha/2} < \frac{\overline{X} - \mu}{\sigma/\sqrt{n}} < Z_{\alpha/2}$$

$$-Z_{\alpha/2}\, \frac{\sigma}{\sqrt{n}} < \overline{X} - \mu < Z_{\alpha/2}\, \frac{\sigma}{\sqrt{n}}$$

$$-\overline{X} - Z_{\alpha/2}\, \frac{\sigma}{\sqrt{n}} < -\mu < -\overline{X} + Z_{\alpha/2}\, \frac{\sigma}{\sqrt{n}}$$

$$\overline{X} + Z_{\alpha/2} \frac{\sigma}{\sqrt{n}} > \mu > \overline{X} - Z_{\alpha/2}\, \frac{\sigma}{\sqrt{n}}$$

$$\overline{X} - Z_{\alpha/2}\, \frac{\sigma}{\sqrt{n}} < \mu < \overline{X} + Z_{\alpha/2}\, \frac{\sigma}{\sqrt{n}}$$

The lower limit of the confidence interval $(1 - \alpha)$ is: $\overline{X} - Z_{\alpha/2} \frac{\sigma}{\sqrt{n}}$ where $\overline{X}$ is the sample mean and $\frac{\sigma}{\sqrt{n}}$ is the standard error of the sample mean. The upper limit of the confidence interval $(1 - \alpha)$ is: $\overline{X} + Z_{\alpha/2} \frac{\sigma}{\sqrt{n}}$

This means the value $Z_{\alpha/2}\dfrac{\sigma}{\sqrt{n}}$ must be subtracted from the sample mean to find the lower limit of the confidence interval, and to add the same value $Z_{\alpha/2}\dfrac{\sigma}{\sqrt{n}}$ to the sample mean to find the upper limit of the confidence interval $(1-\alpha)$. In other words, the mean of the population $\mu = \overline{X} \pm Z_{\alpha/2}\dfrac{\sigma}{\sqrt{n}}$

Example 7.1:
Past records showed that the length of time customers take to shop in a supermarket is normally distributed with variance of 100 minutes. A sample of 25 customers selected randomly yielded an average of 30 minutes to shop. Construct a 99% confidence interval for the mean length of time spent in shopping in this supermarket.
Solution:
   (a)   The variance of the population σ^2 is known ($\sigma^2 = 100$)

   (b) $\overline{X} = 30,\ \sigma = \sqrt{100} = 10,\ \dfrac{\sigma}{\sqrt{n}} = \dfrac{10}{\sqrt{25}} = \dfrac{10}{5} = 2$

   (c) $1 - \alpha = .99,\ P(Z) = \dfrac{.99}{2} = .4950,$ then $Z_{\alpha/2} = 2.58$

$$\overline{X} - Z_{\alpha/2}\frac{\sigma}{\sqrt{}} < \mu < \overline{X} + Z_{\alpha/2}\frac{\sigma}{\sqrt{}}$$

$30 - (2.58)(2) < \mu < 30 + (2.58)(2)$
$\qquad 24.84 < \mu < 35.16$
We are confident 99% that the mean length of time spent in shopping in this supermarket is between 24.84 and 35.16 minutes. Or the probability that a customer will spend time between 24.84 and 35.16 minutes to shop at this store is 0.99.
   If the population variance σ^2 (or standard deviation σ) is unknown, then the sample variance s^2 (or standard deviation s) will be used as a point estimate and t-distribution is applied instead of the Z-distribution. The confidence interval $(1 - \alpha)$ for the population mean μ, when the population variance is unknown is:

$$\overline{X} - t\frac{s}{\sqrt{n-1}} < \mu < \overline{X} + t\frac{s}{\sqrt{n-1}}$$

where $\overline{X}$ = the sample mean, s = sample standard deviation, n — 1 = degree of freedom.
   As mentioned before, to evaluate t one needs to know α and v (degree of freedom).
Example 7.2:
A random sample of 101 students showed an average of $800 as summer earnings for a full-time job, with standard deviation of $100.
   Construct a 95% confidence interval for the mean summer earnings.
Solution:
   (a)   The variance of the population (σ^2) is unknown; however, the standard deviation of the sample s is available (s = 100).

(b) $\overline{X} = 800, \dfrac{s}{\sqrt{n-1}} = \dfrac{100}{\sqrt{101-1}} = 10$

(c) $1 - \alpha = .95$, find $t_{.05,\ 100}$ $(v = n - 1 = 101 - 1 = 100)$

$$\overline{X} - t\ \dfrac{s}{\sqrt{n-1}} < \mu < \overline{X} + t\ \dfrac{s}{\sqrt{n-1}}$$

$$800 - (1.97)(10) < \mu < 800 + (1.97)(10)$$
$$780.3 < \mu < 819.7$$

We are confident 95% that the average summer earnings of the students in this group is between $780.30 and $819.70.

Confidence interval for the population proportion:
Many business phenomena follow a binomial distribution. Therefore the estimation of proportions or rates is desirable. For example, any production process can be viewed to follow a binomial population with π as the population proportion of defectives. It is of great interest for the production management as well as for the quality control department to evaluate the confidence interval for the population proportion π by selecting a random sample of this population.

A binomial population can be approximated by a normal distribution with mean $= np$ and variance $= npq$ or: $n(X; np, npq)$ and the confidence interval $(1 - \alpha)$ for the population π becomes:

$$p - Z_{\alpha/2}\ \sigma_p < \pi < p + Z_{\alpha/2}\ \sigma_p$$

$$\sigma_p = \sqrt{\dfrac{\pi(1-\pi)}{n}}$$

where p = sample proportion and σ_p = standard error of the sampling proportion.

This formula assumes that π is known, which is being estimated.

The realistic situation is when π is unknown and the confidence interval of π becomes:

$$p - Z_{\alpha/2}\ s_p < \pi < p + Z_{\alpha/2}\ s_p$$

$$s_p = \sqrt{\dfrac{P(1-P)}{n}}$$

The sample proportion p is a ratio of the number of successes X and the number of trials n as $n \to \infty$. This means that $p = \dfrac{X}{n}$ as the sample size increases. Using this feature the confidence interval for π becomes:

$$\dfrac{x}{n} - Z_{\alpha/2}\ s_p < \pi < \dfrac{x}{n} + Z_{\alpha/2}\ s_p$$

$$s_p = \sqrt{\dfrac{\dfrac{x}{n}\left(1 - \dfrac{x}{n}\right)}{n}}$$

Example 7.3:

A sample survey showed that 120 of 800 families interviewed in the midwest would like to move to the west coast. Find a 0.90 confidence interval for the actual proportion of families in the midwest willing to move to the west coast.

Solution:

(a) $x = 120$ $n = 800$ $\dfrac{x}{n} = .15$

(b) $s_p = \sqrt{\dfrac{(.15)(.85).}{800}} = .0126$

(c) $P(Z_{\alpha/2}) = .45$ $Z_{\alpha/2} = 1.65$

$$\dfrac{x}{n} - Z_{\alpha/2}\, s_p < \pi < \dfrac{x}{n} + Z_{\alpha/2}\, s_p$$

$.15 - (1.65)(0.126) < \pi < .15 + (1.65)(0.126)$
$$.12921 < \pi < .17079$$
We are confident 90% that the actual proportion of families in the midwest willing to move to the west coast is between 12.921% and 17.079%.

Determination of the sample size:

A question frequently raised is the appropriate size of the sample to be selected from the population at random. The sample size n depends on the degree of confidence or the interval estimation $(1 - \alpha)$, standard deviation (σ or s), the deviation of the sample mean or proportion from the mean or proportion of the population $(\overline{X} - \mu$ or $p - \pi)$.

The sample size n can be derived from:

$$Z = \dfrac{\overline{X} - \mu}{\sigma/\sqrt{n}} \qquad \text{or } Z = \dfrac{p - \pi}{\sqrt{\dfrac{\pi(1-\pi)}{n}}} \qquad \text{and solve for n.}$$

$$Z \dfrac{\sigma}{\sqrt{n}} = \overline{X} - \mu \qquad\qquad Z \sqrt{\dfrac{\pi(1-\pi)}{n}} = p - \pi$$

$$\sqrt{n} = \dfrac{Z\sigma}{\overline{X} - \mu} \qquad\qquad \dfrac{Z^2\pi(1-\pi)}{n} = (p - \pi)^2$$

$$n = \left[\dfrac{Z\sigma}{\overline{X} - \mu}\right]^2 \qquad\qquad n = \dfrac{Z^2\pi(1-\pi)}{(p - \pi)^2}$$

Example 7.4:

A tire manufacturing company wishes to know the average useful life of Brand A tire. What is the proper sample size to estimate this average in order that the probability will be 95% that the true mean does not differ from the sample mean by more than 100 miles? The standard deviation for the useful life of all tires produced is 500 miles.

Solution:

$$n = \left[\frac{Z_\sigma}{\overline{X} - \mu} \right]^2$$

(a) $P(Z_{\alpha/2}) = \frac{.95}{2} = .475$

$\qquad Z_{\alpha/2} = 1.96$

(b) $\overline{X} - \mu = 100$ miles

(c) $\sigma = 500$ miles

$$n = \left[\frac{(1.96)(500)}{100} \right]^2 \cong 96$$

Example 7.5:

A production manager wishes to know the proper size of a sample to estimate the rate of defectives produced by a new machine such as the probability is 99% that the true proportion or rate of defectives does not differ from the sample proportion by more than 3%. The rate of defectives produced by all machines is 5%.

Solution:

$$n = \frac{Z^2 \pi (1 - \pi)}{(p - \pi)^2}$$

(a) $P(Z_{\alpha/2}) = \frac{.99}{2} = .495$

$\qquad Z = 2.58$

(b) $p - \pi = .03$

(c) $\pi = .05$

$$n = \frac{(2.58)^2 (.05)(.95)}{(.03)^2} \cong 351.$$

Statistical Quality Control:

The following brief presentation of statistical quality control is intended to show the reader a direct application of interval estimation in production process.

The value of quality control is to detect in time the variation in production attributed to non-random causes such as tool wear, improper machine setting, change in raw materials, and the change in human element (operator).

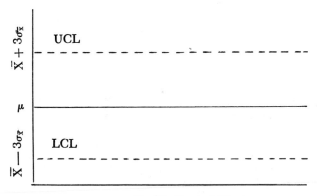

Quality Control Chart

Control charts as shown in the diagram are confidence intervals of 99.7% degree: $\mu = \overline{X} \pm 3\sigma_{\overline{x}}$. The upper control limit (UCL) is $\mu + 3\sigma_{\overline{x}}$ and the lower control limit (LCL) is $\mu - 3\sigma_{\overline{x}}$. A quality control man selects a sample of size n at equal intervals (or quantity). Calculate the sample mean and put it on the chart.

As long as all sample means fall within the two control limits with more points to fall near the central (μ) line and fewer far from it, the process of production is normal. If an upward, downward, or any other pattern noted in the points of the sample means appears on the chart, then this is a red light warning of some attributed variation needing to be adjusted. This situation is true if a sample mean falls outside the upper or lower control limits.

2. Test of Hypotheses:

Test of hypotheses has been developed to decide whether sample statistics ($\overline{X}$, p, s) can represent population parameters (μ, π, σ). A hypothesis is an assumption, and a statistical hypothesis is an assumption about the parameters of a population. A test of statistical hypothesis is a procedure for deciding whether to accept or to reject the hypothesis.

For example, a textile mill may set the desirable average fiber strength of the cotton being used. New shipments of cotton are tested for their average fiber strength to meet the desired average. Samples are taken from the new shipment and the average of these samples ($\overline{X}$) is tested against the desirable average (μ). The test applied in this case is the test of hypothesis. The hypothesis to be tested ($\overline{X} = \mu$) is called the null hypothesis and is denoted by H_o. The null hypothesis assumes that the difference between X and μ is insignificant and due to sampling. If the null hypothesis is rejected, then we might accept its alternative or H_1 (the alternative hypothesis). To decide on accepting or rejecting a null hypothesis, one needs a criterion or a decision rule to determine when to accept or to reject the null hypothesis.

If we are testing the null hypothesis that a coin is fair [$P(H) = P(T)$] against the alternative, then the following decision rule may be applied: "Toss the coin n times, and if the number of heads is $\leq Z_1$ or $\geq Z_2$, reject the null hypothesis."

128

In setting up the decision rule, we are saying that if the probability of the sample occurring by chance falls in the shaded area shown in the diagram, then reject H_o. The probability of this shaded area is denoted by α, the level of significance. The shaded area is called the critical region of a statistical test of hypothesis. which corresponds to the rejection of the hypothesis being tested.

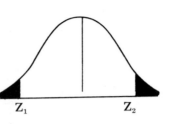

Z_1 Z_2

Types of Error:

There are two types of error that can occur while testing hypotheses:

	H_o is True	H_1 is True
reject H_o	Type I error	correct decision
accept H_o	correct decision	Type II error

Type I error is to reject a true null hypothesis, and the probability of type I error is α. If $\alpha = .05$, this means that the probability of accepting a true hypothesis is 95% and the probability of rejecting a true hypothesis is 5%; or 5% of the time true null hypotheses will be rejected. Type II error is to accept a false hypothesis, and the probability of type II error is β. Probability of type I error plus the probability of type II error is unity or $\alpha + \beta = 1$. To minimize α means to maximize β.

When the decision maker sets an assumption about the parameter of the population to be the null hypothesis, he is usually sure that his assumption is correct. For example, a marketing research department executive making an assumption or hypothesis about the potential average sales of a new product, his assumption is based on many factors as his experience, local and national data, surveys or any type of research concerning this commodity. In short, the executive or the decision maker will not make any hypothesis unless he is sure to a great extent that it is correct. Therefore, the probability of rejecting the null hypothesis is minimized or α is set to be as small as possible.

Another way to decide on the size of α is to construct a power curve which is the outcome of the power function: $P(\text{reject } H_o) = f(\mu)$ as shown in the diagram:

$P(\text{Reject } H_o)$

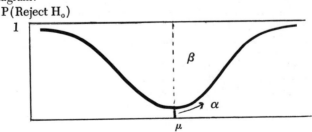

A power curve provides the decision maker with data to select the proper size of α. The common point of all power curves to minimize α is at $\alpha = .05$. The probability of type I error (rejecting a true hypothesis) may decrease with larger samples; also, if α is fixed, then the probability of type II error (accepting a false hypothesis) can be reduced with larger samples.

Types of Test:

There are two types for the test of hypotheses:

(a) Two-tail test:

If the decision maker wishes to test whether the sample statistic is *different* from the population parameter, then the test is a two-tail test because *different* means greater or less than as shown in the diagram. The set of the test is as follows:

H_0: $\overline{X} = \mu$

→ H_1: $\overline{X} = \mu$ indicates a Two-tail test.

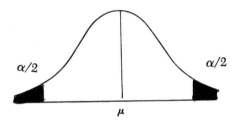

(b) One-tail test:

If the decision maker wishes to test whether the sample statistic is greater than the population parameter, then he runs a one-tail test. In this case he is concerned with the right tail as shown in the diagram. The set of the test can be as follows:

H_0: $p \leqq \pi$

→ H_1: $p > \pi$ indicates a One-tail test.

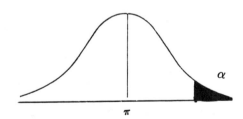

On the other hand, if the decision maker is concerned about whether the sample statistic is less than the population parameter, then he is faced with a one-tail test and α is located at the left tail as shown in the diagram:

H_0: $\overline{X} \geqq \mu$

→ H_1: $X < \mu$ indicates a One-tail test.

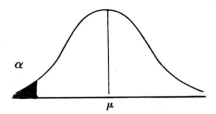

Methods of Testing Hypotheses:

There are different methods to test the hypotheses concerning the mean, the proportion, and the variance. The following methods are considered:
1. Tests concerning the mean:
    a. Test for the difference between μ and $\overline{X}$; σ is known.
    b. Test for the difference between μ and $\overline{X}$; σ is unknown.
    c. Test for the difference between two sample means $(\overline{X}_1, \overline{X}_2)$.
2. Tests concerning the proportion:
    a. Test for the difference between π and p.
    b. Test for the difference between two sample proportions (p_1, p_2).
3. Tests concerning the variance:
    a. Chi-square test.
    b. F-distribution test.

1. Tests concerning the mean:

These tests are conducted to show that the difference between the sample mean and the population mean is due to sampling and no significant difference exists. For example, a part produced by a factory according to specifications such that the diameter is 8″ with standard deviation of .15″. The machine is set to produce the part to meet these specifications. Nonetheless, a quality control or a production management man has to check whether the average length of the diameter of samples selected from the total production is within the acceptable range. If not, the machine needs to be adjusted.

These tests also show the validity of the average of two samples, one taken before introducing a new technique and the other after the application of the new technique. These two sample means may be tested to show whether the new technique has or has not caused any improvement or effect.

a. Test for the difference between μ and $\overline{X}$; σ is known.

If the standard deviation of the population σ is known, then the test for the difference between the population mean μ and the sample mean X requires the calculation of Z_c:

$$Z_c = \frac{\overline{X} - \mu}{\dfrac{\sigma}{\sqrt{n}}}$$

Example 7.6:

An automobile company claimed that the six-cylinder cars produced by the company deliver an average of 20 miles per gallon in town with standard deviation of 4 miles. Fifty of these cars are tested for mileage and they yielded an average of 18.5 miles per gallon. At a .05 level of significance, would you agree with the company's claim?

Solution:

(a) σ is known → use $Z_c = \dfrac{\overline{X} - \mu}{\sigma/\sqrt{n}}$

(b) $\mu = 20$ $\sigma = 4$
      $\overline{X} = 18.5$ $n = 50$

(c)   Set up the test as follows:
$H_0:$ $X \geq \mu$
$H_1:$ $X < \mu$ → One-tail test
$\alpha = .05$

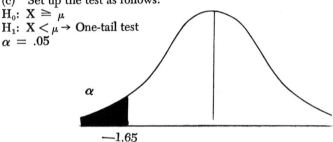

α

-1.65

(d) $Z_c = \dfrac{\overline{X} - \mu}{\sigma/\sqrt{n}} = \dfrac{18.5 - 20}{\dfrac{4}{\sqrt{50}}} = -2.65$

(e) Z_c falls in the shaded area (rejection region)
      H_0 is rejected.

We are confident 95% that the average mileage per gallon delivered by these six-cylinder cars is less than the average mileage per gallon claimd by the company.

b.   Test for the difference between μ and $\overline{X}$; σ is unknown.

In many cases, the standard deviation of the universe σ is unknown, and the standard deviation of the sample s is used as a point estimate of σ. When the standard deviation of the population is unknown, then the t-distribution will be used instead of the Z-distribution:

$$t_c = \dfrac{\overline{X} - \mu}{\dfrac{s}{\sqrt{n-1}}}$$

where n — 1 is the degree of freedom (v).

Example 7.7:

A supermarket, used to issuing trading stamps, showed an average sale of $20.13 per customer in the past. The new manager decided to reduce prices and stop issuing trading stamps. A sample of 200 customers yielded an average sale of $21.50 and a standard deviation of $6.90.

At a level of significance of .01, would you conclude that there is a significant difference between the two policies?

Solution:

(a) σ is unknown → use $t_c = \dfrac{\overline{X} - \mu}{\dfrac{s}{\sqrt{n-1}}}$

(b) $\mu = 20.15 \qquad s = 6.90$
$\overline{X} = 21.50 \qquad n = 200$
$v = n - 1 = 199$

(c) Set up the test:
$H_0: \overline{X} = \mu$
$H_1: \overline{X} \neq \mu \rightarrow$ Two-tail test
$\alpha = .01$
$t_{\alpha/2}, \ v = 2.58$

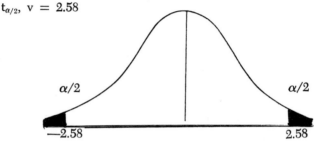

$\alpha/2 \qquad\qquad\qquad\qquad\qquad\qquad\qquad \alpha/2$

$-2.58 \qquad\qquad\qquad\qquad\qquad\qquad\qquad 2.58$

(d) $t_c = \dfrac{\overline{X} - \mu}{\dfrac{s}{\sqrt{n-1}}} = \dfrac{21.50 - 20.15}{\dfrac{6.90}{\sqrt{200-1}}} = 2.76$

(e) t_c falls in the shaded area (rejection region)
H_0 is rejected.

The probability that the two policies differ significantly is 0.99.

c. Test for the difference between two sample means $(\overline{X}_1, \overline{X}_2)$:

In some cases, it is desirable to test the means of two samples to determine whether or not there is a significant difference between them.

To run the test, the calculation of the t_c is required:

$$t_c = \dfrac{\overline{X}_1 - \overline{X}_2}{s_{\bar{x}1 - \bar{x}2}}$$

where $s_{\bar{x}1 - \bar{x}2}$ is the standard error of the difference for the two sample means. The formula for $s_{\bar{x}1 - \bar{x}2}$ for small samples differs from large samples:

For Large samples: $s_{\bar{x}1 - \bar{x}2} = \sqrt{\dfrac{s_1^2}{n_1} + \dfrac{s_2^2}{n_2}}$

For Small samples: $s_{\bar{x}1 - \bar{x}2} = \sqrt{\dfrac{n_1 s_1^2 + n_2 s_2^2}{n_1 + n_2 - 2}} \ \sqrt{\dfrac{1}{n_1} + \dfrac{1}{n_2}}$

Example 7.8 (Large samples):
The manager of a gas station observed the amount of time required for his two attendants to serve the customers. For a sample of 50 customers, it takes Bill an average of 12 minutes with a standard deviation of 4 minutes, while for 52 customers it takes Dick an average of 10 minutes with a standard deviation of 5 minutes.

At a .01 level of significance, is there a significant difference between the performance of Bill and Dick?

Solution:

(a) Samples are large $\rightarrow$ $s_{\bar{x}1 - \bar{x}2} = \sqrt{\dfrac{s_1{}^2}{n_1} + \dfrac{s_2{}^2}{n_2}}$

(b) $n_1 = 50 \qquad \overline{X}_1 = 12 \qquad s_1 = 4$
   $n_2 = 52 \qquad \overline{X}_2 = 10 \qquad s_2 = 5$
   $v = n_1 + n_2 - 2$
   $= 50 + 52 - 2 = 100$ (degree of freedom)

(c) Set up the test:
   $H_0: \overline{X}_1 = \overline{X}_2$
   $H_1: \overline{X}_1 \neq \overline{X}_2 \rightarrow$ Two-tail test
   $\alpha = .01$
   $t_{\alpha/2}, v = 2.617$ (from the table)

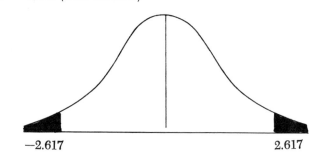

-2.617 $\qquad\qquad\qquad\qquad\qquad\qquad\qquad$ 2.617

(d) $t_c = \dfrac{\overline{X}_1 - \overline{X}_2}{s_{\bar{x}1 - \bar{x}2}}$

   $s_{\bar{x}1 - \bar{x}2} = \sqrt{\dfrac{16}{50} + \dfrac{25}{52.}} = .895$

   $t_c = \dfrac{12 - 10}{.895} = 2.235$

(e) t_c falls in the unshaded area (acceptance region)
   H_0 is accepted.
With probability of 99%, there is no significant difference between the performance of Bill and Dick.

Example 7.9 (Small samples):
Two lots of cotton are tested for fiber strength. The following sample information is made available:

134

I (Pounds)	II (Pounds)
88.5	79.9
90.0	89.4
87.5	90.5
85.9	89.2
79.1	91.0
	88.0

At at .05 level of significance, determine whether or not there is a significant difference in the fiber strength of the two lots.

Solution:

(a) Small samples → $t_c = \dfrac{\overline{X}_1 - \overline{X}_2}{s_{\bar{x}1 - \bar{x}2}}$

$, \quad s_{\bar{x}1 - \bar{x}2} = \sqrt{\dfrac{s_1{}^2 n_1 + s_2{}^2 n_2}{n_1 + n_2 - 2}} \sqrt{\dfrac{1}{n_1} + \dfrac{1}{n_2}}$

(b) $n_1 = 5 \qquad n_2 = 6 \qquad v = n_1 + n_2 - 2 = 9$ (degree of freedom)

(c) Calculate: $X_1, X_2, s_1{}^2, s_2{}^2$:

X_1	$X_1{}^2$	X_2	$X_2{}^2$
88.5	7832.25	79.9	6384.01
90.0	8100.00	89.4	7992.36
87.5	7656.25	90.5	8190.25
85.9	7378.81	89.2	7956.64
79.1	6256.81	91.0	8281.00
		88.0	7744.00
431.0	37224.12	528.0	46548.26

$\overline{X}_1 = 86.20 \qquad\qquad\qquad \overline{X}_2 = 88.0$

$s_1{}^2 = \dfrac{\Sigma X_1{}^2}{n} - (\overline{X}_1)^2 \qquad\qquad s_2{}^2 = \dfrac{\Sigma X_2{}^2}{n} - (\overline{X}_2)^2$

$\qquad = \dfrac{37224.12}{5} - (86.2)^2 \qquad\qquad = \dfrac{46548.26}{6} - (88.0)^2$

$\qquad = 14.38 \qquad\qquad\qquad\qquad\quad = 14.04$

(d) Set up the test:

$\qquad H_0: X_1 = X_2$

$\qquad H_1: X_1 \neq X_2$ → Two-tail test.

$\qquad \alpha = .05$

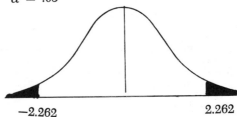

−2.262   2.262

(e) Calculate t_c:

$$s_{\bar{x}1 - \bar{x}2} = \sqrt{\frac{s_1{}^2 n_1 + s_2{}^2 n_2}{n_1 + n_2 - 2}} \ \sqrt{\frac{1}{n_1} + \frac{1}{n_2}}$$

$$= \sqrt{\frac{(14.38)(5) + (14.04)(6)}{5 + 6 - 2}} \ \sqrt{\frac{1}{5} + \frac{1}{6}}$$

$$= 2.54$$

$$t_c = \frac{\overline{X}_1 - \overline{X}_2}{s_{\bar{x}1 - \bar{x}2}}$$

$$= \frac{86.20 - 88.00}{2.54}$$

$$= -.71$$

(f) t_c falls in the acceptance region
     H_0 is accepted.
We are confidence 95% that there is no significant difference in the fiber strength of the two lots of cotton.

2. Tests concerning the proportion:

Testing proportions is commonly used in making business and economic decisions especially in the area of marketing and quality control.

a. Test for the difference between π and p:
To test for the difference between a universe proportion π and a sample proportion p drawn randomly from the population, it is required to calculate Z_c:

$$Z_c = \frac{p - \pi}{\sigma_p}$$

$$, \ \sigma_p = \sqrt{\frac{\pi(1 - \pi)}{n}}$$

Example 7.10:
A manager of a liquor store claimed that 85% of those whose ages range between 21 and 25 years prefer to drink beer. A market research analyst observed 200 customers (whose ages fall between 21 and 25 years) and found that 163 of them prefer to drink beer.
At a level of significance of .05, would the market research analyst agree with the manager's claim?
Solution:

(a) $\pi = .85$

$$p = \frac{163}{200} = .815$$

(b) Set up the test:
$$H_0: p \geq \pi$$
$$H_1: p < \pi \rightarrow \text{One-tail test}$$
$$\alpha = .05$$

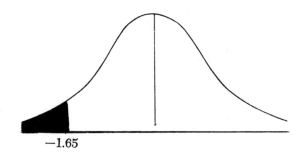

−1.65

(c) $Z_c = \dfrac{p - \pi}{\sqrt{\dfrac{\pi - (1 - \pi)}{n}}}$

$= \dfrac{8.15 - .85}{\sqrt{\dfrac{(.85)(.15)}{200}}}$

$= -1.38$

(d) Z_c falls in the acceptance region.
     H_0 is accepted.

(e) The probability that the market research analyst agrees with the manager's claim is 0.95.

b.   Test for the difference between two sample proportions (p_1, p_2):

In many practical cases, decisions concerning the introduction of new techniques, new machines, or new operators can be made by testing for the difference between two sample proportions. This test can be constructed by calculating Z_c:

$$Z_c = \frac{p_1 - p_2}{s_{p1-p2}}$$

$$, \; s_{p1-p2} = \sqrt{\frac{p_t(1 - p_t)}{n_1} + \frac{p_t(1 - p_t)}{n_2}}$$

where p_t = a proportion constructed for the two samples combined
Example 7.11:

Two new machines, one from Company X and the other from Company Y are tested. Machine X turns out 15 defectives in 250 units produced, and Machine Y turns out 25 defectives in 350 units produced.

At a .05 level of significance, is there a significant difference in the proportion of defectives turned out by the two machines?
Solution:

(a) The test for two-sample proportion:

(b) $p_1 = \dfrac{15}{250} = .06$ $p_2 = \dfrac{25}{350} = .071$

$$P_t = \frac{15 + 25}{250 + 350} = \frac{40}{600} = .067$$

(c) Set up the test:
H_0: $p_1 = p_2$
H_1: $p_1 \neq p_2 \rightarrow$ Two-tail test
$\alpha = .05$

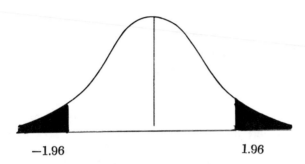

$\quad\quad -1.96 \quad\quad\quad\quad\quad\quad\quad\quad 1.96$

(d) Calculate Z_c:

$$S_{p1-p2} = \sqrt{\frac{P_t(1 - p_t)}{n_1} + \frac{P_t(1 - p_t)}{n_2}}$$

$$= \sqrt{\frac{(.067)(.933)}{250} + \frac{(.067)(.933)}{350}}$$

$$= .0207$$

$$Z_c = \frac{p_1 - p_2}{S_{p1-p2}} = \frac{.06 - .071}{.0207} = -.5314$$

(d) Z_c falls in the acceptance region.
H_0 is accepted.

(e) We are confident 95% that there is no significant difference between the proportion of defectives turned out by the two machines.

3. Tests concerning the variance:

In many cases it is important to test hypotheses concerning variances of populations. For example, a manufacturer of high-precision tools has to test the variability of his product in order to meet the rigid specifications set for these tools. Chi-square (χ^2) distribution can be used for tests concerning variances of populations and samples. Also, χ^2 distribution can be used in other tests such as: test for goodness-of-fit, test of independency, and test of homogeneity.

Another distribution, the F-distribution, can be used for testing hypotheses concerning the equality of two estimated population variances. F-distribution is called the variance ratio and is named in the honor of

138

R. Fisher, the great statistician who developed this distribution. F-distribution is also used in the analysis of variance where a decision should be made whether the difference among sample means are attributed to sampling error or that the difference is statistically significant.

In this section, the χ^2 distribution and F-distribution are applied to different hypotheses.

χ^2-distribution:

A. Test for the difference between the population variance (σ^2) and the sample variance (s^2):

Chi-square is used for testing the variance of a sample and the variance of the population. If X is a normal distribution variable, then the ratio:

$$\frac{s^2\,(n-1)}{\sigma^2}$$

is a χ^2 distribution with $v = n - 1$ (degree of freedom).

Example 7.12:

The diameter of a cylinder should meet rigid specifications and is allowed a variability of $\sigma = .005$. A sample of size 25 selected yielded variance $= .000028$.

At a level of significance of .01, what are the chances that the production of these cylinders will meet the specifications?

Solution:

(a) This is a test concerning the variance of the sample and the

variance of the population, $\chi_c^2 = \dfrac{s^2\,(n-1)}{\sigma^2}$ to be used.

(b) Set up the test:
H_0: $s^2 \leq \sigma^2$
H_1: $s^2 > \sigma^2$
$\alpha = .01$
$\chi^2_{\alpha,v} = \chi^2_{.01,24} = 42.98$

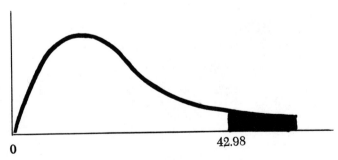

0   42.98

(c) Calculate $\chi_c^2 = \dfrac{s^2\,(n-1)}{\sigma^2} = \dfrac{.000028(24)}{(.005)^2} = 26.88$

(d) χ_c^2 falls in the acceptance region.

H_0 is accepted.

(e) The probability that the production of the cylinders meets its specification is 0.99.

B. Goodness-of-fit test:

A frequent problem that faces those who apply statistics to business and economics is whether a set of observed data may be looked upon as values assumed by a random variable that follows a specific probability distribution. A test for that can be run by using the Chi-square χ^2-distribution expressed in the following formula:

$$\chi_c^2 = \sum_{i=1}^{n} \frac{(O_i - E_i)^2}{E_i} \qquad \text{with } v = n - t - 1$$

where O = observed frequencies, E = Expected frequencies and the degree of freedom v equals the number of classes minus t (refers to the number of estimated parameters), minus one.

Example 7.13:

A quality control supervisor claimed that the distribution of defectives contained in samples of size 50 taken at equal intervals from the weekly production can be looked upon as a random variable following a Poisson probability distribution.

At a .01 level of significance, what is the probability that his claim is right? The following frequency distribution of the defectives for 100 samples each of size 50 is provided to run the test.

Number of Defectives	Observed frequency of samples
0	5
1	10
2	14
3	17
4	16
5	13
6	10
7	6
8	5
9	2
10	1
11	1
12	0
	100

Solution:

(a) To test whether this distribution fits a Poisson probability distribution, $\chi_c^2 = \sum_{i=1}^{n} \frac{(O_i - E_i)^2}{E_i}$ is used.

140

(b) Set up the test:

H_0: The distribution of defectives follows a Poisson distribution with λ = the average of defectives (or $\overline{X}$).

H_1: The distribution of defectives does not follow a Poisson distribution.

$\alpha = .01$

$\chi^2_{.01, v=10} = 23.209$

$v = 12\text{-}1\text{-}1$, where $t = 1$ for the estimated λ

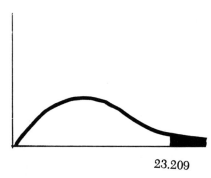

23.209

(c) Calculate χ_c^2:

$$\chi_c^2 = \sum_{i=1}^{n} \frac{(O_i - E_i)^2}{E_i}$$

Number of defectives = X
Observed frequency of samples = f
$\lambda = \Sigma Xf / \Sigma f = \overline{X}$

X	f	Xf	Poisson Probabilities	E_i	O_i	$(O_i - E_i)^2$	$(O_i - E_i)^2 / E_i$
0	5	0	.0183	1.83	5	10.05	5.49
1	10	10	.0733	7.33	10	7.13	.97
2	14	28	.1465	14.65	14	.42	.03
3	17	51	.1954	19.54	17	6.45	.33
4	16	64	.1954	19.54	16	12.53	.64
5	13	65	.1563	15.63	13	6.92	.44
6	10	60	.1042	10.42	10	.18	.02
7	6	42	.0595	5.95	6	.00	.00
8	5	40	.0298	2.98	5	4.08	1.37
9	2	18	.0132	1.32	2	.46	.35
10	1	10	.0053	.53	1	.22	.42
11	1	11	.0019	.19	1	.66	3.47
12	0	0	.0006	.06	0	.00	.00

$\chi_c^2 = \overline{13.53}$

$\overline{}$ 100   399
$\overline{X} = \lambda = 3.99 \cong 4$

(d) $\chi_c{}^2$ falls in the acceptance region
H$_0$ is accepted.
(e) We are confident 99% that the distribution of defectives follows a Poisson distribution.

C. Test of Independence:

Chi-square can be used to test the hypothesis that two variables with different classifications are independent or there is no relationship between the two variables. The two variables are classified in a two-way table called contingency table. The formula of χ^2 distribution used for the test of independence is:

$$\chi_c{}^2 = \sum_{i=1}^{r} \sum_{j=1}^{c} \frac{(O_{ij} - E_{ij})^2}{E_{ij}}$$

with $v = (r - 1)(c - 1)$,   r = number of rows, and c = number of columns.

Example 7.14:

A sample of 500 wives with children was interviewed to test if the education level has anything to do with the number of children in the family. The following data is the result of the research:

Education	Number of Children			
	more than 8	6;7,8	3,4,5	1,2
High School	50	60	70	20
College	20	15	45	50
Graduate	10	20	80	60

At a .05 level of significance, test if these two variables are independent.

Solution:

(a) Set up the test:

H$_0$: The number of children in a family is not related to the mother's level of education.

H$_1$: The number of children in a family is related (not independent) to education.

$\alpha = .05$

(b) $\chi^2{}_{\alpha,v}$

$$v = (r - 1)(c - 1)$$
$$= (2)(3) = 6$$
$$\chi^2{}_{.05,6} = 12.592$$

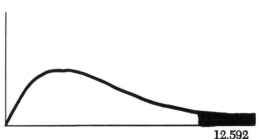

12.592

(c) Calculate

$$\chi^2_c = \sum_{i=1}^{r} \sum_{j=1}^{c} \frac{(O_{ij} - E_{ij})^2}{E_{ij}}$$

1. Observed data or O_{ij}:

Education	Number of Children					
	More than 8	6,7,8	3,4,5	1,2	Total	
High School	50	60	70	20	200	.40
College	20	15	45	50	130	.26
Graduate	10	20	80	60	170	.34
Total	80	95	195	130	500	1.00

$$\text{High School} \quad \frac{200}{500} = .40$$

$$\text{College} \quad \frac{130}{500} = .26$$

$$\text{Graduate} \quad \frac{170}{500} = .34$$

2. **Expected data or E_{ij}:**
For the first column, multiply .4, .26, .34, by 80; for the second column, multiply .4, .26, .34 by 95 and so on and E_{ij} becomes:

	More than 8	6,7,8	3,4,5	1,2
High School	32	38	78	52
College	20.8	24.7	50.7	33.8
Graduate	27.2	32.3	66.3	44.2

3. Calculate χ_c^2:

$$\chi_c^2 = \frac{(50-32)^2}{32} + \frac{(60-38)^2}{38} + \frac{(70-78)^2}{78} + \frac{(20-52)^2}{52}$$

$$+ \frac{(20-20.8)^2}{20.8} + \frac{(15-24.7)^2}{24.7} + \frac{(45-50.7)^2}{50.7} + \frac{(50-33.8)^2}{33.8}$$

$$+ \frac{(10-27.2)^2}{27.2} + \frac{(20-32.3)^2}{32.3} + \frac{(80-66.3)^2}{66.3} + \frac{(60-44.2)^2}{44.2}$$

$$= 10.13 + 12.74 + .82 + 19.69 + .03 + 3.81 + .64 + 7.76 +$$
$$10.88 + 4.68 + 2.83 + 5.65 = 79.66$$

(d) χ_c^2 falls in the shaded or rejection region
H_0 is rejected.

(e) There is a relationship between the number of children in a family and the level of education of the mother, and the probability of that is 0.95.

D. **Test of Homogeneity:**
Chi-square distribution can be used to test for the homogeneity of two samples. The test can determine whether the two samples are drawn from the same population.

Example 7.15:

Two statistics sections, one in the morning and the other in the evening, scored the following grades on the Final:

Grade	Morning Class	Evening Class
A	6	7
B	10	15
C	15	10
D	14	12
F	5	6
	50	50

At a .05 level of significance, test the hypothesis that the two sections are homogeneous.

Solution:

(a) Set up the test:

H_0: The two samples are homogeneous or drawn from the same population.

H_1: The two samples are not homogeneous.

$\alpha = .05$

(b) $\chi^2_{\alpha,v}$

$\chi^2_{.05,4} = 9.488$ $v = (r-1)(c-1) = 4$

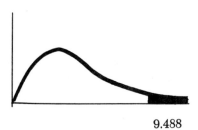

9.488

(c) Calculate $\chi_c^2 = \Sigma \dfrac{(O-E)^2}{E}$

Morning Class (O)	Evening Class (O)	Total	
6	7	13	.13
10	15	25	.25
15	10	25	.25
14	12	26	.26
5	6	11	.11
50	50	100	

The expected values (E) are derived as follows:

For the Morning class: Multiply the percentages .13, .25, .25, .26, .11 all by 50, the total number of students in the class.

For the Evening class: Follow the same steps.

144

Morning class (E)	Evening class (E)
6.5	6.5
12.5	12.5
12.5	12.5
13	13
5.5	5.5

$$\chi_c^2 = \frac{(6-6.5)^2}{6.5} + \frac{(10-12.5)^2}{12.5} + \frac{(15-12.5)^2}{12.5} + \frac{(14-13)^2}{13}$$

$$+ \frac{(5-5.5)^2}{5.5} + \frac{(7-6.5)^2}{6.5} + \frac{(15-12.5)^2}{12.5} + \frac{(10-12.5)^2}{12.5}$$

$$+ \frac{(12-13)^2}{13} + \frac{(6-5.5)^2}{5.5}$$

$$= 2.34$$

(d) χ_c^2 falls in the acceptance region
H$_0$ is accepted.
(e) The probability that the two samples are drawn from the same population is 0.95.

F-distribution:

F-distribution or the variance ratio can be used to test for the difference between two sample variances to determine whether they are from populations with the same variances. Also, F-distribution is being used in the analysis of variance to test for the difference between sample means or estimated population means.

A. Test for the difference between two sample variances:
F-distribution of the following form can be used to run the test for the difference between two sample variances:

$$F_{v1,v2} = \frac{\chi_1^2/v_1}{\chi_2^2/v_2} \quad , \; v_1 = n_1 - 1 \quad \text{and} \quad v_2 = n_2 - 1$$

$$\text{or } F_{v1,v2} = \frac{\hat{s}_1^2}{\hat{s}_2^2}$$

$$\hat{s}_1^2 = s_1^2 \left(\frac{n_1}{n_1 - 1}\right)$$

$$\hat{s}_2^2 = s_2^2 \left(\frac{n_2}{n_2 - 1}\right)$$

v_1 and v_2 degrees of freedom.

Example 7.16:

Two different types of machines are used to produce 12-inch cylinders in two separate factories. A sample of size 50 from the first factory production yielded a variance of 0.18″ while a sample of size 42 of the second factory production yielded a variance of 0.12″.

At 0.05 level of significance, test the hypothesis that the variance of the production in both factories is the same.

Solution:

(a) Set the test:

$$H_0: \sigma_1{}^2 = \sigma_2{}^2$$
$$H_1: \sigma_1{}^2 \neq \sigma_2{}^2$$
$$\alpha = .05$$
$$v_1 = n_1 - 1 = 50 - 1 = 49$$
$$v_2 = n_2 - 1 = 42 - 1 = 41$$
$$F_{49,41} = 1.80$$

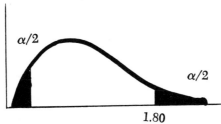

1.80

(b) Calculate

$$F_{v1,v2} = s_1{}^2 \, \frac{n_1}{n_1 - 1} \div s_2{}^2 \, \frac{n_2}{n_2 - 1}$$

$$= .18 \, \frac{50}{49} \div .12 \, \frac{42}{41}$$

$$= 1.496$$

(c) $F_{v1,v2}$ falls in the acceptance region
H_0 is accepted.

(d) The probability is .95 that the variance of the production in both factories is the same.

B. Analysis of variance:

Analysis of variance consists of a set of models constructed to describe different cases for testing the hypothesis that the groups under investigation came from populations of equal means or $\mu_1 = \mu_2 = \mu_3 = \ldots$.

There is no intention to present the different models of analysis of variance in this section. However, a simple model is introduced to show the application of F-distribution in making decisions about the equality of estimated population means. This simple model is:

$$Y_{ij} = \mu + T_i + e_{ij}$$

where Y_{ij} = observations

μ = population mean

T = Treatment or subdivision of the experiment observed associated with the ith group. It is assumed that $\Sigma\, T_i = 0$.

e = random error with mean = 0, and a constant variance. (The random error is assumed to be independent and normally distributed.)

F-distribution to be used for this test is as follows:

$$F_{v1,v2} = \frac{\text{variance among column means}}{\text{variance within columns}}$$

$v_1 = c - 1$ c = number of columns

$v_2 = n - c$ n = number of total observations

variance among column means = sum of squares among column means/v_1

variance within columns = sum of squares within columns /v_2

The data needed to calculate $F_{v1,v2}$ is arranged in a table called Analysis of Variance (ANOV) table where the term Mean Square (MS) is used to denote the variance. The form of ANOV table is as follows:

ANOV Table

Due to	SS	v	MS
Among columns	SS_a	$v_1 = c-1$	$SS_a/v_1 = MS_a$
Within columns	SS_w	$v_2 = n-c$	$SS_w/v_2 = MS_w$
Total	SS_t	$v_1 + v_2 = n-1$	

$$F_{v1,v2} = \frac{MS_a}{MS_w}$$

Example 7.17:

The following is data collected concerning the time, in minutes, spent by 4 workers in producing one part during each day of the week:

Day	A	B	C	D
Monday	20	19	16	22
Tuesday	18	18	19	19
Wednesday	17	19	20	18
Thursday	21	20	22	16
Friday	16	21	20	17

At a .05 level of significance, test the hypothesis that the average time spent by every worker in producing one unit is equal, or $\mu_1 = \mu_2 = \mu_3 = \mu_4$.

Solution:

(a) Set the test:

$H_0: \mu_1 = \mu_2 = \mu_3 = \mu_4$

$H_1: \mu_1 \neq \mu_2 \neq \mu_3 \neq \mu_4$

$\alpha = .05$

$$F_{v1,v2} = F_{3,16} = 4.08$$
$$v1 = c - 1 = 4 - 1 = 3$$
$$v2 = n - c = 20 - 4 = 16$$

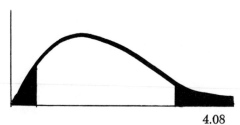

4.08

(b) Calculate $F_{v1,v2}$:

	A	B	C	D	Total
	20	19	16	22	
	18	18	19	19	
	17	19	20	18	
	21	20	22	16	
	16	21	20	17	
Σ	92	97	97	92	378
n	5	5	5	5	20
	18.4	19.4	19.4	18.4	18.4 Average

Total sum of squares $= (20)^2 + (18)^2 + (17)^2 + (21)^2 + (16)^2 + (19)^2 + (18)^2$

$$+ \ldots + (16)^2 + (17)^2 - \frac{(378)^2}{20}$$

$$= 67.8$$

Sum of squares among column means $= \dfrac{(92)^2}{5} + \dfrac{(97)^2}{5} + \dfrac{(97)^2}{5}$

$$+ \frac{(92)^2}{5} - \frac{(378)^2}{20} = 5.0$$

With this information the Analysis of Variance table can be constructed as follows:

Due to	SS	v	MS
Workers (columns)	5.0	3	1.67
Error (within columns)	62.8	16	3.93
Total	67.8	19	

$$F_{3,16} = \frac{1.67}{3.93} = .42$$

(c) F calculated falls in the acceptance region;
    H_0 is accepted.
(d) We are confident 95% that there is no significant difference among the average times spent by each worker in producing one unit.

EXERCISES

7.1 a. Differentiate between point and interval estimation.
     b. What are the reasons for running a test of hypothesis?
     c. What is the difference between type I and type II error?
     d. When do we use a one-tail test?

7.2 a. The variance for the life of incandescent lamps is known to be
         1225 hours. A life test on 108 lamps yielded a mean of 1681
         hours. Construct a 90% confidence interval for the actual popu-
         lation mean.

     b. The variance of usage of brand X tires is found to be 2500 miles.
         A random sample of 10 tires yielded an average usage of 3850
         miles. At a level of confidence of .90, find the two limits between
         which the true average usage falls.

7.3 A car dealer wishes to determine the actual average miles per gallon
     (mpg) a medium sized car can deliver. Ten tests were run and the
     following results are made available:

                           mpg
                           22
                           21
                           18
                           21
                           20
                           19
                           20
                           19
                           18
                           23

     Construct a 99% confidence interval for the actual average miles per
     gallon.

7.4 a. A random sample of 25 test pieces of cotton yielded a sample
         mean of 84 pounds breaking strength with a standard deviation
         of 12 pounds. Construct an 80% confidence interval.

     b. If we want to estimate the average mechanical aptitude of a large
         group of people, how large a sample should we take to be 95%
         confident that our estimate will not differ from the true mean
         by more than 2.5 points?

7.5 a. A random sample of 200 units selected randomly from the total
         production of a machine contains 10 defectives.
         Construct a 99% confidence interval for the actual proportion of
         defectives.

     b. A medical survey showed that 10 of 200 patients failed to recover
         completely from a given disease. Find .95 confidence interval
         for the proportion of those not completely recovered from the
         disease.

7.6 a. A sample survey indicated that 600 of 1100 families in the midwest would like to move to the west coast.
Construct a 99% confidence interval for the actual proportion of the families in the midwest that desire to move to the west coast.

b. A market research survey showed that 400 of 1000 families owning television sets watch a particular program regularly.
Construct a .99 confidence interval for the universe proportion.

7.7 In a big company a level of erroneous entries of 3% is considered acceptable. An internal auditor selected a sample of 250 files randomly and found 10 erroneous vouchers. What inference should you draw at .05 level of significance?

7.8 A machine, when in adjustment, produces parts that have a mean length of 12" with standard deviation of 1.5". A random sample of size 50 parts yielded a mean length of 12.5".
At a .05 level of significance, would you conclude that the machine still is in adjustment?

7.9 The standard time for a certain assembly operation is 3.5 minutes with variance of .81 minutes. Mr. Smith, the new operator, has been observed and timed in this job 25 times and it is found that the average time he spent is 4.2 minutes.
At a level of significance of .01, would you recommend Mr. Smith be retrained?

7.10 The manager of a grocery chain store claimed that the average sales per customer has increased from $18.89 as a result of abolishing trading stamps and decreasing prices.
A random sample of 600 customers selected at random yielded an average sale of $19.06. At a level of significance of .01, would you agree with the manager's claim?

7.11 A survey of 50 families in a large city showed that their average net income is $12,000.00 with a standard deviation of $1,250.00. The state average income is $12,900.00. At a level of significance of .05, test the claim that there is no significant difference between the state and the survey average income.

7.12 A physical education teacher arranged a group of 10 students to test the effectiveness of a newly designed program to lose weight. The following are the weights before and after the program:

Weights before (pounds)	Weights after (pounds)
210	195
176	169
197	189
188	175
156	148
200	169
190	175

220	200
199	189
206	200

At a .01 level of significance, would you agree with the teacher's claim that the new program is effective?

7.13 An electric company claimed that in a certain area 90% of the families use electricity for heating. A sample survey showed that 825 of 1200 families interviewed use electricity for heating.
At a .05 level of significance, test the validity of the company's claim.

7.14 Random samples of the height of basketball players in two universities produced the following results:
$n_1 = 50$ $\quad\quad \overline{X}_1 = 70.9''$ $\quad\quad s_1 = 2.4''$
$n_2 = 100$ $\quad\quad \overline{X}_2 = 69.8''$ $\quad\quad s_2 = 2.9''$
At a .05 level of significance, test the difference between the average height of the two samples.

7.15 The percentage of defectives produced by a certain manufacturing process is .18. A supplier claimed that a special treatment to the new raw material will reduce the percentage of producing defectives. A trial run with the new raw material showed that an output of 700 yielded 90 defective units. Is the claim of the supplier valid? (Use $\alpha = .05$)

7.16 A production manager claimed that the absence of production workers during a particular month appears to follow a Poisson distribution. To investigate his claim the following data have been collected:

Absence (in days)	Frequency
0	35
1	45
2	25
3	18
4	19
5	10
6	5

Would you agree with the production manager? Use $\alpha = .05$.

7.17 A sample of 750 persons of different ages were interviewed to test the relationship between age and smoking. The results of the study are presented in the following table:

	Age			
	less than 20	20 - 40	40 - 60	above 60
Smoker	40	160	100	50
Nonsmoker	50	100	150	100

At a .05 level of significance, would you conclude that a relationship exists between age and smoking?

Chapter VIII

STATISTICAL DECISION MAKING:
DECISION THEORY

In the previous chapter, Estimation and Test of Hypotheses, the two components of the classical approach of statistical decision making, were shown to provide the decision maker with more information concerning the population parameters. Such information helps him to make better decisions. As the economy has become more complex, the modern approach of statistical decision making, called "Decision Theory," is being applied in both business and government to enable the decision maker to select the course of action that optimizes his goal.

Managerial decision makers are faced with alternative courses of action. Each course of action consists of many outcomes or events. The occurrence of these events is uncertain; therefore, probabilities are assigned to these possible outcomes. The main role of a decision maker is the selection of a course of action that maximizes the profit or minimizes the loss.

Structure of a decision problem:

Expected value of alternative courses of action should be calculated and the course of action with the highest expected value of pay off or profit, or the one with the lowest expected value of opportunity loss, is the best course of action to be followed. Therefore, the following three steps are components of any decision problem structure:

1. Pay off tables or opportunity loss tables provide the elements of the decision matrix. (X_{ij}).

2. Probabilities of the possible events $P(E_i)$ are arranged in a column vector.

3. Expected pay off or expected opportunity loss of each action $(E(A_i))$ can be derived by multiplying the decision matrix by probabilities of the events column vector. The result of multiplication yields a column vector of the expected value of each action $E(A_i)$. The decision maker selects the best action to follow according to the decision criterion mentioned before: the action with the highest expected payoff, or that with the lowest expected opportunity loss.

1. Pay off or Opportunity loss tables:

Tables containing estimated or calculated profit for every event of the alternative actions are called "pay off" tables, and those containing estimated or calculated loss of every event of the alternative actions are called "opportunity loss" tables. A Pay off or an Opportunity loss table is, in fact, a decision table. The general form of a decision table is shown below:

Events \ Actions	E_1	E_2	E_3	. . . . . .	E_n
A_1	X_{11}	X_{12}	X_{13}	. . . . . .	X_{1n}
A_2	X_{21}	X_{22}	X_{23}	. . . . . .	X_{2n}
A_3	X_{31}	X_{32}	X_{33}	. . . . . .	X_{3n}
.					
.					
.					
A_m	X_{m1}	X_{m2}	X_{m3}	. . . . . .	X_{mn}

The body of this decision table is the decision matrix X_{ij}, whose elements are:

$$X_{ij} = \begin{bmatrix} X_{11} & X_{12} & X_{13} & \cdots & X_{1n} \\ X_{21} & X_{22} & X_{23} & \cdots & X_{2n} \\ X_{31} & X_{32} & X_{33} & \cdots & X_{3n} \\ \vdots & \vdots & \vdots & & \vdots \\ X_{m1} & X_{m2} & X_{m3} & \cdots & X_{mn} \end{bmatrix}_{m,n}$$

2. Probabilities of the events: $P(E_i)$

Events of alternative courses of action are called states of nature. The occurrence of these events are not known with certainty to the decision maker. Prior or subjective probabilities are assigned to the occurrence of these events. As more information concerning the occurrence of these events becomes available, prior or subjective probabilities can be revised to posterior probabilities. The Bayesian theorem lends itself to the calculation of posterior probabilities. Prior, subjective, or posterior probabilities of the possible events can be arranged in a column vector as follows:

$$P(E_i) = \begin{bmatrix} P(E_1) \\ P(E_2) \\ P(E_3) \\ \vdots \\ P(E_n) \end{bmatrix}_{(n,1)}$$

3. Expected pay off or opportunity loss of alternative actions: $E(A_i)$

To calculate the expected value of pay off or opportunity loss of alternative courses of action A_i, the decision matrix X_{ij} is multiplied by probabilities of the events column vector $P(E_i)$:

$$
\begin{bmatrix}
X_{11} & X_{12} & \cdots & X_{1n} \\
X_{21} & X_{22} & \cdots & X_{2n} \\
\cdot & \cdot & & \cdot \\
\cdot & \cdot & & \cdot \\
\cdot & \cdot & & \cdot \\
X_{m1} & X_{m2} & \cdots & X_{mn}
\end{bmatrix}_{(m,n)}
\cdot
\begin{bmatrix}
P(E_1) \\
P(E_2) \\
\cdot \\
\cdot \\
\cdot \\
P(E_n)
\end{bmatrix}_{(n,1)}
=
\begin{bmatrix}
E(A_1) \\
E(A_2) \\
\cdot \\
\cdot \\
\cdot \\
E(A_m)
\end{bmatrix}_{(m,1)}
$$

The decision to be derived from this is based on the selection of the course of action with highest expected pay off or lowest expected opportunity loss.

Example 8.1:

A company is planning to produce a specific part. A set of machines used at the full capacity level during any month can produce 10,000 units of this part. The sale price is set at $5.00 per unit, the total cost is estimated at $3.00 per unit, and the storage cost is estimated at $0.20 per unit per month. The total cost per unit includes an average storage cost for a month.

A market research analyst suggested the following probabilities of different sales levels:

Event (E_i)	$P(E_i)$
E_1 = sales of 10,000 units	.50
E_2 = sales of 20,000 units	.45
E_3 = sales of 30,000 units	.05
E_4 = sales of 40,000 units	.00
	1.00

The decision is to be made about the total parts to be produced during any month to maximize the profit.

Solution:

This is a decision making problem. Therefore we need to construct a pay off table, derive the decision matrix, derive the expected pay off for each action, and then select the action with the highest expected pay off.

1. Pay off table:

Events / Actions	Sales		
	E_1=10,000	E_2=20,000	E_3=30,000
A_1=Produce 10,000	10,000 × $2.0 = $20,000	10,000 × $2.0 = $20,000	10,000 × $2.0 = $20,000
A_2=Produce 20,000	10,000 × $2.0 −10,000 × $.20 = $18,000	20,000 × $2.0 = 40,000	20,000 × $2.0 = 40,000
A_3=Produce 30,000	10,000 × $2.0 −20,000 × $.20 = $16,000	20,000 × $2.0 −10,000 × $.20 = $38,000	30,000 × $2.0 = 60,000

A sales level of 40,000 has been eliminated because of its zero probability. The decision matrix X_{ij} is as follows: (in thousands of dollars)

$$
\begin{bmatrix}
20 & 20 & 20 \\
18 & 40 & 40 \\
16 & 38 & 60
\end{bmatrix}
$$

2. Probabilities (prior) of events arranged in a column vector:

$$\begin{bmatrix} .50 \\ .45 \\ .05 \end{bmatrix}$$

3. Expected pay off for alternative courses of action (A_1, A_2, A_3):

$$\begin{bmatrix} 20 & 20 & 20 \\ 18 & 40 & 40 \\ 16 & 38 & 60 \end{bmatrix} \cdot \begin{bmatrix} .50 \\ .45 \\ .05 \end{bmatrix} = \begin{bmatrix} (20)(.50) + (20)(.45) + (20)(.05) \\ (18)(.50) + (40)(.45) + (40)(.05) \\ (16)(.50) + (38)(.45) + (60)(.05) \end{bmatrix}$$

$$\begin{bmatrix} E(A_1) \\ E(A_2) \\ E(A_3) \end{bmatrix} = \begin{bmatrix} 20 \\ 29 \\ 28.10 \end{bmatrix} \rightarrow A_2$$

The expected pay off of A_2 is the highest. The decision is made to produce 20,000 units per month in order to maximize profit.

Another Solution:

Instead of constructing a Pay off table, construct an Opportunity loss table and follow the same procedure to derive the expected opportunity loss of all alternative courses of action. To minimize loss, select the course of action with the smallest expected opportunity loss.

1. Opportunity loss table:

Events \ Actions	$E_1 = 10,000$	Sales $E_2 = 20,000$	$E_3 = 30,000$
A_1: Produce 10,000	0	20,000	40,000
A_2: Produce 20,000	2,000 (storage cost)	0	20,000
A_3: Produce 30,000	4,000 (storage cost)	2,000 (storage cost)	0

The Opportunity loss table includes the storage cost and the opportunity loss when sales exceed production.

The decision matrix X_{ij} is as follows: (in thousands of dollars)

$$\begin{bmatrix} 0 & 20 & 40 \\ 2 & 0 & 20 \\ 4 & 2 & 0 \end{bmatrix}$$

2. Probabilities of events:

$$\begin{bmatrix} .50 \\ .45 \\ .05 \end{bmatrix}$$

3. Expected opportunity loss for actions A_1, A_2, and A_3:

$$\begin{bmatrix} 0 & 20 & 40 \\ 2 & 0 & 20 \\ 4 & 2 & 0 \end{bmatrix} \cdot \begin{bmatrix} .50 \\ .45 \\ .05 \end{bmatrix} = \begin{bmatrix} 11 \\ 2 \\ 2.9 \end{bmatrix} \rightarrow A_2$$

Again, the decision is to follow A_2 or produce 20,000 units because of the lowest expected opportunity loss of A_2.

Probability distributions as prior probabilities for events:

Prior probabilities of the states of nature (or events) play an important role in the decision making problems. In the previous example, subjective probabilities have been assigned to the events. However, the occurrence of these states of nature may be viewed as a random variable that follows a discrete or continuous probability distribution. Most economic and business phenomena are discrete. Therefore, the probability distribution representing them are of the discrete type: binomial or Poisson. Two illustrations, one using the binomial, and the second using the Poisson probability distribution, as a prior distribution in decision making problems are presented in the following examples:

Example 8.2:

A trucking company is planning to expand its operation. The manager started to lease more trucks. It costs $50.00 to lease a truck for a day. If the truck is used, it yields net profit of $100.00 per day.

From past experience, the use of trucks is found to follow a binomial distribution with $p = .40$.

What is the number of trucks that the company can lease to maximize the net profit? The maximum number of trucks this company can lease is five.

Solution:

1. An Opportunity loss table can be constructed for this problem as follows:

Events Actions	$E_1=0$	$E_2=1$	$E_3=2$	$E_4=3$	$E_5=4$	$E_6=5$
$A_1 = 0$	0	100	200	300	400	500
$A_2 = 1$	50	0	100	200	300	400
$A_3 = 2$	100	50	0	100	200	300
$A_4 = 3$	150	100	50	0	100	200
$A_5 = 4$	200	150	100	50	0	100
$A_6 = 5$	250	200	150	100	50	0

Actions represent trucks leased; Events represent trucks needed for shipments.

From the Opportunity loss table, the decision matrix is derived:

$$\begin{bmatrix} 0 & 100 & 200 & 300 & 400 & 500 \\ 50 & 0 & 100 & 200 & 300 & 400 \\ 100 & 50 & 0 & 100 & 200 & 300 \\ 150 & 100 & 50 & 0 & 100 & 200 \\ 200 & 150 & 100 & 50 & 0 & 100 \\ 250 & 200 & 150 & 100 & 50 & 0 \end{bmatrix}$$

2. Prior probabilities of events:

The probabilities of trucks needed for shipments or $P(E_i)$ follow a binomial distribution with $p = .40$ and $n = 5$. These probabilities can be calculated using the binomial distribution formula: $(_nC_x)p^x(1-p)^{n-x}$, $x = 0,1,2,3,4,5$, or can be obtained from a binomial distribution table:

E_i	$P(E_i)$
0	.0778
1	.2592
2	.3456
3	.2304
4	.0768
5	.0102

3. Expected opportunity loss for the courses of action is:

$$
\begin{bmatrix}
0 & 100 & 200 & 300 & 400 & 500 \\
50 & 0 & 100 & 200 & 300 & 400 \\
100 & 50 & 0 & 100 & 200 & 300 \\
150 & 100 & 50 & 0 & 100 & 200 \\
200 & 150 & 100 & 50 & 0 & 100 \\
250 & 200 & 150 & 100 & 50 & 0
\end{bmatrix}
\cdot
\begin{bmatrix}
.0778 \\ .2592 \\ .3456 \\ .2304 \\ .0768 \\ .0102
\end{bmatrix}
=
\begin{bmatrix}
199.98 \\ 111.65 \\ 62.20 \\ 64.59 \\ 101.54 \\ 150.01
\end{bmatrix}
\rightarrow A_3
$$

The expected value of opportunity loss for A_3 is the lowest, therefore, the decision is to lease two trucks per day.

Example 8.3:

In the previous example, suppose that the use of trucks for shipments follows a Poisson distribution with $\lambda = 2.5$. What is the optimal decision?

Solution:

1. The decision matrix is the same.
2. Prior probabilities will change because the Poisson distribution =

$$\frac{e^{-\lambda} \lambda^x}{x!}$$

is used to calculate the prior probabilities instead of the binomial distribution.

E_i	$P(E_i)$
0	.0821
1	.2052
2	.2565
3	.2138
4	.1336
5	.0668

3. Expected opportunity loss for the courses of action is:

$$
\begin{bmatrix}
0 & 100 & 200 & 300 & 400 & 500 \\
50 & 0 & 100 & 200 & 300 & 400 \\
100 & 50 & 0 & 100 & 200 & 300 \\
150 & 100 & 50 & 0 & 100 & 200 \\
200 & 150 & 100 & 50 & 0 & 100 \\
250 & 200 & 150 & 100 & 50 & 0
\end{bmatrix}
\cdot
\begin{bmatrix}
.0821 \\ .2052 \\ .2565 \\ .2138 \\ .1336 \\ .0668
\end{bmatrix}
=
\begin{bmatrix}
222.80 \\ 139.32 \\ 86.61 \\ 72.39 \\ 90.22 \\ 128.11
\end{bmatrix}
\rightarrow A_4
$$

The decision is to lease 3 trucks daily or follow Action A_4.

Posterior probability for the Events:

So far decisions made are based on prior probabilities. The decision maker may decide to gather additional information concerning the probabilities of the states of nature to minimize, if not to eliminate, the uncertainty attached to these events. Additional information secured by sampling can be used to calculate the posterior probabilities for the events through the use of Bayesian theorem. New expected values for the courses of action are calculated using the posterior probabilities instead of the prior probabilities and hence new decisions may be reached.

The decision maker should be sure that the estimated cost of the additional information does not exceed the expected value of this information. Another problem to face the decision maker while securing additional information is the optimum size of the sample that provides the additional information. These two problems will not be considered in this chapter. Our assumption is that the decision maker is aware of them.

In the following example, posterior probabilities derived by the application of Bayesian analysis are used instead of the prior probabilities to arrive at the optimal decision:

Example 8.4:

In the previous example of the trucking company, let us assume that a survey has been conducted to provide the management with additional information concerning the probabilities of the number of trucks in use for every action of number of trucks leased. The following table presents the findings of the survey:

	E_1	E_2	E_3	E_4	E_5	E_6
A_1	.15	.20	.25	.15	.10	.20
A_2	.25	.30	.30	.25	.40	.20
A_3	.30	.35	.20	.30	.10	.40
A_4	.15	.05	.05	.10	.10	.10
A_5	.10	.05	.10	.15	.20	.05
A_6	.05	.05	.10	.05	.10	.05

Using prior binomial probabilities, the decision maker arrived at action A_3, or leasing 2 trucks, as the optimal decision. Therefore, the company decided to use the likelihood probabilities $P(A_3/E_i)$ to modify these prior binomial probabilities. Find the new optimal action.

Solution:

1. The decision matrix is:

$$
\begin{bmatrix}
0 & 100 & 200 & 300 & 400 & 500 \\
50 & 0 & 100 & 200 & 300 & 400 \\
100 & 50 & 0 & 100 & 200 & 300 \\
150 & 100 & 50 & 0 & 100 & 200 \\
200 & 150 & 100 & 50 & 0 & 100 \\
250 & 200 & 150 & 100 & 50 & 0
\end{bmatrix}
$$

2. Posterior Probabilities of the events:

Prior Probabilities $P(E_i)$	Likelihood $P(A_3/E_i)$	Joint $P(E_i)P(A_3/E_i)$	Posterior
.0778	.30	.0233	.0883
.2592	.35	.0907	.3436
.3456	.20	.0691	.2617
.2304	.30	.0691	.2617
.0768	.10	.0077	.0292
.0102	.40	.0041	.0155
			1.0000

3. Expected opportunity loss for courses of action:

$$
\begin{bmatrix}
0 & 100 & 200 & 300 & 400 & 500 \\
50 & 0 & 100 & 200 & 300 & 400 \\
100 & 50 & 0 & 100 & 200 & 300 \\
150 & 100 & 50 & 0 & 100 & 200 \\
200 & 150 & 100 & 50 & 0 & 100 \\
250 & 200 & 150 & 100 & 50 & 0
\end{bmatrix}
\cdot
\begin{bmatrix}
.0883 \\
.3436 \\
.2617 \\
.2617 \\
.0292 \\
.0155
\end{bmatrix}
=
\begin{bmatrix}
184.64 \\
97.88 \\
62.67 \\
66.72 \\
110.01 \\
157.69
\end{bmatrix} \to A_3
$$

Action A_3 is optimal whether prior binomial probabilities or posterior probabilities are applied. This is not true in most cases. Additional information may lead to modify the optimal decision.

The material covered in this chapter is a brief presentation of the elements of decision theory which has become an important tool to be used in solving complex problems facing managerial decision makers in business as well as in government.

EXERCISES

8.1   a. What is the difference between statistical inference and decision theory as tools for statistical decision making?
     b. What are the components of any decision problem structure?

8.2   a. What is the role of Bayesian Theorem in decision theory?
     b. How does the decision maker select the optimum solution?

8.3 An appliance dealer makes a net profit of $100 on each washer he sells. The monthly storage is $10 per washer. The dealer is facing a space problem and he has to decide on the optimum number of washers to stock to meet the monthly demand. Knowing that the highest number of washers that had been sold per month over the last five years is seven washers, and the probabilities of monthly sales are as follows:

Sales (washers)	P(sales)
1	.40
2	.22
3	.18
4	.10
5	.05
6	.03
7	.02

find the optimum number of washers to be stocked.

8.4 In Exercise 8.3, if the monthly sales of washers appear to follow a binomial probability distribution with $p = .45$, find the optimal decision.

8.5 In Exercise 8.3, if the monthly sales of washers appear to follow a Poisson probability distribution with $\lambda = .80$, find the optimum number of washers the dealer should keep in stock monthly.

Chapter IX

STATISTICAL DECISION MAKING:
ECONOMETRICS

Econometrics is widely used in decision making and policy formation by government and business. Econometrics is a branch of economics. Its main objective is the analysis of economic phenomena through the application of mathematics and statistical inference. The econometric task is to observe the behavior of economic variables; attempt to construct a mathematical model to describe the relationship among these variables; estimate the parameters of the model; and test the reliability of the model to predict such behavior in non-observed situations.

Econometric models play an important role in portraying economic relationships. They are built to make more systematic use of time series (or statistical data) in assessing their reliability. In general, econometric models are designed to describe the way in which a system actually operates. This system could be the whole economy, a sector or an activity of the economy, or a firm operating in the economy. Econometric models can be used to provide managerial decision makers with information concerning the behavior of national uncertain variables such as income, consumption, prices, interest rates, and others. On the other hand, they can be designed to predict the activity or activities of a firm such as sales. National and/or area econometric models are as important to management as those designed at the industry and the firm level.

A sales forecast econometric model is becoming a popular managerial tool to provide top management with information that can be used to make decisions concerning inventory control, production scheduling, and financial, marketing and hiring strategy for their organizations.

Application of econometrics as a tool of statistical decision making requires the construction of a model. But, what is a model? A model is a set of relationships among a group of variables. This relationship can be expressed algebraically by an equation. Therefore, a business or economic activity can be described by either a one-equation or a multi-equation model expressing the interrelationships among the measurable variables.

The relationship among the variables can be expressed in models of different types: linear and nonlinear, static and dynamic, stochastic and deterministic, and others. There are also many methods for the estimation of parameters of these models: ordinary least square, two-stage and three-stage least square, indirect least square, limited information and full information in maximum likelihood methods. Statistical methods are used to

160

estimate parameters of the model, test their significance and the reliability of the overall model, and for prediction. This function constitutes what is usually known as regression and correlation analysis. In addition, econometricians test for the existence of problems such as identification, multicollinearity, and heteroscedesticity. These problems are beyond the scope of this book.

The ordinary least square method will be considered in this chapter to estimate parameters of linear and nonlinear models.

1. Linear Models:

If the relationship that exists among the variables is linear, then the model is called linear. Linear models are of two types: simple and multiple. A simple linear model represents a linear relationship that exists between two variables, while a multiple linear model has more than two variables.

A. Simple or Two-variable model:

The simplest relationship between two variables can be expressed in a linear form as:

$$Y = a + \beta X$$

where Y and X are variables; Y is the dependent while X is the independent variable. a and β are constants or parameters of the model, a representing the intercept, or the value Y assumes if $X = 0$, and β is the slope or the rate of change of Y on X. The estimate equation is: $\hat{Y} = \hat{a} + \hat{\beta}X$.

Usually a stochastic term e may be added to this linear model to become:

$$\hat{Y} = \hat{a} + \hat{\beta}X + e$$

where $\hat{Y}$, $\hat{a}$, and $\hat{\beta}$ are estimates of Y, a, and β respectively. The disturbance term e represents the residuals $(Y - \hat{Y})$, or the deviation of observed value Y from its estimate $\hat{Y}$. The function of e_i stochastic terms have been included in the model to compensate for the inexact statistical formulation resulting from the following:

1. The omission of certain possible explanatory (or independent) variables.
2. The possible nonlinearity of the above model.
3. The basic and unpredictive element of randomness in human responses.
4. The imperfection of data and the errors of measurement.

The statistical theory upon which the estimating techniques are based requires the following assumption with regard to the distribution of e_i:
1. to be normally distributed random variables, with $\mu = 0$, and $\sigma^2 < \infty$ or $N(e_i; 0, \sigma^2 < \infty)$.
2. Not to be autocorrelated or $Cov(e_i e_j) = 0$ for all $i \neq j$ and $E(e_i e_{i-t}) = 0$ for all i and $t \neq 0$.

The least square method is used to estimate the parameters a and β of the linear model. This method is based on the minimization of the residuals (or Σe_i). If the estimated straight line could pass through every observed value (Y_i), then there would be no residuals or errors, and $\Sigma e_i = 0$; but this is an unattainable situation. The closer the estimates or $\hat{Y}_i$ to the observations Y_i, the smaller the magnitude of the residuals e_i. To calculate the parameters a and β such that the estimated straight line $\hat{Y} = \hat{a} + \hat{\beta}X$ is the best fit, one has to minimize the residuals Σe_i.

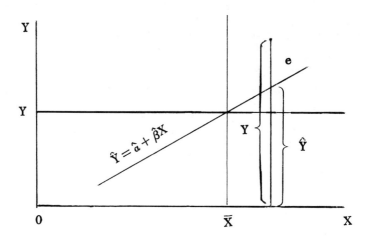

The residuals are either positive, negative, or zero. Nonetheless, $\Sigma e_i = 0$. This means that the sum of all residuals around the regression or estimated line equals zero. Therefore, to find the best straight line that fits the observations, one has to minimize Σe_i^2 rather than Σe_i. Σe_i^2 is a non-negative value and it varies with the dispersion of the observations from the estimated line. This indicates that Σe_i^2 is a function of the parameter estimates $\hat{a}$ and $\hat{\beta}$. In other words, different pairs of $\hat{a}$ and $\hat{\beta}$ yield different values of Σe_i^2. Mathematically this function can be written as follows:

$$\Sigma e_i^2 = f(\hat{a}, \hat{\beta})$$

Now in order to apply the least square method, simply minimize this function:

Min. $\qquad \Sigma e_i^2 = f(\hat{a}, \hat{\beta})$

The necessary condition of minimization is to calculate the first partial derivatives of the function and equate that to zero to locate the stationary points.

$$\Sigma e^2 = \Sigma(Y - \hat{Y})^2 \qquad \text{because } e = Y - \hat{Y}$$

but $\hat{Y} = \hat{a} + \hat{\beta}X$

then $\Sigma e^2 = \Sigma(Y - \hat{a} - \hat{\beta}X)^2$ to be minimized

$$\frac{\partial}{\partial \hat{a}} \Sigma e^2 = (-1)(2)\Sigma(Y - \hat{a} - \hat{\beta}X) = 0 \qquad (1)$$

$$\frac{\partial}{\partial \hat{\beta}} \Sigma e^2 = (-2)\Sigma X(Y - \hat{a} - \hat{\beta}X) = 0 \qquad (2)$$

Equations (1) and (2) can be simplified to yield a system of two-normal equation to calculate the two unknown parameters a and β of the linear model. These two equations are:

$$\Sigma Y = na + \beta \Sigma X$$
$$\Sigma XY = a\Sigma X + \beta \Sigma X^2$$

The parameters a and β can be calculated by solving for their estimated values $\hat{a}$ and $\hat{\beta}$ in the above two normal equations. There are different methods of calculation: by elimination, substitution, graphs, or by using determinants (Cramer's Rule). The last method is considered to calculate $\hat{a}$ and $\hat{\beta}$:

$$\hat{a} = \frac{\begin{vmatrix} \Sigma Y & \Sigma X \\ \Sigma XY & \Sigma X^2 \end{vmatrix}}{\begin{vmatrix} n & \Sigma X \\ \Sigma X & \Sigma X^2 \end{vmatrix}} = \frac{(\Sigma Y)(\Sigma X^2) - (\Sigma XY)(\Sigma X)}{n(\Sigma X^2) - (\Sigma X)^2}$$

$$\hat{\beta} = \frac{\begin{vmatrix} n & \Sigma Y \\ \Sigma X & \Sigma XY \end{vmatrix}}{\begin{vmatrix} n & \Sigma X \\ \Sigma X & \Sigma X^2 \end{vmatrix}} = \frac{n(\Sigma XY) - (\Sigma X)(\Sigma Y)}{n(\Sigma X^2) - (\Sigma X)^2}$$

Example 9.1:

Test the relationship that exists between Y and X, where Y represents personal consumption expenditures on total goods and services and X represents personal outlays (disposable income − personal savings) for the period 1957-1966 in the U.S.A. (The values are in hundred billions of dollars, seasonally adjusted.)

	Y	X
1957	2.81	2.88
1958	2.90	2.97
1959	3.11	3.18
1960	3.25	3.33
1961	3.35	3.43
1962	3.55	3.64
1963	3.75	3.85
1964	4.01	4.12
1965	4.33	4.45
1966	4.66	4.79

Source: Business Statistics 1967, U. S. Department of Commerce, Office of Business Economics.

Estimate the parameters of the model that represents the relationship between personal consumption and personal outlays.

Solution:

(a) For a visual test of the type of relationship that exists between Y and X, a scatter diagram is plotted:

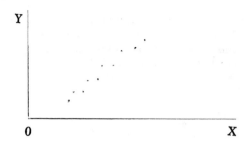

From the scatter diagram, it appears that a linear relationship exists between personal consumption Y and personal outlays X. This relationship can be expressed by a linear model:
$$Y = a + \beta X$$
(b) The next step is to estimate the parameters a and β of the above linear model:
$$\hat{a} = \frac{(\Sigma Y)(\Sigma X^2) - (\Sigma XY)(\Sigma X)}{n(\Sigma X^2) - (\Sigma X)^2}$$
and $\hat{\beta} = \frac{n(\Sigma XY) - (\Sigma Y)(\Sigma X)}{n(\Sigma X^2) - (\Sigma X)^2}$

To calculate a and β, one needs to find the value of:
$$n, \Sigma Y, \Sigma X, \Sigma XY, \Sigma X^2$$
This has been done in the following table:

Y	X	XY	X²
2.81	2.88	8.0928	8.2944
2.90	2.97	8.6130	8.8209
3.11	3.18	9.8898	10.1124
3.25	3.33	10.8225	11.0889
3.35	3.43	11.4905	11.7649
3.55	3.64	12.9220	13.2496
3.75	3.85	14.4375	14.8225
4.01	4.12	16.5212	16.9744
4.33	4.45	19.2685	19.8025
4.66	4.79	22.3214	22.9441
35.72	36.64	134.3792	137.8746
ΣY	ΣX	ΣXY	ΣX^2

n=10

$$\hat{a} = \frac{(35.72)(137.8746) - (134.3792)(36.64)}{10(137.8746) - (36.64)^2}$$
$$= \frac{1.2268}{36.2564}$$
$$= .03383 = .0338$$
$$\hat{\beta} = \frac{(10)(134.3792) - (35.72)(36.64)}{10(137.8746) - (36.64)^2}$$
$$= \frac{35.0112}{36.2564}$$
$$= .96565 = .9657$$

The estimated equation (or the regression line) is:
$$\hat{Y} = .0338 + .9657X$$
To plot the estimated linear equation, determine two points by using two different values for X and connect the two points to a straight line.
Another method to calculate $\hat{a}$ and $\hat{\beta}$ follows:
The system of two normal equations used to derive a and β is:

$$\Sigma Y = n\hat{a} + \hat{\beta}\Sigma X \qquad (1)$$
$$\Sigma XY = \hat{a}\Sigma X + \hat{\beta}\Sigma X^2 \qquad (2)$$

If we divide the elements of equation (1) by n:

$$\frac{\Sigma Y}{n} = \frac{n\hat{a}}{n} + \frac{\hat{\beta}\Sigma X}{n}$$

or $\overline{Y} = \hat{a} + \hat{\beta}\overline{X}$
then $\hat{a} = \overline{Y} - \hat{\beta}\overline{X}$
Also, if we write the second equation in deviation form:
$$\Sigma xy = 0 + \Sigma\beta x^2$$
where $x = X - \overline{X}, \quad y = Y - \overline{Y}$

then $\hat{\beta} = \dfrac{\Sigma xy}{\Sigma x^2}$

Σxy is the covariance that measures the joint variation of X and Y.
Let us apply these new formulas to the previous example:

Y	X	y	x	yx	x^2
2.81	2.88	−.7620	−.7840	.5974	.6147
2.90	2.97	−.6720	−.6940	.4664	.4816
3.11	3.18	−.4620	−.4840	.2236	.2343
3.25	3.33	−.3220	−.3340	.1075	.1116
3.35	3.43	−.2220	−.2340	.0519	.0548
3.55	3.64	−.0220	−.0240	.0005	.0006
3.75	3.85	.1780	.1860	.0331	.0346
4.01	4.12	.4380	.4560	.1997	.2079
4.33	4.45	.7580	.7860	.5958	.6178
4.66	4.79	1.0880	1.1260	1.2251	1.2679
35.72	36.64			3.5010	3.6258

$\overline{Y} = 3.572 \qquad \overline{X} = 3.664$

$\hat{\beta} = \dfrac{\Sigma xy}{\Sigma x^2}$

$\quad = \dfrac{3.5010}{3.6258}$

$\quad = .9656$

$\hat{a} = \overline{Y} - \beta\overline{X}$
$\quad = (3.572) - (.9656)(3.664)$
$\quad = .034$

$\hat{Y} = .034 + .9656X$

Standard Error of Estimate:

The standard deviation of estimate or the standard error of estimate $\hat{\sigma}_{yx}$ is a measure that shows the degree of dispersion of the observed values Y_i around the estimated regression line: $\hat{Y} = \hat{a} + \hat{\beta}X$. It is an absolute measure of goodness-of-fit. If it happened that the standard error $\hat{\sigma}_{yx}$ equals zero, then the regression line should pass through every actual observation of the scatter diagram. This is almost impossible, however, the smaller the magnitude of $\hat{\sigma}_{yx}$, the closer the fit, as shown in the following diagrams:

$$\hat{\sigma}_{yx} \qquad < \qquad \hat{\sigma}_{yx}$$

The standard error when regressing Y on X can be computed by the following formula:

$$\hat{\sigma}_{yx} = \sqrt{\frac{\Sigma(Y - \hat{Y})^2}{n - 2}}$$

where $n - 2$ refers to the degree of freedom.

The loss of two degrees of freedom results from using the estimated parameters $\hat{a}$ and $\hat{\beta}$ in computing the standard error of estimate $\hat{\sigma}_{yx}$.

The standard error of estimate σ_{yx} is computed for the estimated equation: $\hat{Y} = .0338 + .9657X$ as follows:

Y	X		$\hat{Y}$	$(Y-\hat{Y})^2$
2.81	2.88	$.0338 + .9657(2.88) = 2.8150$		.00002500
2.90	2.97	$.0338 + .9657(2.97) = 2.9019$		.00000361
3.11	3.18	$= 3.1047$		.00002809
3.25	3.33	$= 3.2496$		.00000016
3.35	3.43	$= 3.3462$		.00001444
3.55	3.64	$= 3.5489$		.00000121
3.75	3.85	$= 3.7517$		.00000289
4.01	4.12	$= 4.0125$		.00000625
4.33	4.45	$= 4.3312$		.00000144
4.66	4.79	$= 4.6595$		.00000025
				.00008334
				$\Sigma(Y-Y)^2$

$$\hat{\sigma}_{yx} = \sqrt{\frac{.00008334}{10 - 2}}$$

$$= .003249$$

The magnitude of the standard error of estimate .003249 is very small and indicates that the estimated regression line fits the observed data very well.

Another way to interpret $\sigma_{yx} = .003249$ is that about 68% of the observed values Y_i are expected to fall between $Y \pm \sigma_{yx}$ as shown in the diagram:

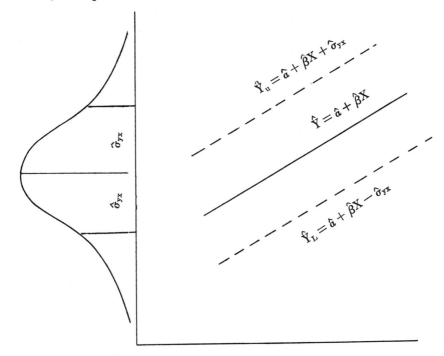

$\hat{Y}_u$ and $\hat{Y}_L$ computed for the previous example are:
$$\hat{Y}_u = .0338 + .9657X + .003249$$
and $\hat{Y}_L = .0338 + .9657X - .003249$

$\hat{Y}_u$ is the upper limit of the band while $\hat{Y}_L$ is the lower limit of the band.

Bands of different limits can be computed; e.g., a band that is expected to contain 95% of the observed data is calculated as follows:
$$\hat{Y}_u = \hat{a} + \hat{\beta}X + 1.96\hat{\sigma}_{yx}$$
$$\hat{Y}_L = \hat{a} + \hat{\beta}X - 1.96\hat{\sigma}_{yx}$$

Standard Error of β:

Errors are expected to occur in the process of estimating the parameters of the model. The standard error of β, $\hat{\sigma}_\beta$ measures the amount of error to determine the significance of the estimated parameter $\hat{\beta}$.

The standard error of β can be calculated by the following formula:
$$\hat{\sigma}_\beta = \frac{\hat{\sigma}_{yx}}{\sqrt{\Sigma(X - \overline{X})^2}}$$

From this formula, one can conclude that the $\hat{\sigma}_\beta$ varies directly with $\hat{\sigma}_{yx}$, and inversely with the variation of the independent variable X.

The following is the standard error of β calculated for the previous example:

X	$(X-\bar{X})^2$
2.88	.6147
2.97	.4816
3.18	.2343
3.33	.1116
3.43	.0548
3.64	.0006
3.85	.0346
4.12	.2079
4.45	.6178
4.79	1.2679

$\Sigma X = 36.64$ 3.6258
$n = 10$
$\bar{X} = 3.664$

$\hat{\sigma}_{yx} = .0032249$

$\hat{\sigma}_\beta = \dfrac{.0032249}{\sqrt{3.6258}}$

$= .0017$

Statistical Significance of β:

A non zero value computed for $\hat{\beta}$ as an estimate of β does not mean in all cases that β is significantly different than zero. To test for the statistical significance of β, one has to apply the following t-test:

$$t_c = \frac{\hat{\beta} - \beta}{\hat{\sigma}_\beta}$$

If $\beta = 0$, then the linear relationship between Y and X is insignificant and one can claim that it does not exist. On the other hand, if $\beta \neq 0$, then there is a significant linear relationship between Y and X. Accordingly, the set up of the test of hypothesis becomes:

$H_o: \beta = 0$
$H_1: \beta \neq 0$

With a level of significance α, if H_o is accepted, then β is not significantly different from zero and there is no linear relationship between Y and X. If H_o is rejected, then accepting H_1 indicates that β is significantly different from zero and hence a linear relationship exists between the two variables Y and X.

Example 9.2:

Test for the significance of β in the previous example at .05 level of significance. Calculate the confidence limits.

Solution:

(a) $\hat{\beta} = .9657$ and $\hat{\sigma}_\beta = .0017$
(b) Set up the test of hypothesis:
$H_o: \beta = 0$
$H_1: \beta \neq 0$
$\alpha = .05$
$v = n - 2 = 8$
$t_{.05,8} = \pm 2.306$

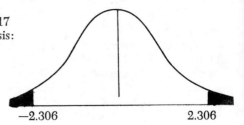

−2.306   2.306

(c) Calculate t_c:

$$t_c = \frac{.9657 - 0}{.0017}$$

$= 568.0588$

t_c falls in the rejection region, H_0 is rejected.

H_1 is accepted. This means that β is significantly different from zero or there is a linear relationship between the two variables Y and X.

(d) Confidence limits ($a = .05$):

The confidence interval ($1 - a$) of 95% has the two limits: upper limit of β and lower limit of β. The two limits of this confidence interval can be calculated as follows:

$$t_{.05,8} = \pm 2.306$$

$$t_{.05,8} = \frac{\hat{\beta} - \beta}{\hat{\sigma}_\beta}$$

$$\pm 2.306 = \frac{.9657 - \beta}{.0017}$$

then solve for the two limits of β:

$$2.306 = \frac{.9657 - \beta}{.0017}$$

$$\beta = .9618$$

$$-2.306 = \frac{.9657 - \beta}{.0017}$$

$$\beta = .9696$$

We are confident 95% that the true value of β falls between .9696 and .9618.

Simple Correlation, or correlation of two variables:

Correlation is a measure of the association that exists between the variables. Simple correlation is a measure of the degree to which the two variables Y and X are related or associated. Correlation analysis does not imply the functional relationship that regression analysis requires between the two variables.

Correlations coefficient R is a measure of closeness of fit. Its magnitude reflects the significance of the overall equation. Instead of using the correlation coefficient R, statisticians are using R^2, the rate of determination, as a measure of association. If the magnitude of R^2 is one, then there is a perfect correlation between the variables. If the magnitude of R^2 is zero, this indicates no correlation between the variables. The closer the magnitude of R^2 to one, the stronger the correlation and the closer to zero, the weaker the association.

R^2, the rate or coefficient of determination, is a ratio of the variation explained by the regression line and the total variation of the observed value.

$$R^2 = \frac{\text{Explained variation}}{\text{Total variation}}$$

or $$R^2 = 1 - \frac{\text{Unexplained variation}}{\text{Total variation}}$$

The concepts total, explained, and unexplained variation can be understood from the inspection of the following diagrams:

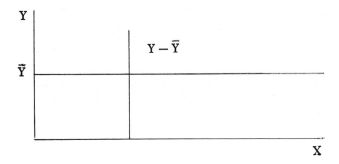

Total variation is the difference between an observation and the mean of all observations: $Y - \overline{Y}$.

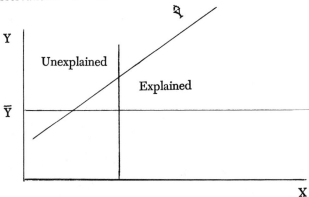

A portion of the total variation will be known or explained or absorbed by the estimated regression line: $\hat{Y} = \hat{a} + \hat{\beta}X$, and is called the explained variation. The explained variation is equal to $\hat{Y} - \overline{Y}$ for each observation.

The portion of the total variation that has not been explained by the regression line is called the unexplained variation which is equal to $Y - \hat{Y}$ for each observation.

Total variation $Y - \overline{Y}$ is equal to the sum of explained and unexplained variation:

$$Y - \overline{Y} = \hat{Y} - \overline{Y} \pm Y - \hat{Y} \qquad \text{(for each observation)}$$
$$\Sigma(Y - \overline{Y}) = \Sigma(\hat{Y} - \overline{Y}) + \Sigma(Y - \hat{Y}) \qquad \text{(for all observations)}$$

Total variation = Explained + Unexplained.

The sum of the total variation $\Sigma(Y - \overline{Y})$ as well as the other sums on the right side of the equation equals zero. Therefore, the sum of squared deviations is used:

$$\Sigma(Y - \overline{Y})^2 = \Sigma(\hat{Y} - \overline{Y})^2 + \Sigma(Y - \hat{Y})^2$$

R^2 formula can be derived from the above equation:

$$R^2 = \frac{\Sigma(\hat{Y} - \overline{Y})^2}{\Sigma(Y - \overline{Y})^2}$$

or $\qquad R^2 = 1 - \dfrac{\Sigma(Y - \hat{Y})^2}{\Sigma(Y - \overline{Y})^2}$

Example 9.3:
Calculate R^2 for the previous example and interpret the results.

Solution:
$$R^2 = 1 - \frac{\Sigma(Y - \hat{Y})^2}{\Sigma(Y - \bar{Y})^2}$$

$\Sigma(Y - \hat{Y})^2 = .00008334$ calculated to find $\hat{\sigma}_{yx}$
So, we need $\Sigma(Y - \bar{Y})^2$

Y	$(Y-\bar{Y})^2$
2.81	.5806
2.90	.4516
3.11	.2134
3.25	.1037
3.35	.0493
3.55	.0005
3.75	.0317
4.01	.1918
4.33	.5746
4.66	1.1837

$\Sigma Y = 35.72$ 3.3809
$n = 10$
$\bar{Y} = 3.572$

$$R^2 = 1 - \frac{.00008334}{3.3809} = .9999$$

The calculation of $R^2 = .9999$ means that 99.99% of the total variation has been explained by the estimated regression line. In other words, there is a very strong (almost perfect) correlation between Y and X.
Other methods of calculation of R^2:
There are many formulas developed to calculate R and R^2. However, the following two are considered because of their practical use:

(1) $R^2 = \hat{\beta}_{yx} \cdot \hat{\beta}_{xy}$

β_{yx} is the slope of the regression line Y on X.
β_{xy} is the slope of the regression line X on Y, or the slope of the regression when rotating the axis.

Example 9.4:
Calculate R^2 for the previous example by using the new formula:
$$R^2 = \hat{\beta}_{yx} \cdot \hat{\beta}_{xy}$$

Solution:
$\hat{\beta}_{yx} = .96565$
To calculate β_{xy} we can use the following formula:
$$\hat{\beta}_{xy} = \frac{n(\Sigma XY) - (\Sigma X)(\Sigma Y)}{n(\Sigma Y^2) - (\Sigma Y)^2}$$

We know the value of:
$n = 10$ $\Sigma XY = 134.3792$
$\Sigma X = 36.64$ $\Sigma Y = 35.72$
then we need the value of: ΣY^2

Y	Y^2
2.81	7.8961
2.90	8.4100
3.11	9.6721
3.25	10.5625
3.35	11.2225
3.55	12.6025
3.75	14.0625
4.01	16.0801
4.33	18.7489
4.66	21.7156
$\overline{35.72}$	$\overline{130.9728}$
ΣY	ΣY^2

$$\hat{\beta}_{xy} = \frac{10(134.3792) - (36.64)(35.72)}{10(130.9728) - (35.72)^2}$$

$$= 1.03554$$
$$R^2 = \hat{\beta}_{yx} \cdot \hat{\beta}_{xy}$$
$$= (.96565)(1.03554)$$
$$= .9999$$

$$(2) \quad R^2 = \frac{(\Sigma xy)^2}{\Sigma x^2 \ \Sigma y^2}$$

From the previous Example 9.1 we have the value of:
$$\Sigma xy = 3.5010 \qquad \qquad \Sigma x^2 = 3.6258$$
We need the value of Σy^2:

y	y^2
−.7620	.5806
−.6720	.4516
−.4620	.2134
−.3220	.1037
−.2220	.0493
−.0220	.0005
.1780	.0317
.4380	.1918
.7580	.5746
1.0880	1.1837
	$\overline{3.3809}$
	Σy^2

$$R^2 = \frac{(3.5010)^2}{(3.6258)(3.3809)}$$
$$= \frac{12.2570}{12.2585}$$
$$= .9999$$

B. Multiple Linear Model:

A simple linear model that represents the relationship between a dependent variable and an independent variable cannot yield satisfactory results if there are other independent variables which can affect that relationship. In other words, if the dependent variable is a function of two or more independent variables: $Y = f(X_1, X_2, \ldots, X_n)$ then a multiple linear model can be constructed to express this function provided that the relationship among the variables is linear. A multiple linear model for this function is:

$$Y = a + \beta_1 X_1 + \beta_2 X_2 + \ldots + \beta_{n-1} X_{n-1} + \beta_n X_n$$

The least square method may be used to estimate the parameters of this multiple linear model: a, β_1, β_2 . . ., β_n. The basic analysis of deriving a system of n + 1 normal equation to solve for the n + 1 unknowns is the same as shown in the simple linear model. The minimization of the function:

$$\Sigma e_i^2 = f(\hat{a}, \hat{\beta}_1, \hat{\beta}_2, \ldots, \hat{\beta}_n)$$

yields the partial derivatives:

$$\frac{\partial}{\partial \hat{a}} \Sigma e_i^2, \quad \frac{\partial}{\partial \hat{\beta}_1} \Sigma e_i^2, \cdots, \quad \frac{\partial}{\partial \hat{\beta}_n} \Sigma e_i^2$$

when set to equal zero, the following system of n + 1 normal equation can be derived:

$$
\begin{aligned}
\Sigma Y &= n\hat{a} + \hat{\beta}_1 \Sigma X_1 + \hat{\beta}_2 \Sigma X_2 + \ldots + \hat{\beta}_n \Sigma X_n \\
\Sigma X_1 Y &= \hat{a}\Sigma X_1 + \hat{\beta}_1 \Sigma X_1^2 + \hat{\beta}_2 \Sigma X_1 X_2 + \ldots + \hat{\beta}_n \Sigma X_1 X_n \\
\Sigma X_2 Y &= \hat{a}\Sigma X_2 + \hat{\beta}_1 \Sigma X_1 X_2 + \hat{\beta}_2 \Sigma X_2^2 + \ldots + \hat{\beta}_n \Sigma X_2 X_n \\
&\quad \cdots \\
\Sigma X_n Y &= \hat{a}\Sigma X_n + \hat{\beta}_1 \Sigma X_1 X_n + \hat{\beta}_2 \Sigma X_2 X_n + \ldots + \hat{\beta}_n \Sigma X_n^2
\end{aligned}
$$

This system of normal equation can be expressed in matrix notation as follows:

$$
\begin{bmatrix}
\Sigma Y \\
\Sigma X_1 Y \\
\Sigma X_2 Y \\
\vdots \\
\Sigma X_n Y
\end{bmatrix}
=
\begin{bmatrix}
n & \Sigma X_1 & \Sigma X_2 & \cdots & \Sigma X_n \\
\Sigma X_1 & \Sigma X_1^2 & \Sigma X_1 X_2 & \cdots & \Sigma X_1 X_n \\
\Sigma X_2 & \Sigma X_1 X_2 & \Sigma X_2^2 & \cdots & \Sigma X_1 X_n \\
\vdots & \vdots & \vdots & & \vdots \\
\Sigma X_n & \Sigma X_1 X_n & \Sigma X_2 X_n & \cdots & \Sigma X_n^2
\end{bmatrix}
\cdot
\begin{bmatrix}
\hat{a} \\
\hat{\beta}_1 \\
\hat{\beta}_2 \\
\vdots \\
\hat{\beta}_n
\end{bmatrix}
$$

or $\mathbf{Y} = \mathbf{XA}$

To solve for the unknown estimated parameters: $\hat{a}$, $\hat{\beta}_1$, $\hat{\beta}_2$, . . ., $\hat{\beta}_n$, simply calculate the inverse of the matrix X and multiply both sides of the matrix equation ($\mathbf{Y=XA}$) by $\mathbf{X^{-1}}$:

$$\mathbf{X^{-1}Y = X^{-1}XA}$$
$$\mathbf{X^{-1}Y = IA}$$

$\mathbf{X^{-1}Y}$ is a column vector of n+1 rows or values representing the values of $\hat{a}$, $\hat{\beta}_1$, $\hat{\beta}_2$, . . ., $\hat{\beta}_n$ respectively, the rows or elements of the column vector A.

This is the general method used to calculate the parameters of a multiple linear model. The computer has been utilized for these calculations and multiple linear computer programs of different types are readily avilable.

For illustration, a multiple linear model for the function: $Y = f(X_1, X_2)$ is considered. The dependent variable Y is affected by two independent variables X_1 and X_2. The relationships existing among the variables are found to be linear. The multiple linear model for this function is:

$$Y = a + \beta_1 X_1 + \beta_2 X_2$$

The least square method is used to estimate the parameters a, β_1, and β_2 of this model. As mentioned before, the least square method requires the minimization of Σe^2 (the sum of squared residuals) which yields a system of three normal equations to solve for the three unknown parameters:

$$\Sigma Y = n\hat{a} + \hat{\beta}\Sigma X_1 + \hat{\beta}_2\Sigma X_2$$
$$\Sigma X_1 Y = \hat{a}\Sigma X_1 + \hat{\beta}\Sigma X_1{}^2 + \hat{\beta}_2\Sigma X_1 X_2$$
$$\Sigma X_2 Y = \hat{a}\Sigma X_2 + \hat{\beta}\Sigma X_1 X_2 + \hat{\beta}\Sigma X_2{}^2$$

In matrix notation, the system becomes:

$$\begin{bmatrix} \Sigma Y \\ \Sigma X_1 Y \\ \Sigma X_2 Y \end{bmatrix} = \begin{bmatrix} n & \Sigma X_1 & \Sigma X_2 \\ \Sigma X_1 & \Sigma X_1{}^2 & \Sigma X_1 X_2 \\ \Sigma X_2 & \Sigma X_1 X_2 & \Sigma X_2{}^2 \end{bmatrix} \cdot \begin{bmatrix} \hat{a} \\ \hat{\beta}_1 \\ \hat{\beta}_2 \end{bmatrix}$$

$$\mathbf{Y = XA}$$

Calculate $\mathbf{X^{-1}}$ and multiply both sides:

$$\mathbf{X^{-1}Y = X^{-1}XA}$$
$$\mathbf{X^{-1}Y = IA}$$

Example 9.5:

Assume the data collected for Y, X_1, and X_2 is as follows:

Y	X_1	X_2
3	2	4
8	1	2
11	4	1
15	7	3
9	13	1
4	7	3
17	15	4
13	19	2
11	12	5
9	19	4

The relationship among the three variables is linear. Estimate the parameters of the model that appropriately represents this relationship.

Solution:

(a) The model:

$$Y = a + \hat{\beta}X_1 + \hat{\beta}_2 X_2$$

(b) The system of normal equation:

$$\Sigma Y = n\hat{a} + \hat{\beta}_1\Sigma X_1 + \hat{\beta}_2\Sigma X_2$$
$$\Sigma X_1 Y = \hat{a}\Sigma X_1 + \hat{\beta}_1\Sigma X_1{}^2 + \hat{\beta}_2\Sigma X_1 X_2$$
$$\Sigma X_2 Y = \hat{a}\Sigma X_2 + \hat{\beta}_1\Sigma X_1 X_2 + \hat{\beta}_2\Sigma X_2{}^2$$

We need the values of: ΣY, ΣX_1, ΣX^2, $\Sigma X_1 Y$, $\Sigma X_2 Y$, $\Sigma X_1{}^2$, $\Sigma X_2{}^2$, $\Sigma X_1 X_2$, n.

Y	X_1	X_2	X_1Y	X_2Y	X_1^2	X_2^2	X_1X_2
3	2	4	6	12	4	16	8
8	1	2	8	16	1	4	2
11	4	1	44	11	16	1	4
15	7	3	105	45	49	9	21
9	13	1	117	9	169	1	13
4	7	3	28	12	49	9	21
17	15	4	255	68	225	16	60
13	19	2	247	26	361	4	38
11	12	5	132	55	144	25	60
9	19	4	171	36	361	16	76
100	99	29	1113	290	1379	101	303
ΣY	ΣX_1	ΣX_2	ΣX_1Y	ΣX_2Y	ΣX_1^2	ΣX_2^2	ΣX_1X_2

Substituting the values in the system of normal equation:

$$100 = 10\hat{a} + 99\hat{\beta_1} + 29\hat{\beta_2}$$
$$1113 = 99\hat{a} + 1379\hat{\beta_1} + 303\hat{\beta_2}$$
$$290 = 29\hat{a} + 303\hat{\beta_1} + 101\hat{\beta_2}$$

$$\begin{bmatrix} 100 \\ 1113 \\ 290 \end{bmatrix} = \begin{bmatrix} 10 & 99 & 29 \\ 99 & 1379 & 303 \\ 29 & 303 & 101 \end{bmatrix} \cdot \begin{bmatrix} \hat{a} \\ \hat{\beta_1} \\ \hat{\beta_2} \end{bmatrix}$$

$$Y = XA$$

Calculate X^{-1}:
1. Find $|X|$
2. Find Adj X
3. $X^{-1} = \dfrac{1}{|X|}$ Adj X

$$X^{-1} = \begin{bmatrix} .7316 & -.0187 & -.1540 \\ -.0187 & .0026 & -.0025 \\ -.1540 & -.0025 & .0615 \end{bmatrix}$$

To solve for $\hat{\alpha}$, $\hat{\beta_1}$, and $\hat{\beta_2}$ multiply X^{-1} by Y:

$$\begin{bmatrix} .7316 & -.0187 & -.1540 \\ -.0187 & .0026 & -.0025 \\ -.1540 & -.0025 & .0615 \end{bmatrix} \cdot \begin{bmatrix} 100 \\ 1113 \\ 290 \end{bmatrix} = \begin{bmatrix} 7.6869 \\ .2988 \\ -.3475 \end{bmatrix} \begin{matrix} \hat{\alpha} \\ \hat{\beta_1} \\ \hat{\beta_2} \end{matrix}$$

The regression line becomes:

$$\hat{Y} = 7.6869 + .2988X_1 - .3475X_2$$

Another method for parameters estimation:

The system of three normal equations can be expressed in deviation form where $y = Y - \overline{Y}$; $x_1 = X_1 - \overline{X}_1$; $x_2 = X_2 - \overline{X}$, and so on.

$$\Sigma y = n\hat{\alpha} + \hat{\beta_1}\Sigma x_1 + \hat{\beta_2}\Sigma x_2$$
$$\Sigma x_1 y = \hat{\alpha}\Sigma x_1 + \hat{\beta_1}\Sigma x_1^2 + \hat{\beta_2}\Sigma x_1 x_2$$
$$\Sigma x_2 y = \hat{\alpha}\Sigma x_2 + \hat{\beta_1}\Sigma x_1 x_2 + \hat{\beta_2}\Sigma x_2^2$$

Σy, Σx_1, Σx_2 are equal to zero, therefore, the three equation system can be reduced to a two equation system:

$$\Sigma x_1 y = \hat{\beta}_1 \Sigma x_1{}^2 + \hat{\beta}_2 \Sigma x_1 x_2$$
$$\Sigma x_2 y = \hat{\beta}_1 \Sigma x_1 x_2 + \hat{\beta}_2 \Sigma x_2{}^2$$

Now we need $\Sigma x_1 y$, $\Sigma x_1{}^2$, $\Sigma x_1 x_2$, $\Sigma x_2 y$, $\Sigma x_2{}^2$ for this two equation system to solve for β_1 and β_2.

$X_1-\overline{X}_1$	$X_2-\overline{X}_2$	$Y-\overline{Y}$	$x_1{}^2$	$x_2{}^2$	$x_1 x_2$	$x_1 y$	$x_2 y$
−7.9	1.1	−7	62.41	1.21	− 8.69	55.3	−7.7
−8.9	− .9	−2	79.21	.81	8.01	17.8	1.8
−5.9	−1.9	1	34.81	3.61	11.21	− 5.9	−1.9
−2.9	.1	5	8.41	.01	− .29	−14.5	.5
3.1	−1.9	−1	9.61	3.61	− 5.89	− 3.1	1.9
−2.9	.1	−6	8.41	.01	− .29	17.4	− .6
5.1	1.1	7	26.01	1.21	5.61	35.7	7.7
9.1	− .9	3	82.81	.81	− 8.19	27.3	−2.7
2.1	2.1	1	4.41	4.41	4.41	2.1	2.1
9.1	1.1	−1	82.81	1.21	10.01	− 9.1	−1.1
			398.9	16.9	15.9	123	0

$$\overline{X}_1 = 9.9 \qquad \overline{X}_2 = 2.9 \qquad \overline{Y} = 10$$

$$123 = 398.9 \hat{\beta}_1 + 15.9 \hat{\beta}_2$$
$$0 = 15.9 \hat{\beta}_1 + 16.9 \hat{\beta}_2$$

$$\beta_1 = \frac{\begin{vmatrix} 123 & 15.9 \\ 0 & 16.9 \end{vmatrix}}{\begin{vmatrix} 398.9 & 15.9 \\ 15.9 & 16.9 \end{vmatrix}} = .3204 \qquad \beta_2 = \frac{\begin{vmatrix} 398.9 & 123 \\ 15.9 & 0 \end{vmatrix}}{\begin{vmatrix} 398.9 & 15.9 \\ 15.9 & 16.9 \end{vmatrix}} = -.3014$$

α is calculated from the following equation:

$$\hat{\alpha} = \overline{Y} - \hat{\beta}_1 X_1 - \hat{\beta}_2 X_2$$
$$= 10-(.3204)(9.9) - (.3014)(2.9)$$
$$= 7.7021$$

The estimated multiple linear equation is:

$$\hat{Y} = 7.7021 + .3204\, X_1 - .3014\, X_2$$

The results achieved by this method of calculation differs insignificantly from those calculated by the application of matrix algebra.

There are many other methods available to calculate the parameters of multiple linear models, however, it will become a problem as the number of the independent variables increases. Therefore, it is easier and more accurate to use computer programs developed for these models.

The regression parameters $\hat{\beta}_1, \hat{\beta}_2, \ldots, \hat{\beta}_n$ are sometimes called partial regression coefficients. They reflect the influence of each independent variable on the dependent variable in units of the original observed data. For example, $\hat{\beta}_1 = .3204$ as calculated above means that holding X_2 constant, a one unit change in X_1 will lead to an average change of .3204 units of Y.

Standard Error of Estimate:

The standard error of estimate, an absolute measure of closeness of fit, can be calculated by a formula similar to that of the simple linear model except for the degrees of freedom which becomes n−k; k refers to the number of parameters being estimated. The formula for the previous example is:

$$\hat{\sigma}_{yx_1x_2} = \sqrt{\frac{\Sigma(Y - \hat{Y})^2}{n - 3}}$$

To calculate the standard error of estimate for the previous example, we need to compute $\hat{Y}$ from the estimated equation:

$$\hat{Y} = 7.6869 + .2988X_1 - .3475X_2$$

$\hat{Y}$ for the 1st observation = 7.6869 + .2988(2) − .3475(4)

$\hat{Y}$	$(Y - \hat{Y})^2$
6.8945	15.1671
7.2907	.5031
8.5346	6.0782
8.7360	39.2377
11.2238	4.9453
8.7360	22.4297
10.7789	38.7021
12.6691	.1095
9.5350	2.1462
11.9741	8.8453
	138.1642

$$\hat{\sigma}_{yx_1x_2} = \sqrt{\frac{138.1642}{10 - 3}}$$

$$= 4.443$$

The magnitude of the standard error of estimation is quite high which may indicate that the regression plane does not fit the data well. To find more about the fit, we need to compute the multiple determination coefficient.

Multiple Determination Coefficient: R^2

Coefficients of multiple determination measures the percentage of variation in Y that has been explained by variations in the independent variables. It is a measure of closeness of the fit of the regression plane to the observed points relative to the fit of the plane going through the means: $\overline{Y}$, $\overline{X}_1$, and $\overline{X}_2$.

The formula for R^2 is the same as the simple linear model:

$$R^2 = \frac{\text{Explained variation (squared)}}{\text{Total variation (squared)}}$$

$$= \frac{\Sigma(\hat{Y} - \overline{Y})^2}{\Sigma(Y - \overline{Y})^2}$$

$$\text{or } R^2 = 1 - \frac{\text{Unexplained variation (squared)}}{\text{Total variation (squared)}}$$

$$= 1 - \frac{\Sigma(Y - \hat{Y})^2}{\Sigma(Y - \overline{Y})^2}$$

We will use the last formula for R^2 because we have already computed $\Sigma(Y - \hat{Y})^2$, so we need to compute $\Sigma(Y - \overline{Y})^2$.

$Y - \overline{Y}$	$(Y - \overline{Y})^2$
-7	49
-2	4
1	1
5	25
-1	1
-6	36
7	49
3	9
1	1
-1	1
	176

$$R^2 = 1 - \frac{138.1642}{176}$$
$$= 1 - .7850$$
$$= .2150$$

The magnitude of R^2 is very small indicating that the linear association among the variables Y, X_1, and X_2 is very weak. In addition, the small value of R^2 means that the regression equation is a poor fit of the plane.

R^2 indicates the degree of association of all variables combined. If the magnitude of R^2 is small, as is the case of the current example, then it might be of interest to determine the independent variable(s) with the lowest association to Y to eliminate. This can be done by examining the simple or two variable correlation coefficients as well as the partial correlation coefficients. Formulas to compute these two types of correlation are presented below.

Two variable correlation coefficients:

For the function of: $Y = f(X_1, X_2)$, we can calculate three simple or two variable correlation coefficients: R_{yx_1}, R_{yx_2}, and $R_{x_1x_2}$ applying the following formulas:

$$R_{yx_1} = \frac{\Sigma yx_1}{\sqrt{\Sigma y^2 \Sigma x_1^2}} \qquad \text{correlation coefficient for Y and } X_1$$

$$R_{yx_2} = \frac{\Sigma yx_2}{\sqrt{\Sigma y^2 \Sigma x_2^2}} \qquad \text{correlation coefficient for Y and } X_2$$

$$R_{x_1x_2} = \frac{\Sigma x_1x_2}{\sqrt{\Sigma x_1^2 \Sigma x_2^2}} \qquad \text{correlation coefficient for } X_1 \text{ and } X_2$$

The simple correlation coefficients for the previous example are calculated and arranged in a matrix. The following values have been previously computed:

$$\Sigma yx_1 = 123 \qquad \Sigma y^2 = 176 \qquad \Sigma x_1^2 = 398.9$$
$$\Sigma yx_2 = 0 \qquad \Sigma x_2^2 = 16.9 \qquad \Sigma x_1 x_2 = 15.9$$

$$R_{yx_1} = \frac{123}{\sqrt{(176)(398.9)}} = .4642$$

$$R_{yx_2} = \frac{0}{\sqrt{(176)(16.9)}} = 0$$

$$R_{x_1 x_2} = \frac{15.9}{\sqrt{(398.9)(16.9)}} = .1937$$

Correlation Matrix

	Y	X_1	X_2
Y	1	.4642	0
X_1	.4642	1	.1937
X_2	0	.1937	1

Partial Correlation Coefficients:

A partial correlation coefficient measures the separate effect of each X on Y provided that the influence of all other X's has been removed. For example, $R_{yx_1 \cdot x_2}$ refers to the partial correlation between Y and X_1, holding X_2 constant, so that its influence on both Y and X_1 has been removed. The calculation of partial correlation coefficients can be done by using the following formulas:

$$R_{yx_1 \cdot x_2} = \frac{R_{yx_1} - R_{yx_2} \cdot R_{x_1 x_2}}{\sqrt{1-R^2_{yx_2}} \sqrt{1-R^2_{x_1 x_2}}}$$

$$R_{yx_2 \cdot x_1} = \frac{R_{yx_2} - R_{yx_1} \cdot R_{x_1 x_2}}{\sqrt{1-R^2_{yx_1}} \sqrt{1-R^2_{x_1 x_2}}}$$

$$R_{x_1 x_2 \cdot y} = \frac{R_{x_1 x_2} - R_{yx_1} \cdot R_{yx_2}}{\sqrt{1-R^2_{yx_1}} \sqrt{1-R^2_{yx_2}}}$$

For the previous example:

$$R_{yx_1 \cdot x_2} = \frac{.4642 - (0)(.1937)}{\sqrt{1-(0)^2} \sqrt{1-(.1937)^2}} = .4731$$

$$R_{yx_2 \cdot x_1} = \frac{0 - (.4642)(.1937)}{\sqrt{1-(.4641)^2} \sqrt{1-(.1937)^2}} = -.1035$$

$$R_{x_1 x_2 \cdot y} = \frac{.1937 - (.4642)(0)}{\sqrt{1-(.4642)^2} \sqrt{1-(0)^2}} = -.3054$$

Standard Error of Regression Coefficients:

The standard errors of β_1, β_2, . . . , β_n measure the expected amount of error that occurs in the estimation of these parameters. These standard errors or $\sigma_{\beta i}$ are computed for use in determining the significance of the estimated parameters β's, and hence the significance of their independent variables.

To calculate the standard error for β_1 and β_2 for the previous example, the following two formulas are introduced:

$$\hat{\sigma}_{\beta 1} = \frac{\hat{\sigma}_{yx_1x_2}}{\sqrt{\Sigma x_1^2(1-R^2_{x_1x_2})}}$$

$$\hat{\sigma}_{\beta 2} = \frac{\hat{\sigma}_{yx_1x_2}}{\sqrt{\Sigma x_2^2(1-R^2_{x_1x_2})}}$$

The magnitudes of $\hat{\sigma}_{\beta 1}$ and $\hat{\sigma}_{\beta 2}$ are:

$$\hat{\sigma}_{\beta 1} = \frac{4.443}{\sqrt{398.9(1-.0375)}} = .2267$$

$$\hat{\sigma}_{\beta 2} = \frac{4.443}{\sqrt{16.9(1-.0375)}} = .2731$$

The estimated regression equation and the standard error of $\hat{\beta}_1$ and $\hat{\beta}_2$ can be written as follows:

$$\hat{Y} = 7.6869 + .2988X_1 - .3475X_2$$
$$(.2267) \qquad (.2731)$$

When compared with the magnitudes of $\hat{\beta}_1$ and $\hat{\sigma}_{\beta i}$, $\hat{\beta}_1$ is not significantly different from zero. This is also true with respect to $\hat{\beta}_2$. A t-test can be run for each $\hat{\beta}$ as applied in the simple two variable regression, to test for the significance of the $\hat{\beta}_i$. The t-test will show that the $\hat{\beta}_i$ are not significant.

In this example, the magnitude of R^2 is very small and the parameter of the model ($\hat{\beta}_i$) is not significantly different from zero, as shown by comparing $\hat{\sigma}_{\beta i}$ and $\hat{\beta}_i$. These two factors indicate that the estimated equation, or the model, is not reliable for prediction. To improve the reliability of the model, other variables and/or the structure of the model need to be changed. It might be worthwhile to use a nonlinear model rather than the linear model.

2. Nonlinear Models:

If the relationship between two or more variables is nonlinear, then any attempt to fit a linear model to the data may fail to produce a reliable, predictive model. An inspection of the scatter diagram is helpful, if not necessary, to decide on the type of model that appropriately fits the data. Even if the decision is made to construct a nonlinear model to represent the nonlinear relationship that exists between the variables, it is important to know the degree of the polynomial from the scatter diagram to properly construct the appropriate model. For example, if the scatter diagram shows that the data follows a polynomial of second degree, then the model becomes:

$$Y = \alpha + \beta_1 X + \beta_2 X^2$$

A higher polynomial curve will determine the elements to be included in the model. In general, any polynomial of second degree or higher can be represented by a nonlinear model. A model for a polynomial of degree n becomes:

$$Y = \alpha + \beta_1 X + \beta_2 X^2 + \beta_3 X^3 + \ldots + \beta_n X^n$$

In addition to polynomials of second degree or higher, growth curves, represented by exponential models, are also nonlinear.

A. Two-variable Nonlinear Model:

Models that express a nonlinear relationship that exists between an independent and a dependent variable are called two-variable or simple nonlinear model. Exponential models of two variables are here considered to illustrate simple nonlinear models. For example, $Y = \alpha X^\beta$ and $Y = \alpha e^{\beta x}$ are two exponential nonlinear models containing two variables, Y and X.

Exponential two-variable models can be transformed to simple- or two-variable linear models by using logarithms. For the model: $Y = \alpha X^\beta$ the transformed linear model becomes:

$$\log_e Y = \log_e \alpha + \beta \log_e X \qquad (1)$$

and $Y = \alpha e^{\beta x}$; a nonlinear exponential model can be transformed to a simple linear model of the form:

$$\log_e Y = \log_e \alpha + \beta X \qquad (2)$$

To estimate the parameters of models (1) and (2), the least square method may be used and a system of normal equation can be derived for each model to solve for the unknown parameters. For the first model, equation (1), the system of two-normal equation is:

$$\Sigma \log Y = n \log \hat{\alpha} + \hat{\beta} \Sigma \log X$$
$$\Sigma \log X \log Y = \log \hat{\alpha} \Sigma \log X + \hat{\beta} \Sigma (\log X)^2$$

while the two-normal equation for model (2) is:

$$\Sigma \log Y = n \log \hat{\alpha} + \hat{\beta} \Sigma X$$
$$\Sigma (\log Y) X = \log \hat{\alpha} \Sigma X + \hat{\beta} \Sigma X^2$$

Solve the first and the second sets of equations for $\log \hat{\alpha}$ and $\hat{\beta}$; then the antilog of $\log \hat{\alpha}$ provides the value of $\hat{\alpha}$.

Having the estimated equations: $\hat{Y} = \hat{\alpha} X^{\hat{\beta}}$ and $\hat{Y} = \hat{\alpha} e^{\hat{\beta} x}$ one can follow the same procedure and use the formula presented in the simple linear model to calculate the standard error of estimate $\hat{\sigma}_{yx}$, the standard error of $\beta(\hat{\sigma}_\beta)$, coefficient of determination R^2, and run tests of significance.

B. Multiple Nonlinear Model:

Polynomials of second or higher degree constitute multiple nonlinear models. For example, if the relationship between Y and X can be represented by a polynomial of third degree then the model becomes:

$$Y = \alpha + \beta_1 X + \beta_2 X^2 + \beta_3 X^3$$

The least square method may be applied to estimate the parameters of this model: α, β_1, β_2, and β_3. The minimization of the sum squared residuals (Σe^2) provides us with a system of four-normal equation to solve for the four unknown parameters. The system of normal equation is:

$$\begin{aligned}
\Sigma Y &= n\hat{\alpha} + \hat{\beta}_1 \Sigma X + \hat{\beta}_2 \Sigma X^2 + \hat{\beta}_3 \Sigma X^3 \\
\Sigma XY &= \hat{\alpha}\Sigma X + \hat{\beta}_1 \Sigma X^2 + \hat{\beta}_2 \Sigma X^3 + \hat{\beta}_3 \Sigma X^4 \\
\Sigma X^2 Y &= \hat{\alpha}\Sigma X^2 + \hat{\beta}_1 \Sigma X^3 + \hat{\beta}_2 \Sigma X^4 + \hat{\beta}_3 \Sigma X^5 \\
\Sigma X^3 Y &= \hat{\alpha}\Sigma X^3 + \hat{\beta}_1 \Sigma X^4 + \hat{\beta}_2 \Sigma X^5 + \hat{\beta}_3 \Sigma X^6
\end{aligned}$$

In matrix notation:

$$
\begin{bmatrix}
\Sigma Y \\
\Sigma XY \\
\Sigma X^2 Y \\
\Sigma X^3 Y
\end{bmatrix}
=
\begin{bmatrix}
n & \Sigma X & \Sigma X^2 & \Sigma X^3 \\
\Sigma X & \Sigma X^2 & \Sigma X^3 & \Sigma X^4 \\
\Sigma X^2 & \Sigma X^3 & \Sigma X^4 & \Sigma X^5 \\
\Sigma X^3 & \Sigma X^4 & \Sigma X^5 & \Sigma X^6
\end{bmatrix}
\cdot
\begin{bmatrix}
\alpha \\
\beta_1 \\
\beta_2 \\
\beta_3
\end{bmatrix}
$$

or $\mathbf{Y} = \mathbf{XA}$

To solve for the values of A, find X^{-1} and multiply:

$$\mathbf{X^{-1}Y} = \mathbf{IA}$$

The estimated equation of this model is:

$$\hat{Y} = \hat{\alpha} + \hat{\beta}_1 X + \hat{\beta}_2 X^2 + \hat{\beta}_3 X^3$$

The standard error of estimate, the standard error for the regression coefficients, and the coefficient of determination can be calculated for this model by following the same procedure presented in the multiple linear model.

The multiple nonlinear model can be transformed into the form of a multiple linear model. For example, in the multiple nonlinear model:

$$Y = \alpha + \beta_1 X + \beta_2 X^2 + \beta_3 X^3$$

if we set $X = X_1$
and $X^2 = X_2$
$ X^3 = X_3$

then this multiple nonlinear model becomes a multiple linear model:

$$Y = \alpha + \beta_1 X_1 + \beta_2 X_2 + \beta_3 X_3$$

As the degree of polynomials increases it will be very difficult to use a desk calculator to estimate the parameters and to calculate measures needed to test the predictive ability of the model. Therefore, it is advisable to use computer programs designed for this type of analysis.

EXERCISES

9.1 Define:
  a. An econometric model
  b. Linear model
  c. Nonlinear model
  d. Multiple linear model
  e. Coefficient of determination

9.2 a. What is the difference between regression and correlation analysis?
  b. Why is the disturbance term included in any econometric model?
  c. What is the difference between the standard error of estimate and the standard error of regression coefficient?

9.3 The following table shows the data for Y and X, where Y represents personal consumption expenditures of durable goods, and X represents total disposable personal income. The data is seasonally adjusted at annual rates, in billions of dollars.

Year	Y	X
1950	30.5	206.9
1951	29.6	226.6
1952	29.3	238.3
1953	33.2	252.6
1954	32.8	257.4
1955	39.6	275.3
1956	38.9	293.2
1957	40.8	308.5
1958	37.9	318.8
1959	44.3	337.3

Construct an appropriate model for the two variables, and determine the reliability of the model to predict.

9.4 Project: $Y_t = f(X_{t-1})$
Y_t represents personal consumption expenditures on automobiles and parts, seasonally adjusted at annual rates for the period 1960 to 1969. X_{t-1} represents personal savings, seasonally adjusted at annual rates for the period 1959 to 1968. (Notice one year lag.)
Construct a model to represent the relationship between the variables; then test the reliability of the model to predict.

9.5 Project: $Y_t = f(X_{1t}, X_{2t-1})$
Y_t represents total personal consumption on nondurable goods, seasonally adjusted at annual rates for the period 1961 to 1970.
X_{1t} represents personal outlays, seasonally adjusted at annual rates for the period from 1961 to 1970.
X_{2t-1} represents personal savings, seasonally adjusted at annual rates for the period from 1960 to 1969.
Test the reliability of the model to predict.

APPENDICES

Appendix A
Σ, Π, and $\sqrt{}$

1. The summation operator Σ:

The upper case of the Greek letter sigma (Σ) is used to denote the sum of the values contained in a variable.

$$\sum_{i=1}^{n} X_i = X_1 + X_2 + X_3 + \ldots + X_n$$

Let X_i be a variable that assumes the following values:

X_i: 5, -2, 0, 15, 10, -12, 4

X_i contains seven observations or n = 7. The sum of the values of the seven observations contained in X_i can be calculated as follows:

$$\sum_{i=1}^{7} X_i = X_1 + X_2 + X_3 + X_4 + X_5 + X_6 + X_7$$
$$= 5 + (-2) + 0 + 15 + 10 + (-12) + 4$$
$$= 20$$

or $\Sigma X = 20$, ΣX indicates that all the observations of X have been added. Remarks concerning the use of Σ:

    a. $\Sigma(X + Y + Z) = \Sigma X + \Sigma Y + \Sigma Z$

    b. $\Sigma cX = c\Sigma X$, c is a constant

    c. $\Sigma c = nc$, c is a constant

    d. $\Sigma YX = \Sigma Y \Sigma X$

2. The multiplication operator Π:

The upper case of the Greek letter PI (Π) is used to denote the product of multiplying the elements contained in a variable.

$$\prod_{i=1}^{n} X_i = X_1 \bullet X_2 \bullet X_3 \ldots X_n$$

Let X_i assume these values: 5, 9, -12, 10, -4 then

$$\prod_{i=1}^{5} X_i = X_1 \bullet X_2 \bullet X_3 \bullet X_4 \bullet X_5$$
$$= 5 \bullet 9 \bullet (-12) \bullet 10 \bullet (-4)$$
$$\text{or } \Pi X = 21600$$

3. The use of square root tables $\sqrt{n}$, $\sqrt{10n}$:

There are two square root tables: $\sqrt{n}$ and $\sqrt{10n}$. To use either, apply the following steps:

    a. Move **even** number of decimals to the left or to the right to reduce the number. If the reduced number falls between one and less than 10, then use $\sqrt{n}$ table. If the reduced number is 10 or more, use $\sqrt{10n}$ table with n = reduced number $\div$ 10.

b.   After finding the square root from $\sqrt{n}$ or $\sqrt{10n}$ from the table, move the decimal to the opposite direction for **half the even** number of decimals moved in a.

Example: Find $\sqrt{10345.07}$

Solution: 4 places
                ←————

10345.07
1.034507 ————→ use $\sqrt{n}$ table, n = 1.03
2 places
————→

1.01489
101.489

Example: Find $\sqrt{.00000673}$

Solution: 6 places
                ————→

.00000673
6.73 ————→ use $\sqrt{n}$ table, n = 6.73
3 places
←————

2.59422
.00259422

Example: Find $\sqrt{.00249}$

Solution: 4 places
                ————→

.00249

24.9 ————→ use $\sqrt{10n}$ table, $n = \dfrac{24.9}{10} = 2.49$

2 places
←————

4.98999
.0498999

Appendix B

MEASURES OF LOCATION
QUARTILES, DECILES, PERCENTILES
(Grouped Data)

Quartiles (Q_1 and Q_3), Deciles (D_i) and Percentiles (P_i) are measures of location used to determine the rank of any observation relation to the whole set of observations. When we say this student ranks in the upper 20% of his graduating class, this means that his grades fall within the limit of the second decile or the 20th percentile.

The formula used to calculate these measures is the same one being used to calculate the median in Chapter II. There is a change in the formula from one measure to another along with the change of the subscripts. The main change in the formula is based on the location of the measure:

$$Q_1 = 1/4\ \Sigma f = \frac{\Sigma f}{4} \qquad \text{indicates the location of } Q_1$$

$$Q_3 = 3/4\ \Sigma f = \frac{3\Sigma f}{4}$$

$$D_1 = 1/10\ \Sigma f = \frac{\Sigma f}{10} \qquad \text{indicates the location of } D_1$$

$$D_2 = 2/10\ \Sigma f = \frac{2\Sigma f}{10}$$

$$D_3 = 3/10\ \Sigma f = \frac{3\Sigma f}{10}$$

- •
- •

$$P_1 = 1/100\ \Sigma f = \frac{\Sigma f}{100} \qquad \text{indicates the location of } P_1$$

$$P_2 = 2/100\ \Sigma f = \frac{2\Sigma f}{100}$$

$$P_3 = 3/100\ \Sigma f = \frac{3\Sigma f}{100}$$

- •
- •
- •

As mentioned above, the formula to calculate Q_1 is the same as the one used to calculate the median except for the change of the subscripts and $\frac{\Sigma f}{4}$ is included in Q_1 formula instead of $\frac{\Sigma f}{2}$ for the median. This is also true with respect to Q_3, D_1, D_2, . . ., P_1, P_2, ...

For example: the formula for the calculation of Q_1:

$$Q_1 = L_{Q_1} + \frac{\dfrac{\Sigma f}{4} - F_{LQ1}}{f_{Q1}} i_{Q1}$$

and for $D_2 = L_{D_2} + \dfrac{\dfrac{2\Sigma f}{10} - F_{LD2}}{f_{D2}} i_{D2}$

and for $P_9 = L_{P_9} + \dfrac{\dfrac{9\Sigma f}{100} - F_{LP9}}{f_{P9}} i_{P9}$

and so on for the other measures.

Appendix C

MATRICES

Matrix algebra is being used extensively in quantitative business and economics to solve for the unknowns of a system of linear equations, to calculate the expected pay off values in decision theory, and to estimate parameters of multiple linear or nonlinear econometric models.

This appendix covers selective parts of matrix algebra either applied or mentioned in the chapters of this book. These parts are: determinants, addition, multiplication, and the inverse of a matrix.

Definition of a matrix:

A matrix is a rectangular array of real numbers arranged in m rows and n columns. Let A be a rectangular array, an m by n (m $\times$ n) matrix. The elements of matrix A are:

$$
A = \begin{bmatrix}
a_{11} & a_{12} & a_{13} & \cdots & a_{1n} \\
a_{21} & a_{22} & a_{23} & \cdots & a_{2n} \\
\cdot & \cdot & \cdot & & \cdot \\
\cdot & \cdot & \cdot & & \cdot \\
\cdot & \cdot & \cdot & & \cdot \\
a_{m1} & a_{m2} & a_{m3} & \cdots & a_{mn}
\end{bmatrix}_{m,n}
$$

or $A = [a_{ij}]_{mn}$; i = 1,2,3, . . . , m and j = 1,2,3, . . . ,n

If the number of rows are equal to the number of columns (m = n), then A becomes a square matrix (n $\times$ n).

An array with m rows and one column is called a column vector while a row vector has one row and n columns.

190

Determinants:

A determinant is a single number associated with a square matrix. The determinant of matrix A is denoted by $|A|$.

$$|A| = \begin{vmatrix} a_{11} & a_{12} & a_{13} & \cdots & a_{1n} \\ a_{21} & a_{22} & a_{23} & \cdots & a_{2n} \\ \cdot & \cdot & \cdot & & \cdot \\ \cdot & \cdot & \cdot & & \cdot \\ \cdot & \cdot & \cdot & & \cdot \\ a_{n1} & a_{n2} & a_{n3} & \cdots & a_{nn} \end{vmatrix}$$

Calculation of determinants:

1. Let X be a 2×2 square matrix:

$$X = \begin{bmatrix} X_{11} & X_{12} \\ X_{21} & X_{22} \end{bmatrix}$$

then $|X| = X_{11} X_{22} - X_{21} X_{22}$

Example:

$$X = \begin{bmatrix} 5 & 9 \\ 4 & 12 \end{bmatrix} \qquad \text{find } |X|$$

Solution: $|X| = (5)(12) - (4)(9)$
$= 24$

2. Let A be a square matrix of higher order than 2×2:

$$A = \begin{bmatrix} a_{11} & a_{12} & a_{13} \\ a_{21} & a_{22} & a_{23} \\ a_{31} & a_{32} & a_{33} \end{bmatrix}$$

$$|A| = \sum_{j=1}^{n} a_{ij} c_{ij}$$

where c_{ij} refers to the co-factors of the minors of A

$c_{ij} = (-1)^{i+j} |M_{ij}|$, $|M_{ij}|$ = determinants of the minor

then $|A| = a_{11}(-1)^{1+1} \begin{vmatrix} a_{22} & a_{23} \\ a_{32} & a_{33} \end{vmatrix} + a_{12}(-1)^{1+2} \begin{vmatrix} a_{21} & a_{23} \\ a_{31} & a_{33} \end{vmatrix}$

$+ a_{13}(-1)^{1+3} \begin{vmatrix} a_{21} & a_{22} \\ a_{31} & a_{32} \end{vmatrix}$

or $|A| = a_{11}(-1)^{1+1} \begin{vmatrix} a_{22} & a_{23} \\ a_{32} & a_{33} \end{vmatrix} + a_{21}(-1)^{2+1} \begin{vmatrix} a_{12} & a_{13} \\ a_{32} & a_{33} \end{vmatrix}$

$+ a_{31}(-1)^{3+1} \begin{vmatrix} a_{12} & a_{13} \\ a_{22} & a_{23} \end{vmatrix}$

Example: Let A be a 3 × 3 matrix:

$$A = \begin{bmatrix} 2 & 4 & 6 \\ 8 & -1 & 3 \\ 5 & 7 & 9 \end{bmatrix}$$

Find |A|.

Solution: $|A| = (2)(-1)^{1+1} \begin{vmatrix} -1 & 3 \\ 7 & 9 \end{vmatrix} + 4(-1)^{1+2} \begin{vmatrix} 8 & 3 \\ 5 & 9 \end{vmatrix}$

$+ 6(-1)^{1+3} \begin{vmatrix} 8 & -1 \\ 5 & 7 \end{vmatrix}$

$= (2)(-9-21) - 4(72-15) + 6(56-(-5))$
$= (2)(-30) - 4(57) + 6(61)$
$= -60 - 228 + 366$
$= 78$

or $|A| = (2)(-1)^{1+1} \begin{vmatrix} -1 & 3 \\ 7 & 9 \end{vmatrix} + 8(-1)^{2+1} \begin{vmatrix} 4 & 6 \\ 7 & 9 \end{vmatrix} + 5(-1)^{3+1} \begin{vmatrix} 4 & 6 \\ -1 & 3 \end{vmatrix}$

$= -60 + 48 + 90$
$= 78$

If the order of a determinant is very large, say 9 or 8, then simplify the determinant order by reducing the rows to zero by some arithmetic operation.

Addition and subtraction of matrices:

Matrices of the same order (m,n) are called conformable for addition or subtraction.

Example: Add the following two matrices:

$$A = \begin{bmatrix} 5 & 6 & -1 \\ 4 & 2 & 9 \end{bmatrix}_{2,3} \qquad B = \begin{bmatrix} 2 & 5 & 9 \\ -6 & 4 & -2 \end{bmatrix}_{2,3}$$

Solution: Let C = A + B

$$C = \begin{bmatrix} 5+2 & 6+5 & -1+9 \\ 4+(-6) & 2+4 & 9+(-2) \end{bmatrix}_{2,3} = \begin{bmatrix} 7 & 11 & 8 \\ -2 & 6 & 7 \end{bmatrix}_{2,3}$$

Example: Subtract the matrices B from A in the above example:

Solution: Let D = A − B

$$D = \begin{bmatrix} 5-2 & 6-5 & -1-9 \\ 4+6 & 2-4 & 9+2 \end{bmatrix} = \begin{bmatrix} 3 & 1 & -10 \\ 10 & -2 & 11 \end{bmatrix}$$

Multiplication of matrices:

Two matrices can be multiplied if the number of columns in one equals the number of rows in the other, or vice versa. If the number of columns in E is equal to the number of rows in F, then E and F can be multiplied. If $E = (e_{ij})_{m,n}$ and $F = (f_{ij})_{n,p}$ then $EF = X = (x_{ik})_{m,p}$

Example: Multiply the following two matrices E and F:

$$E = \begin{bmatrix} 1 & 2 \\ 3 & 4 \end{bmatrix}_{2,2} \qquad F = \begin{bmatrix} 1 & 2 & 3 \\ 3 & 2 & 1 \end{bmatrix}_{2,3}$$

Solution: E is 2×2 matrix, 2 rows and 2 columns.
F is 2×3 matrix, 2 rows and 3 columns.

The number of columns in E = the number of rows in F, then we can multiply E by F to produce X; or
$X = E \quad F$

$$X = \begin{bmatrix} 1 & 2 \\ 3 & 4 \end{bmatrix}_{2,2} \begin{bmatrix} 1 & 2 & 3 \\ 3 & 2 & 1 \end{bmatrix}_{2,3}$$

$$= \begin{bmatrix} (1)(1)+(2)(3) & (1)(2)+(2)(2) & (1)(3)+(2)(1) \\ (3)(1)+(4)(3) & (3)(2)+(4)(2) & (3)(3)+(4)(1) \end{bmatrix}$$

$$= \begin{bmatrix} 7 & 6 & 5 \\ 15 & 14 & 13 \end{bmatrix}_{2,3}$$

Notice that $EF = FE$ even if the number of columns in F equals the number of rows in E.

Transposition of a Matrix:

The term transpose will be mentioned in finding the inverse of a square matrix. It means rows are changed to columns or vice versa. If A is 2×3 matrix, then A transposed (A^T or A') is a matrix of the order 3×2.

Example: Let A be 3×4 matrix, find A^T.

$$A = \begin{bmatrix} -2 & 4 & 7 & 8 \\ 3 & 5 & 0 & 9 \\ 2 & 0 & 5 & 7 \end{bmatrix}_{3,4}$$

Solution:

$$A^T \text{ or } A' = \begin{bmatrix} -2 & 3 & 2 \\ 4 & 5 & 0 \\ 7 & 0 & 5 \\ 8 & 9 & 7 \end{bmatrix}_{4,3}$$

Inverse of a square matrix:

To calculate the inverse of any square matrix, follow these three steps:
1. Find the determinant of X or $|X|$.
2. Find the adjoint matrix of X or Adj X.
3. $X^{-1} = \dfrac{1}{|X|}$Adj X.

Example: Calculate the inverse of the following matrix:

$$X = \begin{bmatrix} 2 & 3 & 4 \\ 5 & 6 & 7 \\ 1 & 7 & 8 \end{bmatrix}$$

Solution: 1. The determinant of X.

$$|X| = 2(-1)^{1+1}\begin{vmatrix} 6 & 7 \\ 7 & 8 \end{vmatrix} + 3(-1)^{1+2}\begin{vmatrix} 5 & 7 \\ 1 & 8 \end{vmatrix} + 4(-1)^{1+3}\begin{vmatrix} 5 & 6 \\ 1 & 7 \end{vmatrix}$$
$$= -2 \ -99 \ +116$$
$$= 15$$

2. Calculate the adjoint matrix of X (Adj X). The adjoint matrix of X can be calculated as follows:

a. Calculate the minors. A minor is the determinant obtained from $|X|$ by deleting the ith row and the jth column.

For example:

$$X = \begin{bmatrix} 2 & 3 & 4 \\ 5 & 6 & 7 \\ 1 & 7 & 8 \end{bmatrix} \qquad |X| = \begin{vmatrix} 2 & 3 & 4 \\ 5 & 6 & 7 \\ 1 & 7 & 8 \end{vmatrix}$$

The minors of X $= \begin{vmatrix} \begin{vmatrix} 6 & 7 \\ 7 & 8 \end{vmatrix} & \begin{vmatrix} 5 & 7 \\ 1 & 8 \end{vmatrix} & \begin{vmatrix} 5 & 6 \\ 1 & 7 \end{vmatrix} \\ \begin{vmatrix} 3 & 4 \\ 7 & 8 \end{vmatrix} & \begin{vmatrix} 2 & 4 \\ 1 & 8 \end{vmatrix} & \begin{vmatrix} 2 & 3 \\ 1 & 7 \end{vmatrix} \\ \begin{vmatrix} 3 & 4 \\ 6 & 7 \end{vmatrix} & \begin{vmatrix} 2 & 4 \\ 5 & 7 \end{vmatrix} & \begin{vmatrix} 2 & 3 \\ 5 & 6 \end{vmatrix} \end{vmatrix}$

b. Find the cofactors of X. The cofactor is a signed minor. The sign attached to the minor can be determined by the following rule: $(-1)^{i+j}$ where i denotes the number of the row and j the number of the column.

For example the sign of the minor $\begin{vmatrix} 6 & 7 \\ 7 & 8 \end{vmatrix}$ is:

$(-1)^{1+1}$ because the minor falls in the first row and in the first column, the sign is $(-1)^2 = +1$. The cofactor for this minor is:

$$+ \begin{vmatrix} 6 & 7 \\ 7 & 8 \end{vmatrix} = (6)(8) - (7)(7) = -1$$

Apply the sign rule to the minor $\begin{vmatrix} 5 & 7 \\ 1 & 8 \end{vmatrix}$ and record the cofactor.

The sign is $(-1)^{1+2}$ because the minor falls in the first row and in the second column. The cofactor becomes:

$$(-1)^3 \begin{vmatrix} 5 & 7 \\ 1 & 8 \end{vmatrix} = (-1)\,[(5)\,(8) - (1)\,(7)] = -33$$

Use the same steps to calculate the cofactor matrix of X:

$$\begin{bmatrix} -1 & -33 & 29 \\ 4 & 12 & -11 \\ -3 & 6 & -3 \end{bmatrix}$$

C. The transpose of the cofactor matrix of X is the Adj X:

$$\text{Adj } X = \begin{bmatrix} -1 & 4 & -3 \\ -33 & 12 & 6 \\ 29 & -11 & -3 \end{bmatrix}$$

3. The inverse of X (X^{-1}) is:

$$X^{-1} = \frac{1}{|X|} \begin{bmatrix} -1 & 4 & -3 \\ -33 & 12 & 6 \\ 29 & -11 & -3 \end{bmatrix}$$

$$= \frac{1}{15} \begin{bmatrix} -1 & 4 & -3 \\ -33 & 12 & 6 \\ 29 & -11 & -3 \end{bmatrix}$$

$$= \begin{bmatrix} -1/15 & 4/15 & -3/15 \\ -33/15 & 12/15 & 6/15 \\ 29/15 & -11/15 & -3/15 \end{bmatrix}$$

$$= \begin{bmatrix} -.07 & .27 & -.20 \\ -2.2 & .80 & .40 \\ 1.93 & -.73 & -.20 \end{bmatrix}$$

If we multiply X by its inverse X^{-1}, the result will be the unit or identity matrix. The identity matrix contains one in the diagonal of the matrix and zeros everywhere and it serves as one in the scalar system. The multiplication of X by X^{-1} produces:

$$X \bullet X^{-1} = \begin{bmatrix} 2 & 3 & 4 \\ 5 & 6 & 7 \\ 1 & 7 & 8 \end{bmatrix} \bullet \begin{bmatrix} -.07 & .27 & -.20 \\ -2.2 & .80 & .40 \\ 1.93 & -.73 & -.20 \end{bmatrix}$$

$$= \begin{bmatrix} .98 & .02 & 0 \\ -.04 & 1.04 & 0 \\ -.03 & .03 & 1 \end{bmatrix} \cong \begin{bmatrix} 1 & 0 & 0 \\ 0 & 1 & 0 \\ 0 & 0 & 1 \end{bmatrix} = I$$

It is also true that $X^{-1} \bullet X = I$, where I refers to the identity matrix. There are different methods besides this one to find the inverse of a matrix.

TABLES

198

Table 1

SQUARES, SQUARE ROOTS, AND RECIPROCALS

n	n^2	$\sqrt{n}$	$\sqrt{10n}$	$1/n$	n	n^2	$\sqrt{n}$	$\sqrt{10n}$	$1/n$
1.00	1.0000	1.00000	3.16228	1.000000	1.50	2.2500	1.22474	3.87298	.666667
1.01	1.0201	1.00499	3.17805	.990099	1.51	2.2801	1.22882	3.88587	.662252
1.02	1.0404	1.00995	3.19374	.980392	1.52	2.3104	1.23288	3.89872	.657895
1.03	1.0609	1.01489	3.20936	.970874	1.53	2.3409	1.23693	3.91152	.653595
1.04	1.0816	1.01980	3.22490	.961538	1.54	2.3716	1.24097	3.92428	.649351
1.05	1.1025	1.02470	3.24037	.952381	1.55	2.4025	1.24499	3.93700	.645161
1.06	1.1236	1.02956	3.25576	.943396	1.56	2.4336	1.24900	3.94968	.641026
1.07	1.1449	1.03441	3.27109	.934579	1.57	2.4649	1.25300	3.96232	.636943
1.08	1.1664	1.03923	3.28634	.925926	1.58	2.4964	1.25698	3.97492	.632911
1.09	1.1881	1.04403	3.30151	.917431	1.59	2.5281	1.26095	3.98748	.628931
1.10	1.2100	1.04881	3.31662	.909091	1.60	2.5600	1.26491	4.00000	.625000
1.11	1.2321	1.05357	3.33167	.900901	1.61	2.5921	1.26886	4.01248	.621118
1.12	1.2544	1.05830	3.34664	.892857	1.62	2.6244	1.27279	4.02492	.617284
1.13	1.2769	1.06301	3.36155	.884956	1.63	2.6569	1.27671	4.03733	.613497
1.14	1.2996	1.06771	3.37639	.877193	1.64	2.6896	1.28062	4.04969	.609756
1.15	1.3225	1.07238	3.39116	.869565	1.65	2.7225	1.28452	4.06202	.606061
1.16	1.3456	1.07703	3.40588	.862069	1.66	2.7556	1.28841	4.07431	.602410
1.17	1.3689	1.08167	3.42053	.854701	1.67	2.7889	1.29228	4.08656	.598802
1.18	1.3924	1.08628	3.43511	.847458	1.68	2.8224	1.29615	4.09878	.595238
1.19	1.4161	1.09087	3.44964	.840336	1.69	2.8561	1.30000	4.11096	.591716
1.20	1.4400	1.09545	3.46410	.833333	1.70	2.8900	1.30384	4.12311	.588235
1.21	1.4641	1.10000	3.47851	.826446	1.71	2.9241	1.30767	4.13521	.584795
1.22	1.4884	1.10454	3.49285	.819672	1.72	2.9584	1.31149	4.14729	.581395
1.23	1.5129	1.10905	3.50714	.813008	1.73	2.9929	1.31529	4.15933	.578035
1.24	1.5376	1.11355	3.52136	.806452	1.74	3.0276	1.31909	4.17133	.574713
1.25	1.5625	1.11803	3.53553	.800000	1.75	3.0625	1.32288	4.18330	.571429
1.26	1.5876	1.12250	3.54965	.793651	1.76	3.0976	1.32665	4.19524	.568182
1.27	1.6129	1.12694	3.56371	.787402	1.77	3.1329	1.33041	4.20714	.564972
1.28	1.6384	1.13137	3.57771	.781250	1.78	3.1684	1.33417	4.21900	.561798
1.29	1.6641	1.13578	3.59166	.775194	1.79	3.2041	1.33791	4.23084	.558659
1.30	1.6900	1.14018	3.60555	.769231	1.80	3.2400	1.34164	4.24264	.555556
1.31	1.7161	1.14455	3.61939	.763359	1.81	3.2761	1.34536	4.25441	.552486
1.32	1.7424	1.14891	3.63318	.757576	1.82	3.3124	1.34907	4.26615	.549451
1.33	1.7689	1.15326	3.64692	.751880	1.83	3.3489	1.35277	4.27785	.546448
1.34	1.7956	1.15758	3.66060	.746269	1.84	3.3856	1.35647	4.28952	.543478
1.35	1.8225	1.16190	3.67423	.740741	1.85	3.4225	1.36015	4.30116	.540541
1.36	1.8496	1.16619	3.68782	.735294	1.86	3.4596	1.36382	4.31277	.537634
1.37	1.8769	1.17047	3.70135	.729927	1.87	3.4969	1.36748	4.32435	.534759
1.38	1.9044	1.17473	3.71484	.724638	1.88	3.5344	1.37113	4.33590	.531915
1.39	1.9321	1.17898	3.72827	.719424	1.89	3.5721	1.37477	4.34741	.529101
1.40	1.9600	1.18322	3.74166	.714286	1.90	3.6100	1.37840	4.35890	.526316
1.41	1.9881	1.18743	3.75500	.709220	1.91	3.6481	1.38203	4.37035	.523560
1.42	2.0164	1.19164	3.76829	.704225	1.92	3.6864	1.38564	4.38178	.520833
1.43	2.0449	1.19583	3.78153	.699301	1.93	3.7249	1.38924	4.39318	.518135
1.44	2.0736	1.20000	3.79473	.694444	1.94	3.7636	1.39284	4.40454	.515464
1.45	2.1025	1.20416	3.80789	.689655	1.95	3.8025	1.39642	4.41588	.512821
1.46	2.1316	1.20830	3.82099	.684932	1.96	3.8416	1.40000	4.42719	.510204
1.47	2.1609	1.21244	3.83406	.680272	1.97	3.8809	1.40357	4.43847	.507614
1.48	2.1904	1.21655	3.84708	.675676	1.98	3.9204	1.40712	4.44972	.505051
1.49	2.2201	1.22066	3.86005	.671141	1.99	3.9601	1.41067	4.46094	.502513
1.50	2.2500	1.22474	3.87298	.666667	2.00	4.0000	1.41421	4.47214	.500000

Charles Clark and Lawrence Schkade, *Statistical Methods for Business Decisions* (Cincinnati: South-Western Publishing Co., 1969), pp. 50-58 by Special Permission.

SQUARES — SQUARE ROOTS — RECIPROCALS (Continued)

n	n^2	$\sqrt{n}$	$\sqrt{10n}$	$1/n$
2.00	4.0000	1.41421	4.47214	.500000
2.01	4.0401	1.41774	4.48330	.497512
2.02	4.0804	1.42127	4.49444	.495050
2.03	4.1209	1.42478	4.50555	.492611
2.04	4.1616	1.42829	4.51664	.490196
2.05	4.2025	1.43178	4.52769	.487805
2.06	4.2436	1.43527	4.53872	.485437
2.07	4.2849	1.43875	4.54973	.483092
2.08	4.3264	1.44222	4.56070	.480769
2.09	4.3681	1.44568	4.57165	.478469
2.10	4.4100	1.44914	4.58258	.476190
2.11	4.4521	1.45258	4.59347	.473934
2.12	4.4944	1.45602	4.60435	.471698
2.13	4.5369	1.45945	4.61519	.469484
2.14	4.5796	1.46287	4.62601	.467290
2.15	4.6225	1.46629	4.63681	.465116
2.16	4.6656	1.46969	4.64758	.462963
2.17	4.7089	1.47309	4.65833	.460829
2.18	4.7524	1.47648	4.66905	.458716
2.19	4.7961	1,47986	4.67974	.456621
2.20	4.8400	1.48324	4.69042	.454545
2.21	4.8841	1.48661	4.70106	.452489
2.22	4.9284	1.48997	4.71169	.450450
2.23	4.9729	1.49332	4.72229	.448430
2.24	5.0176	1.49666	4.73286	.446429
2.25	5.0625	1.50000	4.74342	.444444
2.26	5.1076	1.50333	4.75395	.442478
2.27	5.1529	1.50665	4.76445	.440529
2.28	5.1984	1.50997	4.77493	.438596
2.29	5.2441	1.51327	4.78539	.436681
2.30	5.2900	1.51658	4.79583	.434783
2.31	5.3361	1.51987	4.80625	.432900
2.32	5.3824	1.52315	4.81664	.431034
2.33	5.4289	1.52643	4.82701	.429185
2.34	5.4756	1.52971	4.83735	.427350
2.35	5.5225	1.53297	4.84768	.425532
2.36	5.5696	1.53623	4.85798	.423729
2.37	5.6169	1.53948	4.86826	.421941
2.38	5.6644	1.54272	4.87852	.420168
2.39	5.7121	1.54596	4.88876	.418410
2.40	5.7600	1.54919	4.89898	.416667
2.41	5.8081	1.55242	4.90918	.414938
2.42	5.8564	1.55563	4.91935	.413223
2.43	5.9049	1.55885	4.92950	.411523
2.44	5.9536	1.56205	4.93964	.409836
2.45	6.0025	1.56525	4.94975	.408163
2.46	6.0516	1.56844	4.95984	.406504
2.47	6.1009	1.57162	4.96991	.404858
2.48	6.1504	1.57480	4.97996	.403226
2.49	6.2001	1.57797	4.98999	.401606
2.50	6.2500	1.58114	5.00000	.400000

n	n^2	$\sqrt{n}$	$\sqrt{10n}$	$1/n$
2.50	6.2500	1.58114	5.00000	.400000
2.51	6.3001	1.58430	5.00999	.398406
2.52	6.3504	1.58745	5.01996	.396825
2.53	6.4009	1.59060	5.02991	.395257
2.54	6.4516	1.59374	5.03984	.393701
2.55	6.5025	1.59687	5.04975	.392157
2.56	6.5536	1.60000	5.05964	.390625
2.57	6.6049	1.60312	5.06952	.389105
2.58	6.6564	1.60624	5.07937	.387597
2.59	6.7081	1.60935	5.08920	.386100
2.60	6.7600	1.61245	5.09902	.384615
2.61	6.8121	1.61555	5.10882	.383142
2.62	6.8644	1.61864	5.11859	.381679
2.63	6.9169	1.62173	5.12835	.380228
2.64	6.9696	1.62481	5.13809	.378788
2.65	7.0225	1.62788	5.14782	.377358
2.66	7.0756	1.63095	5.15752	.375940
2.67	7.1289	1.63401	5.16720	.374532
2.68	7.1824	1.63707	5.17687	.373134
2.69	7.2361	1.64012	5.18652	.371747
2.70	7.2900	1.64317	5.19615	.370370
2.71	7.3441	1.64621	5.20577	.369004
2.72	7.3984	1.64924	5.21536	.367647
2.73	7.4529	1.65227	5.22494	.366300
2.74	7.5076	1.65529	5.23450	.364964
2.75	7.5625	1.65831	5.24404	.363636
2.76	7.6176	1.66132	5.25357	.362319
2.77	7.6729	1.66433	5.26308	.361011
2.78	7.7284	1.66733	5.27257	.359712
2.79	7.7841	1.67033	5.28205	.358423
2.80	7.8400	1.67332	5.29150	.357143
2.81	7.8961	1.67631	5.30094	.355872
2.82	7.9524	1.67929	5.31037	.354610
2.83	8.0089	1.68226	5.31977	.353357
2.84	8.0656	1.68523	5.32917	.352113
2.85	8.1225	1.68819	5.33854	.350877
2.86	8.1796	1.69115	5.34790	.349650
2.87	8.2369	1.69411	5.35724	.348432
2.88	8.2944	1.69706	5.36656	.347222
2.89	8.3521	1.70000	5.37587	.346021
2.90	8.4100	1.70294	5.38516	.344828
2.91	8.4681	1.70587	5.39444	.343643
2.92	8.5264	1.70880	5.40370	.342466
2.93	8.5849	1.71172	5.41295	.341297
2.94	8.6436	1.71464	5.42218	.340136
2.95	8.7025	1.71756	5.43139	.338983
2.96	8.7616	1.72047	5.44059	.337838
2.97	8.8209	1.72337	5.44977	.336700
2.98	8.8804	1.72627	5.45894	.335570
2.99	8.9401	1.72916	5.46809	.334448
3.00	9.0000	1.73205	5.47723	.333333

SQUARES — SQUARE ROOTS — RECIPROCALS (Continued)

n	n²	√n	√10n	1/n	n	n²	√n	√10n	1/n
3.00	9.0000	1.73205	5.47723	.333333	3.50	12.2500	1.87083	5.91608	.285714
3.01	9.0601	1.73494	5.48635	.332226	3.51	12.3201	1.87350	5.92453	.284900
3.02	9.1204	1.73781	5.49545	.331126	3.52	12.3904	1.87617	5.93296	.284091
3.03	9.1809	1.74069	5.50454	.330033	3.53	12.4609	1.87883	5.94138	.283286
3.04	9.2416	1.74356	5.51362	.328947	3.54	12.5316	1.88149	5.94979	.282486
3.05	9.3025	1.74642	5.52268	.327869	3.55	12.6025	1.88414	5.95819	.281690
3.06	9.3636	1.74929	5.53173	.326797	3.56	12.6736	1.88680	5.96657	.280899
3.07	9.4249	1.75214	5.54076	.325733	3.57	12.7449	1.88944	5.97495	.280112
3.08	9.4864	1.75499	5.54977	.324675	3.58	12.8164	1.89209	5.98331	.279330
3.09	9.5481	1.75784	5.55878	.323625	3.59	12.8881	1.89473	5.99166	.278552
3.10	9.6100	1.76068	5.56776	.322581	3.60	12.9600	1.89737	6.00000	.277778
3.11	9.6721	1.76352	5.57674	.321543	3.61	13.0321	1.90000	6.00833	.277008
3.12	9.7344	1.76635	5.58570	.320513	3.62	13.1044	1.90263	6.01664	.276243
3.13	9.7969	1.76918	5.59464	.319489	3.63	13.1769	1.90526	6.02495	.275482
3.14	9.8596	1.77200	5.60357	.318471	3.64	13.2496	1.90788	6.03324	.274725
3.15	9.9225	1.77482	5.61249	.317460	3.65	13.3225	1.91050	6.04152	.273973
3.16	9.9856	1.77764	5.62139	.316456	3.66	13.3956	1.91311	6.04979	.273224
3.17	10.0489	1.78045	5.63028	.315457	3.67	13.4689	1.91572	6.05805	.272480
3.18	10.1124	1.78326	5.63915	.314465	3.68	13.5424	1.91833	6.06630	.271739
3.19	10.1761	1.78606	5.64801	.313480	3.69	13.6161	1.92094	6.07454	.271003
3.20	10.2400	1.78885	5.65685	.312500	3.70	13.6900	1.92354	6.08276	.270270
3.21	10.3041	1.79165	5.66569	.311526	3.71	13.7641	1.92614	6.09098	.269542
3.22	10.3684	1.79444	5.67450	.310559	3.72	13.8384	1.92873	6.09918	.268817
3.23	10.4329	1.79722	5.68331	.309598	3.73	13.9129	1.93132	6.10737	.268097
3.24	10.4976	1.80000	5.69210	.308642	3.74	13.9876	1.93391	6.11555	.267380
3.25	10.5625	1.80278	5.70088	.307692	3.75	14.0625	1.93649	6.12372	.266667
3.26	10.6276	1.80555	5.70964	.306748	3.76	14.1376	1.93907	6.13188	.265957
3.27	10.6929	1.80831	5.71839	.305810	3.77	14.2129	1.94165	6.14003	.265252
3.28	10.7584	1.81108	5.72713	.304878	3.78	14.2884	1.94422	6.14817	.264550
3.29	10.8241	1.81384	5.73585	.303951	3.79	14.3641	1.94679	6.15630	.263852
3.30	10.8900	1.81659	5.74456	.303030	3.80	14.4400	1.94936	6.16441	.263158
3.31	10.9561	1.81934	5.75326	.302115	3.81	14.5161	1.95192	6.17252	.262467
3.32	11.0224	1.82209	5.76194	.301205	3.82	14.5924	1.95448	6.18061	.261780
3.33	11.0889	1.82483	5.77062	.300300	3.83	14.6689	1.95704	6.18870	.261097
3.34	11.1556	1.82757	5.77927	.299401	3.84	14.7456	1.95959	6.19677	.260417
3.35	11.2225	1.83030	5.78792	.298507	3.85	14.8225	1.96214	6.20484	.259740
3.36	11.2896	1.83303	5.79655	.297619	3.86	14.8996	1.96469	6.21289	.259067
3.37	11.3569	1.83576	5.80517	.296736	3.87	14.9769	1.96723	6.22093	.258398
3.38	11.4244	1.83848	5.81378	.295858	3.88	15.0544	1.96977	6.22896	.257732
3.39	11.4921	1.84120	5.82237	.294985	3.89	15.1321	1.97231	6.23699	.257069
3.40	11.5600	1.84391	5.83095	.294118	3.90	15.2100	1.97484	6.24500	.256410
3.41	11.6281	1.84662	5.83952	.293255	3.91	15.2881	1.97737	6.25300	.255754
3.42	11.6964	1.84932	5.84808	.292398	3.92	15.3664	1.97990	6.26099	.255102
3.43	11.7649	1.85203	5.85662	.291545	3.93	15.4449	1.98242	6.26897	.254453
3.44	11.8336	1.85472	5.86515	.290698	3.94	15.5236	1.98494	6.27694	.253807
3.45	11.9025	1.85742	5.87367	.289855	3.95	15.6025	1.98746	6.28490	.253165
3.46	11.9716	1.86011	5.88218	.289017	3.96	15.6816	1.98997	6.29285	.252525
3.47	12.0409	1.86279	5.89067	.288184	3.97	15.7609	1.99249	6.30079	.251889
3.48	12.1104	1.86548	5.89915	.287356	3.98	15.8408	1.99499	6.30872	.251256
3.49	12.1801	1.86815	5.90762	.286533	3.99	15.9201	1.99750	6.31664	.250627
3.50	12.2500	1.87083	5.91608	.285714	4.00	16.0000	2.00000	6.32456	.250000
n	n²	√n	√10n	1/n	n	n²	√n	√10n	1/n

SQUARES — SQUARE ROOTS — RECIPROCALS (Continued)

n	n²	√n	√10n	1/n	n	n²	√n	√10n	1/n
4.00	16.0000	2.00000	6.32456	.250000	**4.50**	20.2500	2.12132	6.70820	.222222
4.01	16.0801	2.00250	6.33246	.249377	4.51	20.3401	2.12368	6.71565	.221729
4.02	16.1604	2.00499	6.34035	.248756	4.52	20.4304	2.12603	6.72309	.221239
4.03	16.2409	2.00749	6.34823	.248139	4.53	20.5209	2.12838	6.73053	.220751
4.04	16.3216	2.00998	6.35610	.247525	4.54	20.6116	2.13073	6.73795	.220264
4.05	16.4025	2.01246	6.36396	.246914	4.55	20.7025	2.13307	6.74537	.219780
4.06	16.4836	2.01494	6.37181	.246305	4.56	20.7936	2.13542	6.75278	.219298
4.07	16.5649	2.01742	6.37966	.245700	4.57	20.8849	2.13776	6.76018	.218818
4.08	16.6464	2.01990	6.38749	.245098	4.58	20.9764	2.14009	6.76757	.218341
4.09	16.7281	2.02237	6.39531	.244499	4.59	21.0681	2.14243	6.77495	.217865
4.10	16.8100	2.02485	6.40312	.243902	**4.60**	21.1600	2.14476	6.78233	.217391
4.11	16.8921	2.02731	6.41093	.243309	4.61	21.2521	2.14709	6.78970	.216920
4.12	16.9744	2.02978	6.41872	.242718	4.62	21.3444	2.14942	6.79706	.216450
4.13	17.0569	2.03224	6.42651	.242131	4.63	21.4369	2.15174	6.80441	.215983
4.14	17.1396	2.03470	6.43428	.241546	4.64	21.5296	2.15407	6.81175	.215517
4.15	17.2225	2.03715	6.44205	.240964	4.65	21.6225	2.15639	6.81909	.215054
4.16	17.3056	2.03961	6.44981	.240385	4.66	21.7156	2.15870	6.82642	.214592
4.17	17.3889	2.04206	6.45755	.239808	4.67	21.8089	2.16102	6.83374	.214133
4.18	17.4724	2.04450	6.46529	.239234	4.68	21.9024	2.16333	6.84105	.213675
4.19	17.5561	2.04695	6.47302	.238663	4.69	21.9961	2.16564	6.84836	.213220
4.20	17.6400	2.04939	6.48074	.238095	**4.70**	22.0900	2.16795	6.85565	.212766
4.21	17.7241	2.05183	6.48845	.237530	4.71	22.1841	2.17025	6.86294	.212314
4.22	17.8084	2.05426	6.49615	.236967	4.72	22.2784	2.17256	6.87023	.211864
4.23	17.8929	2.05670	6.50384	.236407	4.73	22.3729	2.17486	6.87750	.211416
4.24	17.9776	2.05913	6.51153	.235849	4.74	22.4676	2.17715	6.88477	.210970
4.25	18.0625	2.06155	6.51920	.235294	4.75	22.5625	2.17945	6.89202	.210526
4.26	18.1476	2.06398	6.52687	.234742	4.76	22.6576	2.18174	6.89928	.210084
4.27	18.2329	2.06640	6.53452	.234192	4.77	22.7529	2.18403	6.90652	.209644
4.28	18.3184	2.06882	6.54217	.233645	4.78	22.8484	2.18632	6.91375	.209205
4.29	18.4041	2.07123	6.54981	.233100	4.79	22.9441	2.18861	6.92098	.208768
4.30	18.4900	2.07364	6.55744	.232558	**4.80**	23.0400	2.19089	6.92820	.208333
4.31	18.5761	2.07605	6.56506	.232019	4.81	23.1361	2.19317	6.93542	.207900
4.32	18.6624	2.07846	6.57267	.231481	4.82	23.2324	2.19545	6.94262	.207469
4.33	18.7489	2.08087	6.58027	.230947	4.83	23.3289	2.19773	6.94982	.207039
4.34	18.8356	2.08327	6.58787	.230415	4.84	23.4256	2.20000	6.95701	.206612
4.35	18.9225	2.08567	6.59545	.229885	4.85	23.5225	2.20227	6.96419	.206186
4.36	19.0096	2.08806	6.60303	.229358	4.86	23.6196	2.20454	6.97137	.205761
4.37	19.0969	2.09045	6.61060	.228833	4.87	23.7169	2.20681	6.97854	.205339
4.38	19.1844	2.09284	6.61816	.228311	4.88	23.8144	2.20907	6.98570	.204918
4.39	19.2721	2.09523	6.62571	.227790	4.89	23.9121	2.21133	6.99285	.204499
4.40	19.3600	2.09762	6.63325	.227273	**4.90**	24.0100	2.21359	7.00000	.204082
4.41	19.4481	2.10000	6.64078	.226757	4.91	24.1081	2.21585	7.00714	.203666
4.42	19.5364	2.10238	6.64831	.226244	4.92	24.2064	2.21811	7.01427	.203252
4.43	19.6249	2.10476	6.65582	.225734	4.93	24.3049	2.22036	7.02140	.202840
4.44	19.7136	2.10713	6.66333	.225225	4.94	24.4036	2.22261	7.02851	.202429
4.45	19.8025	2.10950	6.67083	.224719	4.95	24.5025	2.22486	7.03562	.202020
4.46	19.8916	2.11187	6.67832	.224215	4.96	24.6016	2.22711	7.04273	.201613
4.47	19.9809	2.11424	6.68581	.223714	4.97	24.7009	2.22935	7.04982	.201207
4.48	20.0704	2.11660	6.69328	.223214	4.98	24.8004	2.23159	7.05691	.200803
4.49	20.1601	2.11896	6.70075	.222717	4.99	24.9001	2.23383	7.06399	.200401
4.50	20.2500	2.12132	6.70820	.222222	**5.00**	25.0000	2.23607	7.07107	.200000
n	n²	√n	√10n	1/n	n	n²	√n	√10n	1/n

SQUARES — SQUARE ROOTS — RECIPROCALS (Continued)

n	n²	√n	√10n	1/n	n	n²	√n	√10n	1/n
5.00	25.0000	2.23607	7.07107	.200000	5.50	30.2500	2.34521	7.41620	.181818
5.01	25.1001	2.23830	7.07814	.199601	5.51	30.3601	2.34734	7.42294	.181488
5.02	25.2004	2.24054	7.08520	.199203	5.52	30.4704	2.34947	7.42967	.181159
5.03	25.3009	2.24277	7.09225	.198807	5.53	30.5809	2.35160	7.43640	.180832
5.04	25.4016	2.24499	7.09930	.198413	5.54	30.6916	2.35372	7.44312	.180505
5.05	25.5025	2.24722	7.10634	.198020	5.55	30.8025	2.35584	7.44983	.180180
5.06	25.6036	2.24944	7.11337	.197628	5.56	30.9136	2.35797	7.45654	.179856
5.07	25.7049	2.25167	7.12039	.197239	5.57	31.0249	2.36008	7.46324	.179533
5.08	25.8064	2.25389	7.12741	.196850	5.58	31.1364	2.36220	7.46994	.179211
5.09	25.9081	2.25610	7.13442	.196464	5.59	31.2481	2.36432	7.47663	.178891
5.10	26.0100	2.25832	7.14143	.196078	5.60	31.3600	2.36643	7.48331	.178571
5.11	26.1121	2.26053	7.14843	.195695	5.61	31.4721	2.36854	7.48999	.178253
5.12	26.2144	2.26274	7.15542	.195312	5.62	31.5844	2.37065	7.49667	.177936
5.13	26.3169	2.26495	7.16240	.194932	5.63	31.6969	2.37276	7.50333	.177620
5.14	26.4196	2.26716	7.16938	.194553	5.64	31.8096	2.37487	7.50999	.177305
5.15	26.5225	2.26936	7.17635	.194175	5.65	31.9225	2.37697	7.51665	.176991
5.16	26.6256	2.27156	7.18331	.193798	5.66	32.0356	2.37908	7.52330	.176678
5.17	26.7289	2.27376	7.19027	.193424	5.67	32.1489	2.38118	7.52994	.176367
5.18	26.8324	2.27596	7.19722	.193050	5.68	32.2624	2.38328	7.53658	.176056
5.19	26.9361	2.27816	7.20417	.192678	5.69	32.3761	2.38537	7.54321	.175747
5.20	27.0400	2.28035	7.21110	.192308	5.70	32.4900	2.38747	7.54983	.175439
5.21	27.1441	2.28254	7.21803	.191939	5.71	32.6041	2.38956	7.55645	.175131
5.22	27.2484	2.28473	7.22496	.191571	5.72	32.7184	2.39165	7.56307	.174825
5.23	27.3529	2.28692	7.23187	.191205	5.73	32.8329	2.39374	7.56968	.174520
5.24	27.4576	2.28910	7.23878	.190840	5.74	32.9476	2.39583	7.57628	.174216
5.25	27.5625	2.29129	7.24569	.190476	5.75	33.0625	2.39792	7.58288	.173913
5.26	27.6676	2.29347	7.25259	.190114	5.76	33.1776	2.40000	7.58947	.173611
5.27	27.7729	2.29565	7.25948	.189753	5.77	33.2929	2.40208	7.59605	.173310
5.28	27.8784	2.29783	7.26636	.189394	5.78	33.4084	2.40416	7.60263	.173010
5.29	27.9841	2.30000	7.27324	.189036	5.79	33.5241	2.40624	7.60920	.172712
5.30	28.0900	2.30217	7.28011	.188679	5.80	33.6400	2.40832	7.61577	.172414
5.31	28.1961	2.30434	7.28697	.188324	5.81	33.7561	2.41039	7.62234	.172117
5.32	28.3024	2.30651	7.29383	.187970	5.82	33.8724	2.41247	7.62889	.171821
5.33	28.4089	2.30868	7.30068	.187617	5.83	33.9889	2.41454	7.63544	.171527
5.34	28.5156	2.31084	7.30753	.187266	5.84	34.1056	2.41661	7.64199	.171233
5.35	28.6225	2.31301	7.31437	.186916	5.85	34.2225	2.41868	7.64853	.170940
5.36	28.7296	2.31517	7.32120	.186567	5.86	34.3396	2.42074	7.65506	.170649
5.37	28.8369	2.31733	7.32803	.186220	5.87	34.4569	2.42281	7.66159	.170358
5.38	28.9444	2.31948	7.33485	.185874	5.88	34.5744	2.42487	7.66812	.170068
5.39	29.0521	2.32164	7.34166	.185529	5.89	34.6921	2.42693	7.67463	.169779
5.40	29.1600	2.32379	7.34847	.185185	5.90	34.8100	2.42899	7.68115	.169492
5.41	29.2681	2.32594	7.35527	.184843	5.91	34.9281	2.43105	7.68765	.169205
5.42	29.3764	2.32809	7.36206	.184502	5.92	35.0464	2.43311	7.69415	.168919
5.43	29.4849	2.33024	7.36885	.184162	5.93	35.1649	2.43516	7.70065	.168634
5.44	29.5936	2.33238	7.37564	.183824	5.94	35.2836	2.43721	7.70714	.168350
5.45	29.7025	2.33452	7.38241	.183486	5.95	35.4025	2.43926	7.71362	.168067
5.46	29.8116	2.33666	7.38918	.183150	5.96	35.5216	2.44131	7.72010	.167785
5.47	29.9209	2.33880	7.39594	.182815	5.97	35.6409	2.44336	7.72658	.167504
5.48	30.0304	2.34094	7.40270	.182482	5.98	35.7604	2.44540	7.73305	.167224
5.49	30.1401	2.34307	7.40945	.182149	5.99	35.8801	2.44745	7.73951	.166945
5.50	30.2500	2.34521	7.41620	.181818	6.00	36.0000	2.44949	7.74597	.166667
n	n²	√n	√10n	1/n	n	n²	√n	√10n	1/n

SQUARES — SQUARE ROOTS — RECIPROCALS (Continued)

n	n²	√n	√10n	1/n	n	n²	√n	√10n	1/n
6.00	36.0000	2.44949	7.74597	.166667·	**6.50**	42.2500	2.54951	8.06226	.153846
6.01	36.1201	2.45153	7.75242	.166389	6.51	42.3801	2.55147	8.06846	.153610
6.02	36.2404	2.45357	7.75887	.166113	6.52	42.5104	2.55343	8.07465	.153374
6.03	36.3609	2.45561	7.76531	.165837	6.53	42.6409	2.55539	8.08084	.153139
6.04	36.4816	2.45764	7.77174	.165563	6.54	42.7716	2.55734	8.08703	.152905
6.05	36.6025	2.45967	7.77817	.165289	6.55	42.9025	2.55930	8.09321	.152672
6.06	36.7236	2.46171	7.78460	.165017	6.56	43.0336	2.56125	8.09938	.152439
6.07	36.8449	2.46374	7.79102	.164745	6.57	43.1649	2.56320	8.10555	.152207
6.08	36.9664	2.46577	7.79744	.164474	6.58	43.2964	2.56515	8.11172	.151976
6.09	37.0881	2.46779	7.80385	.164204	6.59	43.4281	2.56710	8.11788	.151745
6.10	37.2100	2.46982	7.81025	.163934	**6.60**	43.5600	2.56905	8.12404	.151515
6.11	37.3321	2.47184	7.81665	.163666	6.61	43.6921	2.57099	8.13019	.151286
6.12	37.4544	2.47386	7.82304	.163399	6.62	43.8244	2.57294	8.13634	.151057
6.13	37.5769	2.47588	7.82943	.163132	6.63	43.9569	2.57488	8.14248	.150830
6.14	37.6996	2.47790	7.83582	.162866	6.64	44.0896	2.57682	8.14862	.150602
6.15	37.8225	2.47992	7.84219	.162602	6.65	44.2225	2.57876	8.15475	.150376
6.16	37.9456	2.48193	7.84857	.162338	6.66	44.3556	2.58070	8.16088	.150150
6.17	38.0689	2.48395	7.85493	.162075	6.67	44.4889	2.58263	8.16701	.149925
6.18	38.1924	2.48596	7.86130	.161812	6.68	44.6224	2.58457	8.17313	.149701
6.19	38.3161	2.48797	7.86766	.161551	6.69	44.7561	2.58650	8.17924	.149477
6.20	38.4400	2.48998	7.87401	.161290	**6.70**	44.8900	2.58844	8.18535	.149254
6.21	38.5641	2.49199	7.88036	.161031	6.71	45.0241	2.59037	8.19146	.149031
6.22	38.6884	2.49399	7.88670	.160772	6.72	45.1584	2.59230	8.19756	.148810
6.23	38.8129	2.49600	7.89303	.160514	6.73	45.2929	2.59422	8.20366	.148588
6.24	38.9376	2.49800	7.89937	.160256	6.74	45.4276	2.59615	8.20975	.148368
6.25	39.0625	2.50000	7.90569	.160000	6.75	45.5625	2.59808	8.21584	.148148
6.26	39.1876	2.50200	7.91202	.159744	6.76	45.6976	2.60000	8.22192	.147929
6.27	39.3129	2.50400	7.91833	.159490	6.77	45.8329	2.60192	8.22800	.147710
6.28	39.4384	2.50599	7.92465	.159236	6.78	45.9684	2.60384	8.23408	.147493
6.29	39.5641	2.50799	7.93095	.158983	6.79	46.1041	2.60576	8.24015	.147275
6.30	39.6900	2.50998	7.93725	.158730	**6.80**	46.2400	2.60768	8.24621	.147059
6.31	39.8161	2.51197	7.94355	.158479	6.81	46.3761	2.60960	8.25227	.146843
6.32	39.9424	2.51396	7.94984	.158228	6.82	46.5124	2.61151	8.25833	.146628
6.33	40.0689	2.51595	7.95613	.157978	6.83	46.6489	2.61343	8.26438	.146413
6.34	40.1956	2.51794	7.96241	.157729	6.84	46.7856	2.61534	8.27043	.146199
6.35	40.3225	2.51992	7.96869	.157480	6.85	46.9225	2.61725	8.27647	.145985
6.36	40.4496	2.52190	7.97496	.157233	6.86	47.0596	2.61916	8.28251	.145773
6.37	40.5769	2.52389	7.98123	.156986	6.87	47.1969	2.62107	8.28855	.145560
6.38	40.7044	2.52587	7.98749	.156740	6.88	47.3344	2.62298	8.29458	.145349
6.39	40.8321	2.52784	7.99375	.156495	6.89	47.4721	2.62488	8.30060	.145138
6.40	40.9600	2.52982	8.00000	.156250	**6.90**	47.6100	2.62679	8.30662	.144928
6.41	41.0881	2.53180	8.00625	.156006	6.91	47.7481	2.62869	8.31264	.144718
6.42	41.2164	2.53377	8.01249	.155763	6.92	47.8864	2.63059	8.31865	.144509
6.43	41.3449	2.53574	8.01873	.155521	6.93	48.0249	2.63249	8.32466	.144300
6.44	41.4736	2.53772	8.02496	.155280	6.94	48.1636	2.63439	8.33067	.144092
6.45	41.6025	2.53969	8.03119	.155039	6.95	48.3025	2.63629	8.33667	.143885
6.46	41.7316	2.54165	8.03741	.154799	6.96	48.4416	2.63818	8.34266	.143678
6.47	41.8609	2.54362	8.04363	.154560	6.97	48.5809	2.64008	8.34865	.143472
6.48	41.9904	2.54558	8.04984	.154321	6.98	48.7204	2.64197	8.35464	.143266
6.49	42.1201	2.54755	8.05605	.154083	6.99	48.8601	2.64386	8.36062	.143062
6.50	42.2500	2.54951	8.06226	.153846	**7.00**	49.0000	2.64575	8.36660	.142857
n	n²	√n	√10n	1/n	n	n²	√n	√10n	1/n

SQUARES — SQUARE ROOTS — RECIPROCALS (Continued)

n	n²	√n	√10n	1/n	n	n²	√n	√10n	1/n
7.00	49.0000	2.64575	8.36660	.142857	7.50	56.2500	2.73861	8.66025	.133333
7.01	49.1401	2.64764	8.37257	.142653	7.51	56.4001	2.74044	8.66603	.133156
7.02	49.2804	2.64953	8.37854	.142450	7.52	56.5504	2.74226	8.67179	.132979
7.03	49.4209	2.65141	8.38451	.142248	7.53	56.7009	2.74408	8.67756	.132802
7.04	49.5616	2.65330	8.39047	.142045	7.54	56.8516	2.74591	8.68332	.132626
7.05	49.7025	2.65518	8.39643	.141844	7.55	57.0025	2.74773	8.68907	.132450
7.06	49.8436	2.65707	8.40238	.141643	7.56	57.1536	2.74955	8.69483	.132275
7.07	49.9849	2.65895	8.40833	.141443	7.57	57.3049	2.75136	8.70057	.132100
7.08	50.1264	2.66083	8.41427	.141243	7.58	57.4564	2.75318	8.70632	.131926
7.09	50.2681	2.66271	8.42021	.141044	7.59	57.6081	2.75500	8.71206	.131752
7.10	50.4100	2.66458	8.42615	.140845	7.60	57.7600	2.75681	8.71780	.131579
7.11	50.5521	2.66646	8.43208	.140647	7.61	57.9121	2.75862	8.72353	.131406
7.12	50.6944	2.66833	8.43801	.140449	7.62	58.0644	2.76043	8.72926	.131234
7.13	50.8369	2.67021	8.44393	.140252	7.63	58.2169	2.76225	8.73499	.131062
7.14	50.9796	2.67208	8.44985	.140056	7.64	58.3696	2.76405	8.74071	.130890
7.15	51.1225	2.67395	8.45577	.139860	7.65	58.5225	2.76586	8.74643	.130719
7.16	51.2656	2.67582	8.46168	.139665	7.66	58.6756	2.76767	8.75214	.130548
7.17	51.4089	2.67769	8.46759	.139470	7.67	58.8289	2.76948	8.75785	.130378
7.18	51.5524	2.67955	8.47349	.139276	7.68	58.9824	2.77128	8.76356	.130208
7.19	51.6961	2.68142	8.47939	.139082	7.69	59.1361	2.77308	8.76926	.130039
7.20	51.8400	2.68328	8.48528	.138889	7.70	59.2900	2.77489	8.77496	.129870
7.21	51.9841	2.68514	8.49117	.138696	7.71	59.4441	2.77669	8.78066	.129702
7.22	52.1284	2.68701	8.49706	.138504	7.72	59.5984	2.77849	8.78635	.129534
7.23	52.2729	2.68887	8.50294	.138313	7.73	59.7529	2.78029	8.79204	.129366
7.24	52.4176	2.69072	8.50882	.138122	7.74	59.9076	2.78209	8.79773	.129199
7.25	52.5625	2.69258	8.51469	.137931	7.75	60.0625	2.78388	8.80341	.129032
7.26	52.7076	2.69444	8.52056	.137741	7.76	60.2176	2.78568	8.80909	.128866
7.27	52.8529	2.69629	8.52643	.137552	7.77	60.3729	2.78747	8.81476	.128700
7.28	52.9984	2.69815	8.53229	.137363	7.78	60.5284	2.78927	8.82043	.128535
7.29	53.1441	2.70000	8.53815	.137174	7.79	60.6841	2.79106	8.82610	.128370
7.30	53.2900	2.70185	8.54400	.136986	7.80	60.8400	2.79285	8.83176	.128205
7.31	53.4361	2.70370	8.54985	.136799	7.81	60.9961	2.79464	8.83742	.128041
7.32	53.5824	2.70555	8.55570	.136612	7.82	61.1524	2.79643	8.84308	.127877
7.33	53.7289	2.70740	8.56154	.136426	7.83	61.3089	2.79821	8.84873	.127714
7.34	53.8756	2.70924	8.56738	.136240	7.84	61.4656	2.80000	8.85438	.127551
7.35	54.0225	2.71109	8.57321	.136054	7.85	61.6225	2.80179	8.86002	.127389
7.36	54.1696	2.71293	8.57904	.135870	7.86	61.7796	2.80357	8.86566	.127226
7.37	54.3169	2.71477	8.58487	.135685	7.87	61.9369	2.80535	8.87130	.127065
7.38	54.4644	2.71662	8.59069	.135501	7.88	62.0944	2.80713	8.87694	.126904
7.39	54.6121	2.71846	8.59651	.135318	7.89	62.2521	2.80891	8.88257	.126743
7.40	54.7600	2.72029	8.60233	.135135	7.90	62.4100	2.81069	8.88819	.126582
7.41	54.9081	2.72213	8.60814	.134953	7.91	62.5681	2.81247	8.89382	.126422
7.42	55.0564	2.72397	8.61394	.134771	7.92	62.7264	2.81425	8.89944	.126263
7.43	55.2049	2.72580	8.61974	.134590	7.93	62.8849	2.81603	8.90505	.126103
7.44	55.3536	2.72764	8.62554	.134409	7.94	63.0436	2.81780	8.91067	.125945
7.45	55.5025	2.72947	8.63134	.134228	7.95	63.2025	2.81957	8.91628	.125786
7.46	55.6516	2.73130	8.63713	.134048	7.96	63.3616	2.82135	8.92188	.125628
7.47	55.8009	2.73313	8.64292	.133869	7.97	63.5209	2.82312	8.92749	.125471
7.48	55.9504	2.73496	8.64870	.133690	7.98	63.6804	2.82489	8.93308	.125313
7.49	56.1001	2.73679	8.65448	.133511	7.99	63.8401	2.82666	8.93868	.125156
7.50	56.2500	2.73861	8.66025	.133333	8.00	64.0000	2.82843	8.94427	.125000
n	n²	√n	√10n	1/n	n	n²	√n	√10n	1/n

SQUARES — SQUARE ROOTS — RECIPROCALS (Continued)

n	n^2	$\sqrt{n}$	$\sqrt{10n}$	$1/n$	n	n^2	$\sqrt{n}$	$\sqrt{10n}$	$1/n$
8.00	64.0000	2.82843	8.94427	.125000	8.50	72.2500	2.91548	9.21954	.117647
8.01	64.1601	2.83019	8.94986	.124844	8.51	72.4201	2.91719	9.22497	.117509
8.02	64.3204	2.83196	8.95545	.124688	8.52	72.5904	2.91890	9.23038	.117371
8.03	64.4809	2.83373	8.96103	.124533	8.53	72.7609	2.92062	9.23580	.117233
8.04	64.6416	2.83549	8.96660	.124378	8.54	72.9316	2.92233	9.24121	.117096
8.05	64.8025	2.83725	8.97218	.124224	8.55	73.1025	2.92404	9.24662	.116959
8.06	64.9636	2.83901	8.97775	.124069	8.56	73.2736	2.92575	9.25203	.116822
8.07	65.1249	2.84077	8.98332	.123916	8.57	73.4449	2.92746	9.25743	.116686
8.08	65.2864	2.84253	8.98888	.123762	5.58	73.6164	2.92916	9.26283	.116550
8.09	65.4481	2.84429	8.99444	.123609	8.59	73.7881	2.93087	9.26823	.116414
8.10	65.6100	2.84605	9.00000	.123457	8.60	73.9600	2.93258	9.27362	.116279
8.11	65.7721	2.84781	9.00555	.123305	8.61	74.1321	2.93428	9.27901	.116144
8.12	65.9344	2.84956	9.01110	.123153	8.62	74.3044	2.93598	9.28440	.116009
8.13	66.0969	2.85132	9.01665	.123001	8.63	74.4769	2.93769	9.28978	.115875
8.14	66.2596	2.85307	9.02219	.122850	8.64	74.6496	2.93939	9.29516	.115741
8.15	66.4225	2.85482	9.02774	.122699	8.65	74.8225	2.94109	9.30054	.115607
8.16	66.5856	2.85657	9.03327	.122549	8.66	74.9956	2.94279	9.30591	.115473
8.17	66.7489	2.85832	9.03881	.122399	8.67	75.1689	2.94449	9.31128	.115340
8.18	66.9124	2.86007	9.04434	.122249	8.68	75.3424	2.94618	9.31665	.115207
8.19	67.0761	2.86182	9.04986	.122100	8.69	75.5161	2.94788	9.32202	.115075
8.20	67.2400	2.86356	9.05539	.121951	8.70	75.6900	2.94958	9.32738	.114943
8.21	67.4041	2.86531	9.06091	.121803	8.71	75.8641	2.95127	9.33274	.114811
8.22	67.5684	2.86705	9.06642	.121655	8.72	76.0384	2.95296	9.33809	.114679
8.23	67.7329	2.86880	9.07193	.121507	8.73	76.2129	2.95466	9.34345	.114548
8.24	67.8976	2.87054	9.07744	.121359	8.74	76.3876	2.95635	9.34880	.114416
8.25	68.0625	2.87228	9.08295	.121212	8.75	76.5625	2.95804	9.35414	.114286
8.26	68.2276	2.87402	9.08845	.121065	8.76	76.7376	2.95973	9.35949	.114155
8.27	68.3929	2.87576	9.09395	.120919	8.77	76.9129	2.96142	9.36483	.114025
8.28	68.5584	2.87750	9.09945	.120773	8.78	77.0884	2.96311	9.37017	.113895
8.29	68.7241	2.87924	9.10494	.120627	8.79	77.2641	2.96479	9.37550	.113766
8.30	68.8900	2.88097	9.11043	.120482	8.80	77.4400	2.96648	9.38083	.113636
8.31	69.0561	2.88271	9.11592	.120337	8.81	77.6161	2.96816	9.38616	.113507
8.32	69.2224	2.88444	9.12140	.120192	8.82	77.7924	2.96985	9.39149	.113379
8.33	69.3889	2.88617	9.12688	.120048	8.83	77.9689	2.97153	9.39681	.113250
8.34	69.5556	2.88791	9.13236	.119904	8.84	78.1456	2.97321	9.40213	.113122
8.35	69.7225	2.88964	9.13783	.119760	8.85	78.3225	2.97489	9.40744	.112994
8.36	69.8896	2.89137	9.14330	.119617	8.86	78.4996	2.97658	9.41276	.112867
8.37	70.0569	2.89310	9.14877	.119474	8.87	78.6769	2.97825	9.41807	.112740
8.38	70.2244	2.89482	9.15423	.119332	8.88	78.8544	2.97993	9.42338	.112613
8.39	70.3921	2.89655	9.15969	.119190	8.89	79.0321	2.98161	9.42868	.112486
8.40	70.5600	2.89828	9.16515	.119048	8.90	79.2100	2.98329	9.43398	.112360
8.41	70.7281	2.90000	9.17061	.118906	8.91	79.3881	2.98496	9.43928	.112233
8.42	70.8964	2.90172	9.17606	.118765	8.92	79.5664	2.98664	9.44458	.112108
8.43	71.0649	2.90345	9.18150	.118624	8.93	79.7449	2.98831	9.44987	.111982
8.44	71.2336	2.90517	9.18695	.118483	8.94	79.9236	2.98998	9.45516	.111857
8.45	71.4025	2.90689	9.19239	.118343	8.95	80.1025	2.99166	9.46044	.111732
8.46	71.5716	2.90861	9.19783	.118203	8.96	80.2816	2.99333	9.46573	.111607
8.47	71.7409	2.91033	9.20326	.118064	8.97	80.4609	2.99500	9.47101	.111483
8.48	71.9104	2.91204	9.20869	.117925	8.98	80.6404	2.99666	9.47629	.111359
8.49	72.0801	2.91376	9.21412	.117786	8.99	80.8201	2.99833	9.48156	.111235
8.50	72.2500	2.91548	9.21954	.117647	9.00	81.0000	3.00000	9.48683	.111111
n	n^2	$\sqrt{n}$	$\sqrt{10n}$	$1/n$	n	n^2	$\sqrt{n}$	$\sqrt{10n}$	$1/n$

SQUARES — SQUARE ROOTS — RECIPROCALS (Continued)

n	n^2	$\sqrt{n}$	$\sqrt{10n}$	$1/n$	n	n^2	$\sqrt{n}$	$\sqrt{10n}$	$1/n$
9.00	81.0000	3.00000	9.48683	.111111	9.50	90.2500	3.08221	9.74679	.105263
9.01	81.1801	3.00167	9.49210	.110988	9.51	90.4401	3.08383	9.75192	.105152
9.02	81.3604	3.00333	9.49737	.110865	9.52	90.6304	3.08545	9.75705	.105042
9.03	81.5409	3.00500	9.50263	.110742	9.53	90.8209	3.08707	9.76217	.104932
9.04	81.7216	3.00666	9.50789	.110619	9.54	91.0116	3.08869	9.76729	.104822
9.05	81.9025	3.00832	9.51315	.110497	9.55	91.2025	3.09031	9.77241	.104712
9.06	82.0836	3.00998	9.51840	.110375	9.56	91.3936	3.09192	9.77753	.104603
9.07	82.2649	3.01164	9.52365	.110254	9.57	91.5849	3.09354	9.78264	.104493
9.08	82.4464	3.01330	9.52890	.110132	9.58	91.7764	3.09516	9.78775	.104384
9.09	82.6281	3.01496	9.53415	.110011	9.59	91.9681	3.09677	9.79285	.104275
9.10	82.8100	3.01662	9.53939	.109890	9.60	92.1600	3.09839	9.79796	.104167
9.11	82.9921	3.01828	9.54463	.109769	9.61	92.3521	3.10000	9.80306	.104058
9.12	83.1744	3.01993	9.54987	.109649	9.62	92.5444	3.10161	9.80816	.103950
9.13	83.3569	3.02159	9.55510	.109529	9.63	92.7369	3.10322	9.81326	.103842
9.14	83.5396	3.02324	9.56033	.109409	9.64	92.9296	3.10483	9.81835	.103734
9.15	83.7225	3.02490	9.56556	.109290	9.65	93.1225	3.10644	9.82344	.103627
9.16	83.9056	3.02655	9.57079	.109170	9.66	93.3156	3.10805	9.82853	.103520
9.17	84.0889	3.02820	9.57601	.109051	9.67	93.5089	3.10966	9.83362	.103413
9.18	84.2724	3.02985	9.58123	.108932	9.68	93.7024	3.11127	9.83870	.103306
9.19	84.4561	3.03150	9.58645	.108814	9.69	93.8961	3.11288	9.84378	.103199
9.20	84.6400	3.03315	9.59166	.108696	9.70	94.0900	3.11448	9.84886	.103093
9.21	84.8241	3.03480	9.59687	.108578	9.71	94.2841	3.11609	9.85393	.102987
9.22	85.0084	3.03645	9.60208	.108460	9.72	94.4784	3.11769	9.85901	.102881
9.23	85.1929	3.03809	9.60729	.108342	9.73	94.6729	3.11929	9.86408	.102775
9.24	85.3776	3.03974	9.61249	.108225	9.74	94.8676	3.12090	9.86914	.102669
9.25	85.5625	3.04138	9.61769	.108108	9.75	95.0625	3.12250	9.87421	.102564
9.26	85.7476	3.04302	9.62289	.107991	9.76	95.2576	3.12410	9.87927	.102459
9.27	85.9329	3.04467	9.62808	.107875	9.77	95.4529	3.12570	9.88433	.102354
9.28	86.1184	3.04631	9.63328	.107759	9.78	95.6484	3.12730	9.88939	.102249
9.29	86.3041	3.04795	9.63846	.107643	9.79	95.8441	3.12890	9.89444	.102145
9.30	86.4900	3.04959	9.64365	.107527	9.80	96.0400	3.13050	9.89949	.102041
9.31	86.6761	3.05123	9.64883	.107411	9.81	96.2361	3.13209	9.90454	.101937
9.32	86.8624	3.05287	9.65401	.107296	9.82	96.4324	3.13369	9.90959	.101833
9.33	87.0489	3.05450	9.65919	.107181	9.83	96.6289	3.13528	9.91464	.101729
9.34	87.2356	3.05614	9.66437	.107066	9.84	96.8256	3.13688	9.91968	.101626
9.35	87.4225	3.05778	9.66954	.106952	9.85	97.0225	3.13847	9.92472	.101523
9.36	87.6096	3.05941	9.67471	.106838	9.86	97.2196	3.14006	9.92975	.101420
9.37	87.7969	3.06105	9.67988	.106724	9.87	97.4169	3.14166	9.93479	.101317
9.38	87.9844	3.06268	9.68504	.106610	9.88	97.6144	3.14325	9.93982	.101215
9.39	88.1721	3.06431	9.69020	.106496	9.89	97.8121	3.14484	9.94485	.101112
9.40	88.3600	3.06594	9.69536	.106383	9.90	98.0100	3.14643	9.94987	.101010
9.41	88.5481	3.06757	9.70052	.106270	9.91	98.2081	3.14802	9.95490	.100908
9.42	88.7364	3.06920	9.70567	.106157	9.92	98.4064	3.14960	9.95992	.100806
9.43	88.9249	3.07083	9.71082	.106045	9.93	98.6049	3.15119	9.96494	.100705
9.44	89.1136	3.07246	9.71597	.105932	9.94	98.8036	3.15278	9.96995	.100604
9.45	89.3025	3.07409	9.72111	.105820	9.95	99.0025	3.15436	9.97497	.100503
9.46	89.4916	3.07571	9.72625	.105708	9.96	99.2016	3.15595	9.97998	.100402
9.47	89.6809	3.07734	9.73139	.105597	9.97	99.4009	3.15753	9.98499	.100301
9.48	89.8704	3.07896	9.73653	.105485	9.98	99.6004	3.15911	9.98999	.100200
9.49	90.0601	3.08058	9.74166	.105374	9.99	99.8001	3.16070	9.99500	.100100
9.50	90.2500	3.08221	9.74679	.105263	10.00	100.000	3.16228	10.0000	.100000
n	n^2	$\sqrt{n}$	$\sqrt{10n}$	$1/n$	n	n^2	$\sqrt{n}$	$\sqrt{10n}$	$1/n$

Table 2

BINOMIAL PROBABILITY DISTRIBUTION

n = 1

r \ p	.01	.02	.03	.04	.05	.06	.07	.08	.09	.10
0	.9900	.9800	.9700	.9600	.9500	.9400	.9300	.9200	.9100	.9000
1	.0100	.0200	.0300	.0400	.0500	.0600	.0700	.0800	.0900	.1000
	.11	.12	.13	.14	.15	.16	.17	.18	.19	.20
0	.8900	.8800	.8700	.8600	.8500	.8400	.8300	.8200	.8100	.8000
1	.1100	.1200	.1300	.1400	.1500	.1600	.1700	.1800	.1900	.2000
	.21	.22	.23	.24	.25	.26	.27	.28	.29	.30
0	.7900	.7800	.7700	.7600	.7500	.7400	.7300	.7200	.7100	.7000
1	.2100	.2200	.2300	.2400	.2500	.2600	.2700	.2800	.2900	.3000
	.31	.32	.33	.34	.35	.36	.37	.38	.39	.40
0	.6900	.6800	.6700	.6600	.6500	.6400	.6300	.6200	.6100	.6000
1	.3100	.3200	.3300	.3400	.3500	.3600	.3700	.3800	.3900	.4000
	.41	.42	.43	.44	.45	.46	.47	.48	.49	.50
0	.5900	.5800	.5700	.5600	.5500	.5400	.5300	.5200	.5100	.5000
1	.4100	.4200	.4300	.4400	.4500	.4600	.4700	.4800	.4900	.5000

n = 2

r \ p	.01	.02	.03	.04	.05	.06	.07	.08	.09	.10
0	.9801	.9604	.9409	.9216	.9025	.8836	.8649	.8464	.8281	.8100
1	.0198	.0392	.0582	.0768	.0950	.1128	.1302	.1472	.1638	.1800
2	.0001	.0004	.0009	.0016	.0025	.0036	.0049	.0064	.0081	.0100
	.11	.12	.13	.14	.15	.16	.17	.18	.19	.20
0	.7921	.7744	.7569	.7396	.7225	.7056	.6889	.6724	.6561	.6400
1	.1958	.2112	.2262	.2408	.2550	.2688	.2822	.2952	.3078	.3200
2	.0121	.0144	.0169	.0196	.0225	.0256	.0289	.0324	.0361	.0400
	.21	.22	.23	.24	.25	.26	.27	.28	.29	.30
0	.6241	.6084	.5929	.5776	.5625	.5476	.5329	.5184	.5041	.4900
1	.3318	.3432	.3542	.3648	.3750	.3848	.3942	.4032	.4118	.4200
2	.0441	.0484	.0529	.0576	.0625	.0676	.0729	.0784	.0841	.0900
	.31	.32	.33	.34	.35	.36	.37	.38	.39	.40
0	.4761	.4624	.4489	.4356	.4225	.4096	.3969	.3844	.3721	.3600
1	.4278	.4352	.4422	.4488	.4550	.4608	.4662	.4712	.4758	.4800
2	.0961	.1024	.1089	.1156	.1225	.1296	.1369	.1444	.1521	.1600
	.41	.42	.43	.44	.45	.46	.47	.48	.49	.50
0	.3481	.3364	.3249	.3136	.3025	.2916	.2809	.2704	.2601	.2500
1	.4838	.4872	.4902	.4928	.4950	.4968	.4982	.4992	.4998	.5000
2	.1681	.1764	.1849	.1936	.2025	.2116	.2209	.2304	.2401	.2500

Charles Clark and Lawrence Schkade, *Statistical Methods for Business Decisions* (Cincinnati: South-Western Publishing Co., 1969), pp. 77-94, by Special Permission.

n = 3

p \ r	.01	.02	.03	.04	.05	.06	.07	.08	.09	.10
0	.9704	.9412	.9127	.8847	.8574	.8306	.8044	.7787	.7536	.7290
1	.0294	.0576	.0847	.1106	.1354	.1590	.1816	.2031	.2236	.2430
2	.0003	.0012	.0026	.0046	.0071	.0102	.0137	.0177	.0221	.0270
3	.0000	.0000	.0000	.0001	.0001	.0002	.0003	.0005	.0007	.0010

p \ r	.11	.12	.13	.14	.15	.16	.17	.18	.19	.20
0	.7050	.6815	.6585	.6361	.6141	.5927	.5718	.5514	.5314	.5120
1	.2614	.2788	.2952	.3106	.3251	.3387	.3513	.3631	.3740	.3840
2	.0323	.0380	.0441	.0506	.0574	.0645	.0720	.0797	.0877	.0960
3	.0013	.0017	.0022	.0027	.0034	.0041	.0049	.0058	.0069	.0080

p \ r	.21	.22	.23	.24	.25	.26	.27	.28	.29	.30
0	.4930	.4746	.4565	.4390	.4219	.4052	.3890	.3732	.3579	.3430
1	.3932	.4015	.4091	.4159	.4219	.4271	.4316	.4355	.4386	.4410
2	.1045	.1133	.1222	.1313	.1406	.1501	.1597	.1693	.1791	.1890
3	.0093	.0106	.0122	.0138	.0156	.0176	.0197	.0220	.0244	.0270

p \ r	.31	.32	.33	.34	.35	.36	.37	.38	.39	.40
0	.3285	.3144	.3008	.2875	.2746	.2621	.2500	.2383	.2270	.2160
1	.4428	.4439	.4444	.4443	.4436	.4424	.4406	.4382	.4354	.4320
2	.1989	.2089	.2189	.2289	.2389	.2488	.2587	.2686	.2783	.2880
3	.0298	.0328	.0359	.0393	.0429	.0467	.0507	.0549	.0593	.0640

p \ r	.41	.42	.43	.44	.45	.46	.47	.48	.49	.50
0	.2054	.1951	.1852	.1756	.1664	.1575	.1489	.1406	.1327	.1250
1	.4282	.4239	.4191	.4140	.4084	.4024	.3961	.3894	.3823	.3750
2	.2975	.3069	.3162	.3252	.3341	.3428	.3512	.3594	.3674	.3750
3	.0689	.0741	.0795	.0852	.0911	.0973	.1038	.1106	.1176	.1250

n = 4

p \ r	.01	.02	.03	.04	.05	.06	.07	.08	.09	.10
0	.9606	.9224	.8853	.8493	.8145	.7807	.7481	.7164	.6857	.6561
1	.0388	.0753	.1095	.1416	.1715	.1993	.2252	.2492	.2713	.2916
2	.0006	.0023	.0051	.0088	.0135	.0191	.0254	.0325	.0402	.0486
3	.0000	.0000	.0001	.0002	.0005	.0008	.0013	.0019	.0027	.0036
4	.0000	.0000	.0000	.0000	.0000	.0000	.0000	.0000	.0001	.0001

p \ r	.11	.12	.13	.14	.15	.16	.17	.18	.19	.20
0	.6274	.5997	.5729	.5470	.5220	.4979	.4746	.4521	.4305	.4096
1	.3102	.3271	.3424	.3562	.3685	.3793	.3888	.3970	.4039	.4096
2	.0575	.0669	.0767	.0870	.0975	.1084	.1195	.1307	.1421	.1536
3	.0047	.0061	.0076	.0094	.0115	.0138	.0163	.0191	.0222	.0256
4	.0001	.0002	.0003	.0004	.0005	.0007	.0008	.0010	.0013	.0016

p \ r	.21	.22	.23	.24	.25	.26	.27	.28	.29	.30
0	.3895	.3702	.3515	.3336	.3164	.2999	.2840	.2687	.2541	.2401
1	.4142	.4176	.4200	.4214	.4219	.4214	.4201	.4180	.4152	.4116
2	.1651	.1767	.1882	.1996	.2109	.2221	.2331	.2439	.2544	.2646
3	.0293	.0332	.0375	.0420	.0469	.0520	.0575	.0632	.0693	.0756
4	.0019	.0023	.0028	.0033	.0039	.0046	.0053	.0061	.0071	.0081

p \ r	.31	.32	.33	.34	.35	.36	.37	.38	.39	.40
0	.2267	.2138	.2015	.1897	.1785	.1678	.1575	.1478	.1385	.1296
1	.4074	.4025	.3970	.3910	.3845	.3775	.3701	.3623	.3541	.3456
2	.2745	.2841	.2933	.3021	.3105	.3185	.3260	.3330	.3396	.3456
3	.0822	.0891	.0963	.1038	.1115	.1194	.1276	.1361	.1447	.1536
4	.0092	.0105	.0119	.0134	.0150	.0168	.0187	.0209	.0231	.0256

p \ r	.41	.42	.43	.44	.45	.46	.47	.48	.49	.50
0	.1212	.1132	.1056	.0983	.0915	.0850	.0789	.0731	.0677	.0625
1	.3368	.3278	.3185	.3091	.2995	.2897	.2799	.2700	.2600	.2500
2	.3511	.3560	.3604	.3643	.3675	.3702	.3723	.3738	.3747	.3750
3	.1627	.1719	.1813	.1908	.2005	.2102	.2201	.2300	.2400	.2500
4	.0283	.0311	.0342	.0375	.0410	.0448	.0488	.0531	.0576	.0625

r = X

n = 5

p \ r	.01	.02	.03	.04	.05	.06	.07	.08	.09	.10
0	.9510	.9039	.8587	.8154	.7738	.7339	.6957	.6591	.6240	.5905
1	.0480	.0922	.1328	.1699	.2036	.2342	.2618	.2866	.3086	.3280
2	.0010	.0038	.0082	.0142	.0214	.0299	.0394	.0498	.0610	.0729
3	.0000	.0001	.0003	.0006	.0011	.0019	.0030	.0043	.0060	.0081
4	.0000	.0000	.0000	.0000	.0000	.0001	.0001	.0002	.0003	.0004

p \ r	.11	.12	.13	.14	.15	.16	.17	.18	.19	.20
0	.5584	.5277	.4984	.4704	.4437	.4182	.3939	.3707	.3487	.3277
1	.3451	.3598	.3724	.3829	.3915	.3983	.4034	.4069	.4089	.4096
2	.0853	.0981	.1113	.1247	.1382	.1517	.1652	.1786	.1919	.2048
3	.0105	.0134	.0166	.0203	.0244	.0289	.0338	.0392	.0450	.0512
4	.0007	.0009	.0012	.0017	.0022	.0028	.0035	.0043	.0053	.0064
5	.0000	.0000	.0000	.0001	.0001	.0001	.0001	.0002	.0002	.0003

p \ r	.21	.22	.23	.24	.25	.26	.27	.28	.29	.30
0	.3077	.2887	.2707	.2536	.2373	.2219	.2073	.1935	.1804	.1681
1	.4090	.4072	.4043	.4003	.3955	.3898	.3834	.3762	.3685	.3602
2	.2174	.2297	.2415	.2529	.2637	.2739	.2836	.2926	.3010	.3087
3	.0578	.0648	.0721	.0798	.0879	.0962	.1049	.1138	.1229	.1323
4	.0077	.0091	.0108	.0126	.0146	.0169	.0194	.0221	.0251	.0284
5	.0004	.0005	.0006	.0008	.0010	.0012	.0014	.0017	.0021	.0024

p \ r	.31	.32	.33	.34	.35	.36	.37	.38	.39	.40
0	.1564	.1454	.1350	.1252	.1160	.1074	.0992	.0916	.0845	.0778
1	.3513	.3421	.3325	.3226	.3124	.3020	.2914	.2808	.2700	.2592
2	.3157	.3220	.3275	.3323	.3364	.3397	.3423	.3441	.3452	.3456
3	.1418	.1515	.1613	.1712	.1811	.1911	.2010	.2109	.2207	.2304
4	.0319	.0357	.0397	.0441	.0488	.0537	.0590	.0646	.0706	.0768
5	.0029	.0034	.0039	.0045	.0053	.0060	.0069	.0079	.0090	.0102

p \ r	.41	.42	.43	.44	.45	.46	.47	.48	.49	.50
0	.0715	.0656	.0602	.0551	.0503	.0459	.0418	.0380	.0345	.0312
1	.2484	.2376	.2270	.2164	.2059	.1956	.1854	.1755	.1657	.1562
2	.3452	.3442	.3424	.3400	.3369	.3332	.3289	.3240	.3185	.3125
3	.2399	.2492	.2583	.2671	.2757	.2838	.2916	.2990	.3060	.3125
4	.0834	.0902	.0974	.1049	.1128	.1209	.1293	.1380	.1470	.1562
5	.0116	.0131	.0147	.0165	.0185	.0206	.0229	.0255	.0282	.0312

P

n = 6

p \ r	.01	.02	.03	.04	.05	.06	.07	.08	.09	.10
0	.9415	.8858	.8330	.7828	.7351	.6899	.6470	.6064	.5679	.5314
1	.0571	.1085	.1546	.1957	.2321	.2642	.2922	.3164	.3370	.3543
2	.0014	.0055	.0120	.0204	.0305	.0422	.0550	.0688	.0833	.0984
3	.0000	.0002	.0005	.0011	.0021	.0036	.0055	.0080	.0110	.0146
4	.0000	.0000	.0000	.0000	.0001	.0002	.0003	.0005	.0008	.0012
5	.0000	.0000	.0000	.0000	.0000	.0000	.0000	.0000	.0000	.0001

p \ r	.11	.12	.13	.14	.15	.16	.17	.18	.19	.20
0	.4970	.4644	.4336	.4046	.3771	.3513	.3269	.3040	.2824	.2621
1	.3685	.3800	.3888	.3952	.3993	.4015	.4018	.4004	.3975	.3932
2	.1139	.1295	.1452	.1608	.1762	.1912	.2057	.2197	.2331	.2458
3	.0188	.0236	.0289	.0349	.0415	.0486	.0562	.0643	.0729	.0819
4	.0017	.0024	.0032	.0043	.0055	.0069	.0086	.0106	.0128	.0154
5	.0001	.0001	.0002	.0003	.0004	.0005	.0007	.0009	.0012	.0015
6	.0000	.0000	.0000	.0000	.0000	.0000	.0000	.0000	.0000	.0001

p \ r	.21	.22	.23	.24	.25	.26	.27	.28	.29	.30
0	.2431	.2252	.2084	.1927	.1780	.1642	.1513	.1393	.1281	.1176
1	.3877	.3811	.3735	.3651	.3560	.3462	.3358	.3251	.3139	.3025
2	.2577	.2687	.2789	.2882	.2966	.3041	.3105	.3160	.3206	.3241
3	.0913	.1011	.1111	.1214	.1318	.1424	.1531	.1639	.1746	.1852
4	.0182	.0214	.0249	.0287	.0330	.0375	.0425	.0478	.0535	.0595
5	.0019	.0024	.0030	.0036	.0044	.0053	.0063	.0074	.0087	.0102
6	.0001	.0001	.0001	.0002	.0002	.0003	.0004	.0005	.0006	.0007

n = 6 (Continued)

r \ p	.31	.32	.33	.34	.35	.36	.37	.38	.39	.40
0	.1079	.0989	.0905	.0827	.0754	.0687	.0625	.0568	.0515	.0467
1	.2909	.2792	.2673	.2555	.2437	.2319	.2203	.2089	.1976	.1866
2	.3267	.3284	.3292	.3290	.3280	.3261	.3235	.3201	.3159	.3110
3	.1957	.2061	.2162	.2260	.2355	.2446	.2533	.2616	.2693	.2765
4	.0660	.0727	.0799	.0873	.0951	.1032	.1116	.1202	.1291	.1382
5	.0119	.0137	.0157	.0180	.0205	.0232	.0262	.0295	.0330	.0369
6	.0009	.0011	.0013	.0015	.0018	.0022	.0026	.0030	.0035	.0041

r \ p	.41	.42	.43	.44	.45	.46	.47	.48	.49	.50
0	.0422	.0381	.0343	.0308	.0277	.0248	.0222	.0198	.0176	.0156
1	.1759	.1654	.1552	.1454	.1359	.1267	.1179	.1095	.1014	.0938
2	.3055	.2994	.2928	.2856	.2780	.2699	.2615	.2527	.2436	.2344
3	.2831	.2891	.2945	.2992	.3032	.3065	.3091	.3110	.3121	.3125
4	.1475	.1570	.1666	.1763	.1861	.1958	.2056	.2153	.2249	.2344
5	.0410	.0455	.0503	.0554	.0609	.0667	.0729	.0795	.0864	.0938
6	.0048	.0055	.0063	.0073	.0083	.0095	.0108	.0122	.0138	.0156

n = 7

r \ p	.01	.02	.03	.04	.05	.06	.07	.08	.09	.10
0	.9321	.8681	.8080	.7514	.6983	.6485	.6017	.5578	.5168	.4783
1	.0659	.1240	.1749	.2192	.2573	.2897	.3170	.3396	.3578	.3720
2	.0020	.0076	.0162	.0274	.0406	.0555	.0716	.0886	.1061	.1240
3	.0000	.0003	.0008	.0019	.0036	.0059	.0090	.0128	.0175	.0230
4	.0000	.0000	.0000	.0001	.0002	.0004	.0007	.0011	.0017	.0026
5	.0000	.0000	.0000	.0000	.0000	.0000	.0000	.0001	.0001	.0002

r \ p	.11	.12	.13	.14	.15	.16	.17	.18	.19	.20
0	.4423	.4087	.3773	.3479	.3206	.2951	.2714	.2493	.2288	.2097
1	.3827	.3901	.3946	.3965	.3960	.3935	.3891	.3830	.3756	.3670
2	.1419	.1596	.1769	.1936	.2097	.2248	.2391	.2523	.2643	.2753
3	.0292	.0363	.0441	.0525	.0617	.0714	.0816	.0923	.1033	.1147
4	.0036	.0049	.0066	.0086	.0109	.0136	.0167	.0203	.0242	.0287
5	.0003	.0004	.0006	.0008	.0012	.0016	.0021	.0027	.0034	.0043
6	.0000	.0000	.0000	.0000	.0001	.0001	.0001	.0002	.0003	.0004

r \ p	.21	.22	.23	.24	.25	.26	.27	.28	.29	.30
0	.1920	.1757	.1605	.1465	.1335	.1215	.1105	.1003	.0910	.0824
1	.3573	.3468	.3356	.3237	.3115	.2989	.2860	.2731	.2600	.2471
2	.2850	.2935	.3007	.3067	.3115	.3150	.3174	.3186	.3186	.3177
3	.1263	.1379	.1497	.1614	.1730	.1845	.1956	.2065	.2169	.2269
4	.0336	.0389	.0447	.0510	.0577	.0648	.0724	.0803	.0886	.0972
5	.0054	.0066	.0080	.0097	.0115	.0137	.0161	.0187	.0217	.0250
6	.0005	.0006	.0008	.0010	.0013	.0016	.0020	.0024	.0030	.0036
7	.0000	.0000	.0000	.0000	.0001	.0001	.0001	.0001	.0002	.0002

r \ p	.31	.32	.33	.34	.35	.36	.37	.38	.39	.40
0	.0745	.0672	.0606	.0546	.0490	.0440	.0394	.0352	.0314	.0280
1	.2342	.2215	.2090	.1967	.1848	.1732	.1619	.1511	.1407	.1306
2	.3156	.3127	.3088	.3040	.2985	.2922	.2853	.2778	.2698	.2613
3	.2363	.2452	.2535	.2610	.2679	.2740	.2793	.2838	.2875	.2903
4	.1062	.1154	.1248	.1345	.1442	.1541	.1640	.1739	.1838	.1935
5	.0286	.0326	.0369	.0416	.0466	.0520	.0578	.0640	.0705	.0774
6	.0043	.0051	.0061	.0071	.0084	.0098	.0113	.0131	.0150	.0172
7	.0003	.0003	.0004	.0005	.0006	.0008	.0009	.0011	.0014	.0016

r \ p	.41	.42	.43	.44	.45	.46	.47	.48	.49	.50
0	.0249	.0221	.0195	.0173	.0152	.0134	.0117	.0103	.0090	.0078
1	.1211	.1119	.1032	.0950	.0872	.0798	.0729	.0664	.0604	.0547
2	.2524	.2431	.2336	.2239	.2140	.2040	.1940	.1840	.1740	.1641
3	.2923	.2934	.2937	.2932	.2918	.2897	.2867	.2830	.2786	.2734
4	.2031	.2125	.2216	.2304	.2388	.2468	.2543	.2612	.2676	.2734
5	.0847	.0923	.1003	.1086	.1172	.1261	.1353	.1447	.1543	.1641
6	.0196	.0223	.0252	.0284	.0320	.0358	.0400	.0445	.0494	.0547
7	.0019	.0023	.0027	.0032	.0037	.0044	.0051	.0059	.0068	.0078

n = 8

r \ p	.01	.02	.03	.04	.05	.06	.07	.08	.09	.10
0	.9227	.8508	.7837	.7214	.6634	.6096	.5596	.5132	.4703	.4305
1	.0746	.1389	.1939	.2405	.2793	.3113	.3370	.3570	.3721	.3826
2	.0026	.0099	.0210	.0351	.0515	.0695	.0888	.1087	.1288	.1488
3	.0001	.0004	.0013	.0029	.0054	.0089	.0134	.0189	.0255	.0331
4	.0000	.0000	.0001	.0002	.0004	.0007	.0013	.0021	.0031	.0046
5	.0000	.0000	.0000	.0000	.0000	.0000	.0001	.0001	.0002	.0004

r \ p	.11	.12	.13	.14	.15	.16	.17	.18	.19	.20
0	.3937	.3596	.3282	.2992	.2725	.2479	.2252	.2044	.1853	.1678
1	.3892	.3923	.3923	.3897	.3847	.3777	.3691	.3590	.3477	.3355
2	.1684	.1872	.2052	.2220	.2376	.2518	.2646	.2758	.2855	.2936
3	.0416	.0511	.0613	.0723	.0839	.0959	.1084	.1211	.1339	.1468
4	.0064	.0087	.0115	.0147	.0185	.0228	.0277	.0332	.0393	.0459
5	.0006	.0009	.0014	.0019	.0026	.0035	.0045	.0058	.0074	.0092
6	.0000	.0001	.0001	.0002	.0002	.0003	.0005	.0006	.0009	.0011
7	.0000	.0000	.0000	.0000	.0000	.0000	.0000	.0000	.0001	.0001

r \ p	.21	.22	.23	.24	.25	.26	.27	.28	.29	.30
0	.1517	.1370	.1236	.1113	.1001	.0899	.0806	.0722	.0646	.0576
1	.3226	.3092	.2953	.2812	.2670	.2527	.2386	.2247	.2110	.1977
2	.3002	.3052	.3087	.3108	.3115	.3108	.3089	.3058	.3017	.2965
3	.1596	.1722	.1844	.1963	.2076	.2184	.2285	.2379	.2464	.2541
4	.0530	.0607	.0689	.0775	.0865	.0959	.1056	.1156	.1258	.1361
5	.0113	.0137	.0165	.0196	.0231	.0270	.0313	.0360	.0411	.0467
6	.0015	.0019	.0025	.0031	.0038	.0047	.0058	.0070	.0084	.0100
7	.0001	.0002	.0002	.0003	.0004	.0005	.0006	.0008	.0010	.0012
8	.0000	.0000	.0000	.0000	.0000	.0000	.0000	.0000	.0001	.0001

r \ p	.31	.32	.33	.34	.35	.36	.37	.38	.39	.40
0	.0514	.0457	.0406	.0360	.0319	.0281	.0248	.0218	.0192	.0168
1	.1847	.1721	.1600	.1484	.1373	.1267	.1166	.1071	.0981	.0896
2	.2904	.2835	.2758	.2675	.2587	.2494	.2397	.2297	.2194	.2090
3	.2609	.2668	.2717	.2756	.2786	.2805	.2815	.2815	.2806	.2787
4	.1465	.1569	.1673	.1775	.1875	.1973	.2067	.2157	.2242	.2322
5	.0527	.0591	.0659	.0732	.0808	.0888	.0971	.1058	.1147	.1239
6	.0118	.0139	.0162	.0188	.0217	.0250	.0285	.0324	.0367	.0413
7	.0015	.0019	.0023	.0028	.0033	.0040	.0048	.0057	.0067	.0079
8	.0001	.0001	.0001	.0002	.0002	.0003	.0003	.0004	.0005	.0007

r \ p	.41	.42	.43	.44	.45	.46	.47	.48	.49	.50
0	.0147	.0128	.0111	.0097	.0084	.0072	.0062	.0053	.0046	.0039
1	.0816	.0742	.0672	.0608	.0548	.0493	.0442	.0395	.0352	.0312
2	.1985	.1880	.1776	.1672	.1569	.1489	.1371	.1275	.1183	.1094
3	.2759	.2723	.2679	.2627	.2568	.2503	.2431	.2355	.2273	.2188
4	.2397	.2465	.2526	.2580	.2627	.2665	.2695	.2717	.2730	.2734
5	.1332	.1428	.1525	.1622	.1719	.1816	.1912	.2006	.2098	.2188
6	.0463	.0517	.0575	.0637	.0703	.0774	.0848	.0926	.1008	.1094
7	.0092	.0107	.0124	.0143	.0164	.0188	.0215	.0244	.0277	.0312
8	.0008	.0010	.0012	.0014	.0017	.0020	.0024	.0028	.0033	.0039

n = 9

r \ p	.01	.02	.03	.04	.05	.06	.07	.08	.09	.10
0	.9135	.8337	.7602	.6925	.6302	.5730	.5204	.4722	.4279	.3874
1	.0830	.1531	.2116	.2597	.2985	.3292	.3525	.3695	.3809	.3874
2	.0034	.0125	.0262	.0433	.0629	.0840	.1061	.1285	.1507	.1722
3	.0001	.0006	.0019	.0042	.0077	.0125	.0186	.0261	.0348	.0446
4	.0000	.0000	.0001	.0003	.0006	.0012	.0021	.0034	.0052	.0074
5	.0000	.0000	.0000	.0000	.0000	.0001	.0002	.0003	.0005	.0008
6	.0000	.0000	.0000	.0000	.0000	.0000	.0000	.0000	.0000	.0001

				n = 9 (Continued)					
p r	.11	.12	.13	.14	.15	.16	.17	.18	.19	.20
0	.3504	.3165	.2855	.2573	.2316	.2082	.1869	.1676	.1501	.1342
1	.3897	.3884	.3840	.3770	.3679	.3569	.3446	.3312	.3169	.3020
2	.1927	.2119	.2295	.2455	.2597	.2720	.2823	.2908	.2973	.3020
3	.0556	.0674	.0800	.0933	.1069	.1209	.1349	.1489	.1627	.1762
4	.0103	.0138	.0179	.0228	.0283	.0345	.0415	.0490	.0573	.0661
5	.0013	.0019	.0027	.0037	.0050	.0066	.0085	.0108	.0134	.0165
6	.0001	.0002	.0003	.0004	.0006	.0008	.0012	.0016	.0021	.0028
7	.0000	.0000	.0000	.0000	.0000	.0001	.0001	.0001	.0002	.0003

p r	.21	.22	.23	.24	.25	.26	.27	.28	.29	.30
0	.1199	.1069	.0952	.0846	.0751	.0665	.0589	.0520	.0458	.0404
1	.2867	.2713	.2558	.2404	.2253	.2104	.1960	.1820	.1685	.1556
2	.3049	.3061	.3056	.3037	.3003	.2957	.2899	.2831	.2754	.2668
3	.1891	.2014	.2130	.2238	.2336	.2424	.2502	.2569	.2624	.2668
4	.0754	.0852	.0954	.1060	.1168	.1278	.1388	.1499	.1608	.1715
5	.0200	.0240	.0285	.0335	.0389	.0449	.0513	.0583	.0657	.0735
6	.0036	.0045	.0057	.0070	.0087	.0105	.0127	.0151	.0179	.0210
7	.0004	.0005	.0007	.0010	.0012	.0016	.0020	.0025	.0031	.0039
8	.0000	.0000	.0001	.0001	.0001	.0001	.0002	.0002	.0003	.0004

p r	.31	.32	.33	.34	.35	.36	.37	.38	.39	.40
0	.0355	.0311	.0272	.0238	.0207	.0180	.0156	.0135	.0117	.0101
1	.1433	.1317	.1206	.1102	.1004	.0912	.0826	.0747	.0673	.0605
2	.2576	.2478	.2376	.2270	.2162	.2052	.1941	.1831	.1721	.1612
3	.2701	.2721	.2731	.2729	.2716	.2693	.2660	.2618	.2567	.2508
4	.1820	.1921	.2017	.2109	.2194	.2272	.2344	.2407	.2462	.2508
5	.0818	.0904	.0994	.1086	.1181	.1278	.1376	.1475	.1574	.1672
6	.0245	.0284	.0326	.0373	.0424	.0479	.0539	.0603	.0671	.0743
7	.0047	.0057	.0069	.0082	.0098	.0116	.0136	.0158	.0184	.0212
8	.0005	.0007	.0008	.0011	.0013	.0016	.0020	.0024	.0029	.0035
9	.0000	.0000	.0000	.0001	.0001	.0001	.0001	.0002	.0002	.0003

p r	.41	.42	.43	.44	.45	.46	.47	.48	.49	.50
0	.0087	.0074	.0064	.0054	.0046	.0039	.0033	.0028	.0023	.0020
1	.0542	.0484	.0431	.0383	.0339	.0299	.0263	.0231	.0202	.0176
2	.1506	.1402	.1301	.1204	.1110	.1020	.0934	.0853	.0776	.0703
3	.2442	.2369	.2291	.2207	.2119	.2027	.1933	.1837	.1739	.1641
4	.2545	.2573	.2592	.2601	.2600	.2590	.2571	.2543	.2506	.2461
5	.1769	.1863	.1955	.2044	.2128	.2207	.2280	.2347	.2408	.2461
6	.0819	.0900	.0983	.1070	.1160	.1253	.1348	.1445	.1542	.1641
7	.0244	.0279	.0318	.0360	.0407	.0458	.0512	.0571	.0635	.0703
8	.0042	.0051	.0060	.0071	.0083	.0097	.0114	.0132	.0153	.0176
9	.0003	.0004	.0005	.0006	.0008	.0009	.0011	.0014	.0016	.0020

				n = 10					
p r	.01	.02	.03	.04	.05	.06	.07	.08	.09	.10
0	.9044	.8171	.7374	.6648	.5987	.5386	.4840	.4344	.3894	.3487
1	.0914	.1667	.2281	.2770	.3151	.3438	.3643	.3777	.3851	.3874
2	.0042	.0153	.0317	.0519	.0746	.0988	.1234	.1478	.1714	.1937
3	.0001	.0008	.0026	.0058	.0105	.0168	.0248	.0343	.0452	.0574
4	.0000	.0000	.0001	.0004	.0010	.0019	.0033	.0052	.0078	.0112
5	.0000	.0000	.0000	.0000	.0001	.0001	.0003	.0005	.0009	.0015
6	.0000	.0000	.0000	.0000	.0000	.0000	.0000	.0000	.0001	.0001

p r	.11	.12	.13	.14	.15	.16	.17	.18	.19	.20
0	.3118	.2785	.2484	.2213	.1969	.1749	.1552	.1374	.1216	.1074
1	.3854	.3798	.3712	.3603	.3474	.3331	.3178	.3017	.2852	.2684
2	.2143	.2330	.2496	.2639	.2759	.2856	.2929	.2980	.3010	.3020
3	.0706	.0847	.0995	.1146	.1298	.1450	.1600	.1745	.1883	.2013
4	.0153	.0202	.0260	.0326	.0401	.0483	.0573	.0670	.0773	.0881
5	.0023	.0033	.0047	.0064	.0085	.0111	.0141	.0177	.0218	.0264
6	.0002	.0004	.0006	.0009	.0012	.0018	.0024	.0032	.0043	.0055
7	.0000	.0000	.0000	.0001	.0001	.0002	.0003	.0004	.0006	.0008
8	.0000	.0000	.0000	.0000	.0000	.0000	.0000	.0000	.0001	.0001

n = 10 (Continued)

r \ p	.21	.22	.23	.24	.25	.26	.27	.28	.29	.30
0	.0947	.0834	.0733	.0643	.0563	.0492	.0430	.0374	.0326	.0282
1	.2517	.2351	.2188	.2030	.1877	.1730	.1590	.1456	.1330	.1211
2	.3011	.2984	.2942	.2885	.2816	.2735	.2646	.2548	.2444	.2335
3	.2134	.2244	.2343	.2429	.2503	.2563	.2609	.2642	.2662	.2668
4	.0993	.1108	.1225	.1343	.1460	.1576	.1689	.1798	.1903	.2001
5	.0317	.0375	.0439	.0509	.0584	.0664	.0750	.0839	.0933	.1029
6	.0070	.0088	.0109	.0134	.0162	.0195	.0231	.0272	.0317	.0368
7	.0011	.0014	.0019	.0024	.0031	.0039	.0049	.0060	.0074	.0090
8	.0001	.0002	.0002	.0003	.0004	.0005	.0007	.0009	.0011	.0014
9	.0000	.0000	.0000	.0000	.0000	.0000	.0001	.0001	.0001	.0001

r \ p	.31	.32	.33	.34	.35	.36	.37	.38	.39	.40
0	.0245	.0211	.0182	.0157	.0135	.0115	.0098	.0084	.0071	.0060
1	.1099	.0995	.0898	.0808	.0725	.0649	.0578	.0514	.0456	.0403
2	.2222	.2107	.1990	.0873	.1757	.1642	.1529	.1419	.1312	.1209
3	.2662	.2644	.2614	.2573	.2522	.2462	.2394	.2319	.2237	.2150
4	.2093	.2177	.2253	.2320	.2377	.2424	.2461	.2487	.2503	.2508
5	.1128	.1229	.1332	.1434	.1536	.1636	.1734	.1829	.1920	.2007
6	.0422	.0482	.0547	.0616	.0689	.0767	.0849	.0934	.1023	.1115
7	.0108	.0130	.0154	.0181	.0212	.0247	.0285	.0327	.0374	.0425
8	.0018	.0023	.0028	.0035	.0043	.0052	.0063	.0075	.0090	.0106
9	.0002	.0002	.0003	.0004	.0005	.0006	.0008	.0010	.0013	.0016
10	.0000	.0000	.0000	.0000	.0000	.0000	.0000	.0001	.0001	.0001

r \ p	.41	.42	.43	.44	.45	.46	.47	.48	.49	.50
0	.0051	.0043	.0036	.0030	.0025	.0021	.0017	.0014	.0012	.0010
1	.0355	.0312	.0273	.0238	.0207	.0180	.0155	.0133	.0114	.0098
2	.1111	.1017	.0927	.0843	.0763	.0688	.0619	.0554	.0494	.0439
3	.2058	.1963	.1865	.1765	.1665	.1564	.1464	.1364	.1267	.1172
4	.2503	.2488	.2462	.2427	.2384	.2331	.2271	.2204	.2130	.2051
5	.2087	.2162	.2229	.2289	.2340	.2383	.2417	.2441	.2456	.2461
6	.1209	.1304	.1401	.1499	.1596	.1692	.1786	.1878	.1966	.2051
7	.0480	.0540	.0604	.0673	.0746	.0824	.0905	.0991	.1080	.1172
8	.0125	.0147	.0171	.0198	.0229	.0263	.0301	.0343	.0389	.0439
9	.0019	.0024	.0029	.0035	.0042	.0050	.0059	.0070	.0083	.0098
10	.0001	.0002	.0002	.0003	.0003	.0004	.0005	.0006	.0008	.0010

n = 11

r \ p	.01	.02	.03	.04	.05	.06	.07	.08	.09	.10
0	.8953	.8007	.7153	.6382	.5688	.5063	.4501	.3996	.3544	.3138
1	.0995	.1798	.2433	.2925	.3293	.3555	.3727	.3823	.3855	.3835
2	.0050	.0183	.0376	.0609	.0867	.1135	.1403	.1662	.1906	.2131
3	.0002	.0011	.0035	.0076	.0137	.0217	.0317	.0434	.0566	.0710
4	.0000	.0000	.0002	.0006	.0014	.0028	.0048	.0075	.0112	.0158
5	.0000	.0000	.0000	.0000	.0001	.0002	.0005	.0009	.0015	.0025
6	.0000	.0000	.0000	.0000	.0000	.0000	.0000	.0001	.0002	.0003

r \ p	.11	.12	.13	.14	.15	.16	.17	.18	.19	.20
0	.2775	.2451	.2161	.1903	.1673	.1469	.1288	.1127	.0985	.0859
1	.3773	.3676	.3552	.3408	.3248	.3078	.2901	.2721	.2541	.2362
2	.2332	.2507	.2654	.2774	.2866	.2932	.2971	.2987	.2980	.2953
3	.0865	.1025	.1190	.1355	.1517	.1675	.1826	.1967	.2097	.2215
4	.0214	.0280	.0356	.0441	.0536	.0638	.0748	.0864	.0984	.1107
5	.0037	.0053	.0074	.0101	.0132	.0170	.0214	.0265	.0323	.0388
6	.0005	.0007	.0011	.0016	.0023	.0032	.0044	.0058	.0076	.0097
7	.0000	.0001	.0001	.0002	.0003	.0004	.0006	.0009	.0013	.0017
8	.0000	.0000	.0000	.0000	.0000	.0000	.0001	.0001	.0001	.0002

n = 11 (Continued)

r \ p	.21	.22	.23	.24	.25	.26	.27	.28	.29	.30
0	.0748	.0650	.0564	.0489	.0422	.0364	.0314	.0270	.0231	.0198
1	.2187	.2017	.1854	.1697	.1549	.1408	.1276	.1153	.1038	.0932
2	.2907	.2845	.2768	.2680	.2581	.2474	.2360	.2242	.2121	.1998
3	.2318	.2407	.2481	.2539	.2581	.2608	.2619	.2616	.2599	.2568
4	.1232	.1358	.1482	.1603	.1721	.1832	.1937	.2035	.2123	.2201
5	.0459	.0536	.0620	.0709	.0803	.0901	.1003	.1108	.1214	.1321
6	.0122	.0151	.0185	.0224	.0268	.0317	.0371	.0431	.0496	.0566
7	.0023	.0030	.0039	.0050	.0064	.0079	.0098	.0120	.0145	.0173
8	.0003	.0004	.0006	.0008	.0011	.0014	.0018	.0023	.0030	.0037
9	.0000	.0000	.0001	.0001	.0001	.0002	.0002	.0003	.0004	.0005

r \ p	.31	.32	.33	.34	.35	.36	.37	.38	.39	.40
0	.0169	.0144	.0122	.0104	.0088	.0074	.0062	.0052	.0044	.0036
1	.0834	.0744	.0662	.0587	.0518	.0457	.0401	.0351	.0306	.0266
2	.1874	.1751	.1630	.1511	.1395	.1284	.1177	.1075	.0978	.0887
3	.2526	.2472	.2408	.2335	.2254	.2167	.2074	.1977	.1876	.1774
4	.2269	.2326	.2372	.2406	.2428	.2438	.2436	.2423	.2399	.2365
5	.1427	.1533	.1636	.1735	.1830	.1920	.2003	.2079	.2148	.2207
6	.0641	.0721	.0806	.0894	.0985	.1080	.1176	.1274	.1373	.1471
7	.0206	.0242	.0283	.0329	.0379	.0434	.0494	.0558	.0627	.0701
8	.0046	.0057	.0070	.0085	.0102	.0122	.0145	.0171	.0200	.0234
9	.0007	.0009	.0011	.0015	.0018	.0023	.0028	.0035	.0043	.0052
10	.0001	.0001	.0001	.0001	.0002	.0003	.0003	.0004	.0005	.0007

r \ p	.41	.42	.43	.44	.45	.46	.47	.48	.49	.50
0	.0030	.0025	.0021	.0017	.0014	.0011	.0009	.0008	.0006	.0005
1	.0231	.0199	.0171	.0147	.0125	.0107	.0090	.0076	.0064	.0054
2	.0801	.0721	.0646	.0577	.0513	.0454	.0401	.0352	.0308	.0269
3	.1670	.1566	.1462	.1359	.1259	.1161	.1067	.0976	.0888	.0806
4	.2321	.2267	.2206	.2136	.2060	.1978	.1892	.1801	.1707	.1611
5	.2258	.2299	.2329	.2350	.2360	.2359	.2348	.2327	.2296	.2256
6	.1569	.1664	.1757	.1846	.1931	.2010	.2083	.2148	.2206	.2256
7	.0779	.0861	.0947	.1036	.1128	.1223	.1319	.1416	.1514	.1611
8	.0271	.0312	.0357	.0407	.0462	.0521	.0585	.0654	.0727	.0806
9	.0063	.0075	.0090	.0107	.0126	.0148	.0173	.0201	.0233	.0269
10	.0009	.0011	.0014	.0017	.0021	.0025	.0031	.0037	.0045	.0054
11	.0001	.0001	.0001	.0001	.0002	.0002	.0002	.0003	.0004	.0005

n = 12

r \ p	.01	.02	.03	.04	.05	.06	.07	.08	.09	.10
0	.8864	.7847	.6938	.6127	.5404	.4759	.4186	.3677	.3225	.2824
1	.1074	.1922	.2575	.3064	.3413	.3645	.3781	.3837	.3827	.3766
2	.0060	.0216	.0438	.0702	.0988	.1280	.1565	.1835	.2082	.2301
3	.0002	.0015	.0045	.0098	.0173	.0272	.0393	.0532	.0686	.0852
4	.0000	.0001	.0003	.0009	.0021	.0039	.0067	.0104	.0153	.0213
5	.0000	.0000	.0000	.0001	.0002	.0004	.0008	.0014	.0024	.0038
6	.0000	.0000	.0000	.0000	.0000	.0000	.0001	.0001	.0003	.0005

r \ p	.11	.12	.13	.14	.15	.16	.17	.18	.19	.20
0	.2470	.2157	.1880	.1637	.1422	.1234	.1069	.0924	.0798	.0687
1	.3663	.3529	.3372	.3197	.3012	.2821	.2627	.2434	.2245	.2062
2	.2490	.2647	.2771	.2863	.2924	.2955	.2960	.2939	.2897	.2835
3	.1026	.1203	.1380	.1553	.1720	.1876	.2021	.2151	.2265	.2362
4	.0285	.0369	.0464	.0569	.0683	.0804	.0931	.1062	.1195	.1329
5	.0056	.0081	.0111	.0148	.0193	.0245	.0305	.0373	.0449	.0532
6	.0008	.0013	.0019	.0028	.0040	.0054	.0073	.0096	.0123	.0155
7	.0001	.0001	.0002	.0004	.0006	.0009	.0013	.0018	.0025	.0033
8	.0000	.0000	.0000	.0000	.0001	.0001	.0002	.0002	.0004	.0005
9	.0000	.0000	.0000	.0000	.0000	.00000	.0000	.0000	.0000	.0001

n = 12 (Continued)

r \ p	.21	.22	.23	.24	.25	.26	.27	.28	.29	.30
0	.0591	.0507	.0434	.0371	.0317	.0270	.0229	.0194	.0164	.0138
1	.1885	.1717	.1557	.1407	.1267	.1137	.1016	.0906	.0804	.0712
2	.2756	.2663	.2558	.2444	.2323	.2197	.2068	.1937	.1807	.1678
3	.2442	.2503	.2547	.2573	.2581	.2573	.2549	.2511	.2460	.2397
4	.1460	.1589	.1712	.1828	.1936	.2034	.2122	.2197	.2261	.2311
5	.0621	.0717	.0818	.0924	.1032	.1143	.1255	.1367	.1477	.1585
6	.0193	.0236	.0285	.0340	.0401	.0469	.0542	.0620	.0704	.0792
7	.0044	.0057	.0073	.0092	.0115	.0141	.0172	.0207	.0246	.0291
8	.0007	.0010	.0014	.0018	.0024	.0031	.0040	.0050	.0063	.0078
9	.0001	.0001	.0002	.0003	.0004	.0005	.0007	.0009	.0011	.0015
10	.0000	.0000	.0000	.0000	.0000	.0001	.0001	.0001	.0001	.0002

r \ p	.31	.32	.33	.34	.35	.36	.37	.38	.39	.40
0	.0116	.0098	.0082	.0068	.0057	.0047	.0039	.0032	.0027	.0022
1	.0628	.0552	.0484	.0422	.0368	.0319	.0276	.0237	.0204	.0174
2	.1552	.1429	.1310	.1197	.1088	.0986	.0890	.0800	.0716	.0639
3	.2324	.2241	.2151	.2055	.1954	.1849	.1742	.1634	.1526	.1419
4	.2349	.2373	.2384	.2382	.2367	.2340	.2302	.2254	.2195	.2128
5	.1688	.1787	.1879	.1963	.2039	.2106	.2163	.2210	.2246	.2270
6	.0885	.0981	.1079	.1180	.1281	.1382	.1482	.1580	.1675	.1766
7	.0341	.0396	.0456	.0521	.0591	.0666	.0746	.0830	.0918	.1009
8	.0096	.0116	.0140	.0168	.0199	.0234	.0274	.0318	.0367	.0420
9	.0019	.0024	.0031	.0038	.0048	.0059	.0071	.0087	.0104	.0125
10	.0003	.0003	.0005	.0006	.0008	.0010	.0013	.0016	.0020	.0025
11	.0000	.0000	.0000	.0001	.0001	.0001	.0001	.0002	.0002	.0003

r \ p	.41	.42	.43	.44	.45	.46	.47	.48	.49	.50
0	.0018	.0014	.0012	.0010	.0008	.0006	.0005	.0004	.0003	.0002
1	.0148	.0126	.0106	.0090	.0075	.0063	.0052	.0043	.0036	.0029
2	.0567	.0502	.0442	.0388	.0339	.0294	.0255	.0220	.0189	.0161
3	.1314	.1211	.1111	.1015	.0923	.0836	.0754	.0676	.0604	.0537
4	.2054	.1973	.1886	.1794	.1700	.1602	.1504	.1405	.1306	.1208
5	.2284	.2285	.2276	.2256	.2225	.2184	.2134	.2075	.2008	.1934
6	.1851	.1931	.2003	.2068	.2124	.2171	.2208	.2234	.2250	.2256
7	.1103	.1198	.1295	.1393	.1489	.1585	.1678	.1768	.1853	.1934
8	.0479	.0542	.0611	.0684	.0762	.0844	.0930	.1020	.1113	.1208
9	.0148	.0175	.0205	.0239	.0277	.0319	.0367	.0418	.0475	.0537
10	.0031	.0038	.0046	.0056	.0068	.0082	.0098	.0116	.0137	.0161
11	.0004	.0005	.0006	.0008	.0010	.0013	.0016	.0019	.0024	.0029
12	.0000	.0000	.0000	.0001	.0001	.0001	.0001	.0001	.0002	.0002

n = 13

r \ p	.01	.02	.03	.04	.05	.06	.07	.08	.09	.10
0	.8775	.7690	.6730	.5882	.5133	.4474	.3893	.3383	.2935	.2542
1	.1152	.2040	.2706	.3186	.3512	.3712	.3809	.3824	.3773	.3672
2	.0070	.0250	.0502	.0797	.1109	.1422	.1720	.1995	.2239	.2448
3	.0003	.0019	.0057	.0122	.0214	.0333	.0475	.0636	.0812	.0997
4	.0000	.0001	.0004	.0013	.0028	.0053	.0089	.0138	.0201	.0277
5	.0000	.0000	.0000	.0001	.0003	.0006	.0012	.0022	.0036	.0055
6	.0000	.0000	.0000	.0000	.0000	.0001	.0001	.0003	.0005	.0008
7	.0000	.0000	.0000	.0000	.0000	.0000	.0000	.0000	.0000	.0001

r \ p	.11	.12	.13	.14	.15	.16	.17	.18	.19	.20
0	.2198	.1898	.1636	.1408	.1209	.1037	.0887	.0758	.0646	.0550
1	.3532	.3364	.3178	.2979	.2774	.2567	.2362	.2163	.1970	.1787
2	.2619	.2753	.2849	.2910	.2937	.2934	.2903	.2848	.2773	.2680
3	.1187	.1376	.1561	.1737	.1900	.2049	.2180	.2293	.2385	.2457
4	.0367	.0469	.0583	.0707	.0838	.0976	.1116	.1258	.1399	.1535
5	.0082	.0115	.0157	.0207	.0266	.0335	.0412	.0497	.0591	.0691
6	.0013	.0021	.0031	.0045	.0063	.0085	.0112	.0145	.0185	.0230
7	.0002	.0003	.0005	.0007	.0011	.0016	.0023	.0032	.0043	.0058
8	.0000	.0000	.0001	.0001	.0001	.0002	.0004	.0005	.0008	.0011
9	.0000	.0000	.0000	.0000	.0000	.0000	.0000	.0001	.0001	.0001

n = 13 (Continued)

p / r	.21	.22	.23	.24	.25	.26	.27	.28	.29	.30
0	.0467	.0396	.0334	.0282	.0238	.0200	.0167	.0140	.0117	.0097
1	.1613	.1450	.1299	.1159	.1029	.0911	.0804	.0706	.0619	.0540
2	.2573	.2455	.2328	.2195	.2059	.1921	.1784	.1648	.1516	.1388
3	.2508	.2539	.2550	.2542	.2517	.2475	.2419	.2351	.2271	.2181
4	.1667	.1790	.1904	.2007	.2097	.2174	.2237	.2285	.2319	.2337
5	.0797	.0909	.1024	.1141	.1258	.1375	.1489	.1600	.1705	.1803
6	.0283	.0342	.0408	.0480	.0559	.0644	.0734	.0829	.0928	.1030
7	.0075	.0096	.0122	.0152	.0186	.0226	.0272	.0323	.0379	.0442
8	.0015	.0020	.0027	.0036	.0047	.0060	.0075	.0094	.0116	.0142
9	.0002	.0003	.0005	.0006	.0009	.0012	.0015	.0020	.0026	.0034
10	.0000	.0000	.0001	.0001	.0001	.0002	.0002	.0003	.0004	.0006
11	.0000	.0000	.0000	.0000	.0000	.0000	.0000	.0000	.0000	.0001

p / r	.31	.32	.33	.34	.35	.36	.37	.38	.39	.40
0	.0080	.0066	.0055	.0045	.0037	.0030	.0025	.0020	.0016	.0013
1	.0469	.0407	.0351	.0302	.0259	.0221	.0188	.0159	.0135	.0113
2	.1265	.1148	.1037	.0933	.0836	.0746	.0663	.0586	.0516	.0453
3	.2084	.1981	.1874	.1763	.1651	.1538	.1427	.1317	.1210	.1107
4	.2341	.2331	.2307	.2270	.2222	.2163	.2095	.2018	.1934	.1845
5	.1893	.1974	.2045	.2105	.2154	.2190	.2215	.2227	.2226	.2214
6	.1134	.1239	.1343	.1446	.1546	.1643	.1734	.1820	.1898	.1968
7	.0509	.0583	.0662	.0745	.0833	.0924	.1019	.1115	.1213	.1312
8	.0172	.0206	.0244	.0288	.0336	.0390	.0449	.0513	.0582	.0656
9	.0043	.0054	.0067	.0082	.0101	.0122	.0146	.0175	.0207	.0243
10	.0008	.0010	.0013	.0017	.0022	.0027	.0034	.0043	.0053	.0065
11	.0001	.0001	.0002	.0002	.0003	.0004	.0006	.0007	.0009	.0012
12	.0000	.0000	.0000	.0000	.0000	.0000	.0001	.0001	.0001	.0001

p / r	.41	.42	.43	.44	.45	.46	.47	.48	.49	.50
0	.0010	.0008	.0007	.0005	.0004	.0003	.0003	.0002	.0002	.0001
1	.0095	.0079	.0066	.0054	.0045	.0037	.0030	.0024	.0020	.0016
2	.0395	.0344	.0298	.0256	.0220	.0188	.0160	.0135	.0114	.0095
3	.1007	.0913	.0823	.0739	.0660	.0587	.0519	.0457	.0401	.0349
4	.1750	.1653	.1553	.1451	.1350	.1250	.1151	.1055	.0962	.0873
5	.2189	.2154	.2108	.2053	.1989	.1917	.1838	.1753	.1664	.1571
6	.2029	.2080	.2121	.2151	.2169	.2177	.2173	.2158	.2131	.2095
7	.1410	.1506	.1600	.1690	.1775	.1854	.1927	.1992	.2048	.2095
8	.0735	.0818	.0905	.0996	.1089	.1185	.1282	.1379	.1476	.1571
9	.0284	.0329	.0379	.0435	.0495	.0561	.0631	.0707	.0788	.0873
10	.0079	.0095	.0114	.0137	.0162	.0191	.0224	.0261	.0303	.0349
11	.0015	.0019	.0024	.0029	.0036	.0044	.0054	.0066	.0079	.0095
12	.0002	.0002	.0003	.0004	.0005	.0006	.0008	.0010	.0013	.0016
13	.0000	.0000	.0000	.0000	.0000	.0000	.0001	.0001	.0001	.0001

n = 14

p / r	.01	.02	.03	.04	.05	.06	.07	.08	.09	.10
0	.8687	.7536	.6528	.5647	.4877	.4205	.3620	.3112	.2670	.2288
1	.1229	.2153	.2827	.3294	.3593	.3758	.3815	.3788	.3698	.3559
2	.0081	.0286	.0568	.0892	.1229	.1559	.1867	.2141	.2377	.2570
3	.0003	.0023	.0070	.0149	.0259	.0398	.0562	.0745	.0940	.1142
4	.0000	.0001	.0006	.0017	.0037	.0070	.0116	.0178	.0256	.0349
5	.0000	.0000	.0000	.0001	.0004	.0009	.0018	.0031	.0051	.0078
6	.0000	.0000	.0000	.0000	.0000	.0001	.0002	.0004	.0008	.0013
7	.0000	.0000	.0000	.0000	.0000	.0000	.0000	.0000	.0001	.0002

p / r	.11	.12	.13	.14	.15	.16	.17	.18	.19	.20
0	.1956	.1670	.1423	.1211	.1028	.0871	.0736	.0621	.0523	.0440
1	.3385	.3188	.2977	.2759	.2539	.2322	.2112	.1910	.1719	.1539
2	.2720	.2826	.2892	.2919	.2912	.2875	.2811	.2725	.2620	.2501
3	.1345	.1542	.1728	.1901	.2056	.2190	.2303	.2393	.2459	.2501
4	.0457	.0578	.0710	.0851	.0998	.1147	.1297	.1444	.1586	.1720
5	.0113	.0158	.0212	.0277	.0352	.0437	.0531	.0634	.0744	.0860
6	.0021	.0032	.0048	.0068	.0093	.0125	.0163	.0209	.0262	.0322
7	.0003	.0005	.0008	.0013	.0019	0027	.0038	.0052	.0070	.0092
8	.0000	.0001	.0001	.0002	.0003	.0005	.0007	.0010	.0014	.0020
9	.0000	.0000	.0000	.0000	.0000	.0001	.0001	.0001	.0002	.0003

n = 14 (Continued)

p\r	.21	.22	.23	.24	.25	.26	.27	.28	.29	.30
0	.0369	.0309	.0258	.0214	.0178	.0148	.0122	.0101	.0083	.0068
1	.1372	.1218	.1077	.0948	.0832	.0726	.0632	.0548	.0473	.0407
2	.2371	.2234	.2091	.1946	.1802	.1659	.1519	.1385	.1256	.1134
3	.2521	.2520	.2499	.2459	.2402	.2331	.2248	.2154	.2052	.1943
4	.1843	.1955	.2052	.2135	.2202	.2252	.2286	.2304	.2305	.2290
5	.0980	.1103	.1226	.1348	.1468	.1583	.1691	.1792	.1883	.1963
6	.0391	.0466	.0549	.0639	.0734	.0834	.0938	.1045	.1153	.1262
7	.0119	.0150	.0188	.0231	.0280	.0335	.0397	.0464	.0538	.0618
8	.0028	.0037	.0049	.0064	.0082	.0103	.0128	.0158	.0192	.0232
9	.0005	.0007	.0010	.0013	.0018	.0024	.0032	.0041	.0052	.0066
10	.0001	.0001	.0001	.0002	.0003	.0004	.0006	.0008	.0011	.0014
11	.0000	.0000	.0000	.0000	.0000	.0001	.0001	.0001	.0002	.0002

	.31	.32	.33	.34	.35	.36	.37	.38	.39	.40
0	.0055	.0045	.0037	.0030	.0024	.0019	.0016	.0012	.0010	.0008
1	.0349	.0298	.0253	.0215	.0181	.0152	.0128	.0106	.0088	.0073
2	.1018	.0911	.0811	.0719	.0634	.0557	.0487	.0424	.0367	.0317
3	.1830	.1715	.1598	.1481	.1366	.1253	.1144	.1039	.0940	.0845
4	.2261	.2219	.2164	.2098	.2022	.1938	.1848	.1752	.1652	.1549
5	.2032	.2088	.2132	.2161	.2178	.2181	.2170	.2147	.2112	.2066
6	.1369	.1474	.1575	.1670	.1759	.1840	.1912	.1974	.2026	.2066
7	.0703	.0793	.0886	.0983	.1082	.1183	.1283	.1383	.1480	.1574
8	.0276	.0326	.0382	.0443	.0510	.0582	.0659	.0742	.0828	.0918
9	.0083	.0102	.0125	.0152	.0183	.0218	.0258	.0303	.0353	.0408
10	.0019	.0024	.0031	.0039	.0049	.0061	.0076	.0093	.0113	.0136
11	.0003	.0004	.0006	.0007	.0010	.0013	.0016	.0021	.0026	.0033
12	.0000	.0000	.0001	.0001	.0001	.0002	.0002	.0003	.0004	.0005
13	.0000	.0000	.0000	.0000	.0000	.0000	.0000	.0000	.0000	.0001

	.41	.42	.43	.44	.45	.46	.47	.48	.49	.50
0	.0006	.0005	.0004	.0003	.0002	.0002	.0001	.0001	.0001	.0001
1	.0060	.0049	.0040	.0033	.0027	.0021	.0017	.0014	.0011	.0009
2	.0272	.0233	.0198	.0168	.0141	.0118	.0099	.0082	.0068	.0056
3	.0757	.0674	.0597	.0527	.0462	.0403	.0350	.0303	.0260	.0222
4	.1446	.1342	.1239	.1138	.1040	.0945	.0854	.0768	.0687	.0611
5	.2009	.1943	.1869	.1788	.1701	.1610	.1515	.1418	.1320	.1222
6	.2094	.2111	.2115	.2108	.2088	.2057	.2015	.1963	.1902	.1833
7	.1663	.1747	.1824	.1892	.1952	.2003	.2043	.2071	.2089	.2095
8	.1011	.1107	.1204	.1301	.1398	.1493	.1585	.1673	.1756	.1833
9	.0469	.0534	.0605	.0682	.0762	.0848	.0937	.1030	.1125	.1222
10	.0163	.0193	.0228	.0268	.0312	.0361	.0415	.0475	.0540	.0611
11	.0041	.0051	.0063	.0076	.0093	.0112	.0134	.0160	.0189	.0222
12	.0007	.0009	.0012	.0015	.0019	.0024	.0030	.0037	.0045	.0056
13	.0001	.0001	.0001	.0002	.0002	.0003	.0004	.0005	.0007	.0009
14	.0000	.0000	.0000	.0000	.0000	.0000	.0000	.0000	.0000	.0001

n = 15

p\r	.01	.02	.03	.04	.05	.06	.07	.08	.09	.10
0	.8601	.7386	.6333	.5421	.4633	.3953	.3367	.2863	.2430	.2059
1	.1303	.2261	.2938	.3388	.3658	.3785	.3801	.3734	.3605	.3432
2	.0092	.0323	.0636	.0988	.1348	.1691	.2003	.2273	.2496	.2669
3	.0004	.0029	.0085	.0178	.0307	.0468	.0653	.0857	.1070	.1285
4	.0000	.0002	.0008	.0022	.0049	.0090	.0148	.0223	.0317	.0428
5	.0000	.0000	.0001	.0002	.0006	.0013	.0024	.0043	.0069	.0105
6	.0000	.0000	.0000	.0000	.0000	.0001	.0003	.0006	.0011	.0019
7	.0000	.0000	.0000	.0000	.0000	.0000	.0000	.0001	.0001	.0003

n = 15 (Continued)									
p\r	.11	.12	.13	.14	.15	.16	.17	.18	.19	.20
0	.1741	.1470	.1238	.1041	.0874	.0731	.0611	.0510	.0424	.0352
1	.3228	.3006	.2775	.2542	.2312	.2090	.1978	.1678	.1492	.1319
2	.2793	.2870	.2903	.2897	.2856	.2787	.2692	.2578	.2449	.2309
3	.1496	.1696	.1880	.2044	.2184	.2300	.2389	.2452	.2489	.2501
4	.0555 ·	.0694	.0843	.0998	.1156	.1314	.1468	.1615	.1752	.1876
5	.0151	.0208	.0277	.0357	.0449	.0551	.0662	.0780	.0904	.1032
6	.0031	.0047	.0069	.0097	.0132	.0175	.0226	.0285	.0353	.0430
7	.0005	.0008	.0013	.0020	.0030	.0043	.0059	.0081	.0107	.0138
8	.0001	.0001	.0002	.0003	.0005	.0008	.0012	.0018	.0025	.0035
9	.0000	.0000	.0000	.0000	.0001	.0001	.0002	.0003	.0005	.0007
10	.0000	.0000	.0000	.0000	.0000	.0000	.0000	.0000	.0001	.0001

	.21	.22	.23	.24	.25	.26	.27	.28	.29	.30
0	.0291	.0241	.0198	.0163	.0134	.0109	.0089	.0072	.0059	.0047
1	.1162	.1018	.0889	.0772	.0668	.0576	.0494	.0423	.0360	.0305
2	.2162	.2010	.1858	.1707	.1559	.1416	.1280	.1150	.1029	.0916
3	.2490	.2457	.2405	.2336	.2252	.2156	.2051	.1939	.1821	.1700
4	.1986	.2079	.2155	.2213	.2252	.2273	.2276	.2262	.2231	.2186
5	.1161	.1290	.1416	.1537	.1651	.1757	.1852	.1935	.2005	.2061
6	.0514	.0606	.0705	.0809	.0917	.1029	.1142	.1254	.1365	.1472
7	.0176	.0220	.0271	.0329	.0393	.0465	.0543	.0627	.0717	.0811
8	.0047	.0062	.0081	.0104	.0131	.0163	.0201	.0244	.0293	.0348
9	.0010	.0014	.0019	.0025	.0034	.0045	.0058	.0074	.0093	.0116
10	.0002	.0002	.0003	.0005	.0007	.0009	.0013	.0017	.0023	.0030
11	.0000	.0000	.0000	.0001	.0001	.0002	.0002	.0003	.0004	.0006
12	.0000	.0000	.0000	.0000	.0000	.0000	.0000	.0000	.0001	.0001

	.31	.32	.33	.34	.35	.36	.37	.38	.39	.40
0	.0038	.0031	.0025	.0020	.0016	.0012	.0010	.0008	.0006	.0005
1	.0258	.0217	.0182	.0152	.0126	.0104	.0086	.0071	.0058	.0047
2	.0811	.0715	.0627	.0547	.0476	.0411	.0354	.0303	.0259	.0219
3	.1579	.1457	.1338	.1222	.1110	.1002	.0901	.0805	.0716	.0634
4	.2128	.2057	.1977	.1888	.1792	.1692	.1587	.1481	.1374	.1268
5	.210	.2130	.2142	.2140	.2123	.2093	.2051	.1997	.1933	.1859
6	.1575	.1671	.1759	.1837	.1906	.1963	.2008	.2040	.2059	.2066
7	.0910	.1011	.1114	.1217	.1319	.1419	.1516	.1608	.1693	.1771
8	.0409	.0476	.0549	.0627	.0710	.0798	.0890	.0985	.1082	.1181
9	.0143	.0174	.0210	.0251	.0298	.0349	.0407	.0470	.0538	.0612
10	.0038	.0049	.0062	.0078	.0096	.0118	.0143	.0173	.0206	.0245
11	.0008	.0011	.0014	.0018	.0024	.0030	.0038	.0048	.0060	.0074
12	.0001	.0002	.0002	.0003	.0004	.0006	.0007	.0010	.0013	.0016
13	.0000	.0000	.0000	.0000	.0001	.0001	.0001	.0001	.0002	.0003

	.41	.42	.43	.44	.45	.46	.47	.48	.49	.50
0	.0004	.0003	.0002	.0002	.0001	.0001	.0001	.0001	.0000	.0000
1	.0038	.0031	.0025	.0020	.0016	.0012	.0010	.0008	.0006	.0005
2	.0185	.0156	.0130	.0108	.0090	.0074	.0060	.0049	.0040	.0032
3	.0558	.0489	.0426	.0369	.0318	.0272	.0232	.0197	.0166	.0139
4	.1163	.1061	.0963	.0869	.0780	.0696	.0617	.0545	.0478	.0417
5	.1778	.1691	.1598	.1502	.1404	.1304	.1204	.1106	.1010	.0916
6	.2060	.2041	.2010	.1967	.1914	.1851	.1780	.1702	.1617	.1527
7	.1840	.1900	.1949	.1987	.2013	.2028	.2030	.2020	.1997	.1964
8	.1279	.1376	.1470	.1561	.1647	.1727	.1800	.1864	.1919	.1964
9	.0691	.0775	.0863	.0954	.1048	.1144	.1241	.1338	.1434	.1527
10	.0288	.0337	.0390	.0450	.0515	.0585	.0661	.0741	.0827	.0916
11	.0091	.0111	.0134	.0161	.0191	.0226	.0266	.0311	.0361	.0417
12	.0021	.0027	.0034	.0042	.0052	.0064	.0079	.0096	.0116	.0139
13	.0003	.0004	.0006	.0008	.0010	.0013	.0016	.0020	.0026	.0032
14	.0000	.0000	.0001	.0001	.0001	.0002	.0002	.0003	.0004	.0005

n = 16

r \ p	.01	.02	.03	.04	.05	.06	.07	.08	.09	.10
0	.8515	.7238	.6143	.5204	.4401	.3716	.3131	.2634	.2211	.1853
1	.1376	.2363	.3040	.3469	.3706	.3795	.3771	.3665	.3499	.3294
2	.0104	.0362	.0705	.1084	.1463	.1817	.2129	.2390	.2596	.2745
3	.0005	.0034	.0102	.0211	.0359	.0541	.0748	.0970	.1198	.1423
4	.0000	.0002	.0010	.0029	.0061	.0112	.0183	.0274	.0385	.0514
5	.0000	.0000	.0001	.0003	.0008	.0017	.0033	.0057	.0091	.0137
6	.0000	.0000	.0000	.0000	.0001	.0002	.0005	.0009	.0017	.0028
7	.0000	.0000	.0000	.0000	.0000	.0000	.0000	.0000	.0002	.0004
8	.0000	.0000	.0000	.0000	.0000	.0000	.0000	.0000	.0000	.0001

r \ p	.11	.12	.13	.14	.15	.16	.17	.18	.19	.20
0	.1550	.1293	.1077	.0895	.0743	.0614	.0507	.0418	.0343	.0281
1	.3065	.2822	.2575	.2332	.2097	.1873	.1662	.1468	.1289	.1126
2	.2841	.2886	.2886	.2847	.2775	.2675	.2554	.2416	.2267	.2111
3	.1638	.1837	.2013	.2163	.2285	.2378	.2441	.2475	.2482	.2463
4	.0658	.0814	.0977	.1144	.1311	.1472	.1625	.1766	.1892	.2001
5	.0195	.0266	.0351	.0447	.0555	.0673	.0799	.0930	.1065	.1201
6	.0044	.0067	.0096	.0133	.0180	.0235	.0300	.0374	.0458	.0550
7	.0008	.0013	.0020	.0031	.0045	.0064	.0088	.0117	.0153	.0197
8	.0001	.0002	.0003	.0006	.0009	.0014	.0020	.0029	.0041	.0055
9	.0000	.0000	.0000	.0001	.0001	.0002	.0004	.0006	.0008	.0012
10	.0000	.0000	.0000	.0000	.0000	.0000	.0001	.0001	.0001	.0002

r \ p	.21	.22	.23	.24	.25	.26	.27	.28	.29	.30
0	.0230	.0188	.0153	.0124	.0100	.0081	.0065	.0052	.0042	.0033
1	.0979	.0847	.0730	.0626	.0535	.0455	.0385	.0325	.0273	.0228
2	.1952	.1792	.1635	.1482	.1336	.1198	.1068	.0947	.0835	.0732
3	.2421	.2359	.2279	.2185	.2079	.1964	.1843	.1718	.1591	.1465
4	.2092	.2162	.2212	.2242	.2252	.2243	.2215	.2171	.2112	.2040
5	.1334	.1464	.1586	.1699	.1802	.1891	.1966	.2026	.2071	.2099
6	.0650	.0757	.0869	.0984	.1101	.1218	.1333	.1445	.1551	.1649
7	.0247	.0305	.0371	.0444	.0524	.0611	.0704	.0803	.0905	.1010
8	.0074	.0097	.0125	.0158	.0197	.0242	.0293	.0351	.0416	.0487
9	.0017	.0024	.0033	.0044	.0058	.0075	.0096	.0121	.0151	.0185
10	.0003	.0005	.0007	.0010	.0014	.0019	.0025	.0033	.0043	.0056
11	.0000	.0001	.0001	.0002	.0002	.0004	.0005	.0007	.0010	.0013
12	.0000	.0000	.0000	.0000	.0000	.0001	.0001	.0001	.0002	.0002

r \ p	.31	.32	.33	.34	.35	.36	.37	.38	.39	.40
0	.0026	.0021	.0016	.0013	.0010	.0008	.0006	.0005	.0004	.0003
1	.0190	.0157	.0130	.0107	.0087	.0071	.0058	.0047	.0038	.0030
2	.0639	.0555	.0480	.0413	.0353	.0301	.0255	.0215	.0180	.0150
3	.1341	.1220	.1103	.0992	.0888	.0790	.0699	.0615	.0538	.0468
4	.1958	.1865	.1766	.1662	.1553	.1444	.1333	.1224	.1118	.1014
5	.2111	.2107	.2088	.2054	.2008	.1949	.1879	.1801	.1715	.1623
6	.1739	.1818	.1885	.1940	.1982	.2010	.2024	.2024	.2010	.1983
7	.1116	.1222	.1326	.1428	.1524	.1615	.1698	.1772	.1836	.1889
8	.0564	.0647	.0735	.0827	.0923	.1022	.1122	.1222	.1320	.1417
9	.0225	.0271	.0322	.0379	.0442	.1511	.0586	.0666	.0750	.0840
10	.0071	.0089	.0111	.0137	.0167	.0201	.0241	.0286	.0336	.0392
11	.0017	.0023	.0030	.0038	.0049	.0062	.0077	.0095	.0117	.0142
12	.0003	.0004	.0006	.0008	.0011	.0014	.0019	.0024	.0031	.0040
13	.0000	.0001	.0001	.0001	.0002	.0003	.0003	.0005	.0006	.0008
14	.0000	.0000	.0000	.0000	.0000	.0000	.0000	.0001	.0001	.0001

r \ p	.41	.42	.43	.44	.45	.46	.47	.48	.49	.50
0	.0002	.0002	.0001	.0001	.0001	.0001	.0000	.0000	.0000	.0000
1	.0024	.0019	.0015	.0012	.0009	.0007	.0005	.0004	.0003	.0002
2	.0125	.0103	.0085	.0069	.0056	.0046	.0037	.0029	.0023	.0018
3	.0405	.0349	.0299	.0254	.0215	.0181	.0151	.0126	.0104	.0085
4	.0915	.0821	.0732	.0649	.0572	.0501	.0436	.0378	.0325	.0278
5	.1526	.1426	.1325	.1224	.1123	.1024	.0929	.0837	.0749	.0667
6	.1944	.1894	.1833	.1762	.1684	.1600	.1510	.1416	.1319	.1222
7	.1930	.1959	.1975	.1978	.1969	.1947	.1912	.1867	.1811	.1746
8	.1509	.1596	.1676	.1749	.1812	.1865	.1908	.1939	.1958	.1964
9	.0932	.1027	.1124	.1221	.1318	.1413	.1504	.1591	.1672	.1746
10	.0453	.0521	.0594	.0672	.0755	.0842	.0934	.1028	.1124	.1222
11	.0172	.0206	.0244	.0288	.0337	.0391	.0452	.0518	.0589	.0667
12	.0050	.0062	.0077	.0094	.0115	.0139	.0167	.0199	.0236	.0278
13	.0011	.0014	.0018	.0023	.0029	.0036	.0046	.0057	.0070	.0085
14	.0002	.0002	.0003	.0004	.0005	.0007	.0009	.0011	.0014	.0018
15	.0000	.0000	.0000	.0000	.0001	.0001	.0001	.0001	.0002	.0002

n = 17

r \ p	.01	.02	.03	.04	.05	.06	.07	.08	.09	.10
0	.8429	.7093	.5958	.4996	.4181	.3493	.2912	.2423	.2012	.1668
1	.1447	.2461	.3133	.3539	.3741	.3790	.3726	.3582	.3383	.3150
2	.0117	.0402	.0775	.1180	.1575	.1935	.2244	.2492	.2677	.2800
3	.0006	.0041	.0120	.0246	.0415	.0618	.0844	.1083	.1324	.1556
4	.0000	.0003	.0013	.0036	.0076	.0138	.0222	.0330	.0458	.0605
5	.0000	.0000	.0001	.0004	.0010	.0023	.0044	.0075	.0118	.0175
6	.0000	.0000	.0000	.0000	.0001	.0003	.0007	.0013	.0023	.0039
7	.0000	.0000	.0000	.0000	.0000	.0000	.0001	.0002	.0004	.0007
8	.0000	.0000	.0000	.0000	.0000	.0000	.0000	.0000	.0000	.0001

r \ p	.11	.12	.13	.14	.15	.16	.17	.18	.19	.20
0	.1379	.1138	.0937	.0770	.0631	.0516	.0421	.0343	.0278	.0225
1	.2898	.2638	.2381	.2131	.1893	.1671	.1466	.1279	.1109	.0957
2	.2865	.2878	.2846	.2775	.2673	.2547	.2402	.2245	.2081	.1914
3	.1771	.1963	.2126	.2259	.2359	.2425	.2460	.2464	.2441	.2393
4	.0766	.0937	.1112	.1287	.1457	.1617	.1764	.1893	.2004	.2093
5	.0246	.0332	.0432	.0545	.0668	.0801	.0939	.1081	.1222	.1361
6	.0061	.0091	.0129	.0177	.0236	.0305	.0385	.0474	.0573	.0680
7	.0012	.0019	.0030	.0045	.0065	.0091	.0124	.0164	.0211	.0267
8	.0002	.0003	.0006	.0009	.0014	.0022	.0032	.0045	.0062	.0084
9	.0000	.0000	.0001	.0002	.0003	.0004	.0006	.0010	.0015	.0021
10	.0000	.0000	.0000	.0000	.0000	.0001	.0001	.0002	.0003	.0004
11	.0000	.0000	.0000	.0000	.0000	.0000	.0000	.0000	.0000	.0001

r \ p	.21	.22	.23	.24	.25	.26	.27	.28	.29	.30
0	.0182	.0146	.0118	.0094	.0075	.0060	.0047	.0038	.0030	.0023
1	.0822	.0702	.0597	.0505	.0426	.0357	.0299	.0248	.0206	.0169
2	.1747	.1584	.1427	.1277	.1136	.1005	.0883	.0772	.0672	.0581
3	.2322	.2234	.2131	.2016	.1893	.1765	.1634	.1502	.1372	.1245
4	.2161	.2205	.2228	.2228	.2209	.2170	.2115	.2044	.1961	.1868
5	.1493	.1617	.1730	.1830	.1914	.1982	.2033	.2067	.2083	.2081
6	.0794	.0912	.1034	.1156	.1276	.1393	.1504	.1608	.1701	.1784
7	.0332	.0404	.0485	.0573	.0668	.0769	.0874	.0982	.1092	.1201
8	.0110	.0143	.0181	.0226	.0279	.0338	.0404	.0478	.0558	.0644
9	.0029	.0040	.0054	.0071	.0093	.0119	.0150	.0186	.0228	.0276
10	.0006	.0009	.0013	.0018	.0025	.0033	.0044	.0058	.0074	.0095
11	.0001	.0002	.0002	.0004	.0005	.0007	.0010	.0014	.0019	.0026
12	.0000	.0000	.0000	.0001	.0001	.0001	.0002	.0003	.0004	.0006
13	.0000	.0000	.0000	.0000	.0000	.0000	.0000	.0000	.0001	.0001

r \ p	.31	.32	.33	.34	.35	.36	.37	.38	.39	.40
0	.0018	.0014	.0011	.0009	.0007	.0005	.0004	.0003	.0002	.0002
1	.0139	.0114	.0093	.0075	.0060	.0048	.0039	.0031	.0024	.0019
2	.0500	.0428	.0364	.0309	.0260	.0218	.0182	.0151	.0125	.0102
3	.1123	.1007	.0898	.0795	.0701	.0614	.0534	.0463	.0398	.0341
4	.1766	.1659	.1547	.1434	.1320	.1208	.1099	.0993	.0892	.0796
5	.2063	.2030	.1982	.1921	.1849	.1767	.1677	.1582	.1482	.1379
6	.1854	.1910	.1952	.1979	.1991	.1988	.1970	.1939	.1895	.1839
7	.1309	.1413	.1511	.1602	.1685	.1757	.1818	.1868	.1904	.1927
8	.0735	.0831	.0930	.1032	.1134	.1235	.1335	.1431	.1521	.1606
9	.0330	.0391	.0458	.0531	.0611	.0695	.0784	.0877	.0973	.1070
10	.0119	.0147	.0181	.0219	.0263	.0313	.0368	.0430	.0498	.0571
11	.0034	.0044	.0057	.0072	.0090	.0112	.0138	.0168	.0202	.0242
12	.0008	.0010	.0014	.0018	.0024	.0031	.0040	.0051	.0065	.0081
13	.0001	.0002	.0003	.0004	.0005	.0007	.0009	.0012	.0016	.0021
14	.0000	.0000	.0000	.0001	.0001	.0001	.0002	.0002	.0003	.0004
15	.0000	.0000	.0000	.0000	.0000	.0000	.0000	.0000	.0000	.0001

n = 17 (Continued)

p / r	.41	.42	.43	.44	.45	.46	.47	.48	.49	.50
0	.0001	.0001	.0001	.0001	.0000	.0000	.0000	.0000	.0000	.0000
1	.0015	.0012	.0009	.0007	.0005	.0004	.0003	.0002	.0002	.0001
2	.0084	.0068	.0055	.0044	.0035	.0028	.0022	.0017	.0013	.0010
3	.0290	.0246	.0207	.0173	.0144	.0119	.0097	.0079	.0064	.0052
4	.0706	.0622	.0546	.0475	.0411	.0354	.0302	.0257	.0217	.0182
5	.1276	.1172	.1070	.0971	.0875	.0784	.0697	.0616	.0541	.0472
6	.1773	.1697	.1614	.1525	.1432	.1335	.1237	.1138	.1040	.0944
7	.1936	.1932	.1914	.1883	.1841	.1787	.1723	.1650	.1570	.1484
8	.1682	.1748	.1805	.1850	.1883	.1903	.1910	.1904	.1886	.1855
9	.1169	.1266	.1361	.1453	.1540	.1621	.1694	.1758	.1812	.1855
10	.0650	.0733	.0822	.0914	.1008	.1105	.1202	.1298	.1393	.1484
11	.0287	.0338	.0394	.0457	.0525	.0599	.0678	.0763	.0851	.0944
12	.0100	.0122	.0149	.0179	.0215	.0255	.0301	.0352	.0409	.0472
13	.0027	.0034	.0043	.0054	.0068	.0084	.0103	.0125	.0151	.0182
14	.0005	.0007	.0009	.0012	.0016	.0020	.0026	.0033	.0041	.0052
15	.0001	.0001	.0001	.0002	.0003	.0003	.0005	.0006	.0008	.0010
16	.0000	.0000	.0000	.0000	.0000	.0000	.0001	.0001	.0001	.0001

n = 18

p / r	.01	.02	.03	.04	.05	.06	.07	.08	.09	.10
0	.8345	.6951	.5780	.4796	.3972	.3283	.2708	.2229	.1831	.1501
1	.1517	.2554	.3217	.3597	.3763	.3772	.3669	.3489	.3260	.3002
2	.0130	.0443	.0846	.1274	.1683	.2047	.2348	.2579	.2741	.2835
3	.0007	.0048	.0140	.0283	.0473	.0697	.0942	.1196	.1446	.1680
4	.0000	.0004	.0016	.0044	.0093	.0167	.0266	.0390	.0536	.0700
5	.0000	.0000	.0001	.0005	.0014	.0030	.0056	.0095	.0148	.0218
6	.0000	.0000	.0000	.0000	.0002	.0004	.0009	.0018	.0032	.0052
7	.0000	.0000	.0000	.0000	.0000	.0000	.0001	.0003	.0005	.0010
8	.0000	.0000	.0000	.0000	.0000	.0000	.0000	.0000	.0001	.0002

p / r	.11	.12	.13	.14	.15	.16	.17	.18	.19	.20
0	.1227	.1002	.0815	.0662	.0536	.0434	.0349	.0281	.0225	.0180
1	.2731	.2458	.2193	.1940	.1704	.1486	.1288	.1110	.0951	.0811
2	.2869	.2850	.2785	.2685	.2556	.2407	.2243	.2071	.1897	.1723
3	.1891	.2072	.2220	.2331	.2406	.2445	.2450	.2425	.2373	.2297
4	.0877	.1060	.1244	.1423	.1592	.1746	.1882	.1996	.2087	.2153
5	.0303	.0405	.0520	.0649	.0787	.0931	.1079	.1227	.1371	.1507
6	.0081	.0120	.0168	.0229	.0301	.0384	.0479	.0584	.0697	.0816
7	.0017	.0028	.0043	.0064	.0091	.0126	.0168	.0220	.0280	.0350
8	.0003	.0005	.0009	.0014	.0022	.0033	.0047	.0066	.0090	.0120
9	.0000	.0001	.0001	.0003	.0004	.0007	.0011	.0016	.0024	.0033
10	.0000	.0000	.0000	.0000	.0001	.0001	.0002	.0003	.0005	.0008
11	.0000	.0000	.0000	.0000	.0000	.0000	.0000	.0001	.0001	.0001

p / r	.21	.22	.23	.24	.25	.26	.27	.28	.29	.30
0	.0144	.0114	.0091	.0072	.0056	.0044	.0035	.0027	.0021	.0016
1	.0687	.0580	.0487	.0407	.0338	.0280	.0231	.0189	.0155	.0126
2	.1553	.1390	.1236	.1092	.0958	.0836	.0725	.0626	.0537	.0458
3	.2202	.2091	.1969	.1839	.1704	.1567	.1431	.1298	.1169	.1046
4	.2195	.2212	.2205	.2177	.2130	.2065	.1985	.1892	.1790	.1681
5	.1634	.1747	.1845	.1925	.1988	.2031	.2055	.2061	.2048	.2017
6	.0941	.1067	.1194	.1317	.1436	.1546	.1647	.1736	.1812	.1873
7	.0429	.0516	.0611	.0713	.0820	.0931	.1044	.1157	.1269	.1376
8	.0157	.0200	.0251	.0310	.0376	.0450	.0531	.0619	.0713	.0811
9	.0046	.0063	.0083	.0109	.0139	.0176	.0218	.0267	.0323	.0386
10	.0011	.0016	.0022	.0031	.0042	.0056	.0073	.0094	.0119	.0149
11	.0002	.0003	.0005	.0007	.0010	.0014	.0020	.0026	.0035	.0046
12	.0000	.0001	.0001	.0001	.0002	.0003	.0004	.0006	.0008	.0012
13	.0000	.0000	.0000	.0000	.0000	.0000	.0001	.0001	.0002	.0002

222

	n = 18 (Continued)								
r \ p	.31	.32	.33	.34	.35	.36	.37	.38	.39	.40
0	.0013	.0010	.0007	.0006	.0004	.0003	.0002	.0002	.0001	.0001
1	.0102	.0082	.0066	.0052	.0042	.0033	.0026	.0020	.0016	.0012
2	.0388	.0327	.0275	.0229	.0190	.0157	.0129	.0105	.0086	.0069
3	.0930	.0822	.0722	.0630	.0547	.0471	.0404	.0344	.0292	.0246
4	.1567	.1450	.1333	.1217	.1104	.0994	.0890	.0791	.0699	.0614
5	.1971	.1911	.1838	.1755	.1664	.1566	.1463	.1358	.1252	.1146
6	.1919	.1948	.1962	.1959	.1941	.1908	.1862	.1803	.1734	.1655
7	.1478	.1572	.1656	.1730	.1792	.1840	.1875	.1895	.1900	.1892
8	.0913	.1017	.1122	.1226	.1327	.1423	.1514	.1597	.1671	.1734
9	.0456	.0532	.0614	.0701	.0794	.0890	.0988	.1087	.1187	.1284
10	.0184	.0225	.0272	.0325	.0385	.0450	.0522	.0600	.0683	.0771
11	.0060	.0077	.0097	.0122	.0151	.0184	.0223	.0267	.0318	.0374
12	.0016	.0021	.0028	.0037	.0047	.0060	.0076	.0096	.0118	.0145
13	.0003	.0005	.0006	.0009	.0012	.0016	.0021	.0027	.0035	.0045
14	.0001	.0001	.0001	.0002	.0002	.0003	.0004	.0006	.0008	.0011
15	.0000	.0000	.0000	.0000	.0000	.0000	.0001	.0001	.0001	.0002

r \ p	.41	.42	.43	.44	.45	.46	.47	.48	.49	.50
0	.0001	.0001	.0000	.0000	.0000	.0000	.0000	.0000	.0000	.0000
1	.0009	.0007	.0005	.0004	.0003	.0002	.0002	.0001	.0001	.0001
2	.0055	.0044	.0035	.0028	.0022	.0017	.0013	.0010	.0008	.0006
3	.0206	.0171	.0141	.0116	.0095	.0077	.0062	.0050	.0039	.0031
4	.0536	.0464	.0400	.0342	.0291	.0246	.0206	.0172	.0142	.0117
5	.1042	.0941	.0844	.0753	.0666	.0586	.0512	.0444	.0382	.0327
6	.1569	.1477	.1380	.1281	.1181	.1081	.0983	.0887	.0796	.0708
7	.1869	.1833	.1785	.1726	.1657	.1579	.1494	.1404	.1310	.1214
8	.1786	.1825	.1852	.1864	.1864	.1850	.1822	.1782	.1731	.1669
9	.1379	.1469	.1552	.1628	.1694	.1751	.1795	.1828	.1848	.1855
10	.0862	.0957	.1054	.1151	.1248	.1342	.1433	.1519	.1598	.1669
11	.0436	.0504	.0578	.0658	.0742	.0831	.0924	.1020	.1117	.1214
12	.0177	.0213	.0254	.0301	.0354	.0413	.0478	.0549	.0626	.0708
13	.0057	.0071	.0089	.0109	.0134	.0162	.0196	.0234	.0278	.0327
14	.0014	.0018	.0024	.0031	.0039	.0049	.0062	.0077	.0095	.0117
15	.0003	.0004	.0005	.0006	.0009	.0011	.0015	.0019	.0024	.0031
16	.0000	.0000	.0001	.0001	.0001	.0002	.0002	.0003	.0004	.0006
17	.0000	.0000	.0000	.0000	.0000	.0000	.0000	.0000	.0000	.0001

	n = 19								
r \ p	.01	.02	.03	.04	.05	.06	.07	.08	.09	.10
0	.8262	.6812	.5606	.4604	.3774	.3086	.2519	.2051	.1666	.1351
1	.1586	.2642	.3294	.3645	.3774	.3743	.3602	.3389	.3131	.2852
2	.0144	.0485	.0917	.1367	.1787	.2150	.2440	.2652	.2787	.2852
3	.0008	.0056	.0161	.0323	.0533	.0778	.1041	.1307	.1562	.1796
4	.0000	.0005	.0020	.0054	.0112	.0199	.0313	.0455	.0618	.0798
5	.0000	.0000	.0002	.0007	.0018	.0038	.0071	.0119	.0183	.0266
6	.0000	.0000	.0000	.0001	.0002	.0006	.0012	.0024	.0042	.0069
7	.0000	.0000	.0000	.0000	.0000	.0001	.0002	.0004	.0008	.0014
8	.0000	.0000	.0000	.0000	.0000	.0000	.0000	.0001	.0001	.0002

r \ p	.11	.12	.13	.14	.15	.16	.17	.18	.19	.20
0	.1092	.0881	.0709	.0569	.0456	.0364	.0290	.0230	.0182	.0144
1	.2565	.2284	.2014	.1761	.1529	.1318	.1129	.0961	.0813	.0685
2	.2854	.2803	.2708	.2581	.2428	.2259	.2081	.1898	.1717	.1540
3	.1999	.2166	.2293	.2381	.2428	.2439	.2415	.2361	.2282	.2182
4	.0988	.1181	.1371	.1550	.1714	.1858	.1979	.2073	.2141	.2182
5	.0366	.0483	.0614	.0757	.0907	.1062	.1216	.1365	.1507	.1636
6	.0106	.0154	.0214	.0288	.0374	.0472	.0581	.0699	.0825	.0955
7	.0024	.0039	.0059	.0087	.0122	.0167	.0221	.0285	.0359	.0443
8	.0004	.0008	.0013	.0021	.0032	.0048	.0068	.0094	.0126	.0166
9	.0001	.0001	.0002	.0004	.0007	.0011	.0017	.0025	.0036	.0051
10	.0000	.0000	.0000	.0001	.0001	.0002	.0003	.0006	.0009	.0013
11	.0000	.0000	.0000	.0000	.0000	.0000	.0001	.0001	.0002	.0003

n = 19 (Continued)

r \ p	.21	.22	.23	.24	.25	.26	.27	.28	.29	.30
0	.0113	.0089	.0070	.0054	.0042	.0033	.0025	.0019	.0015	.0011
1	.0573	.0477	.0396	.0326	.0268	.0219	.0178	.0144	.0116	.0093
2	.1371	.1212	.1064	.0927	.0803	.0692	.0592	.0503	.0426	.0358
3	.2065	.1937	.1800	.1659	.1517	.1377	.1240	.1109	.0985	.0869
4	.2196	.2185	.2151	.2096	.2023	.1935	.1835	.1726	.1610	.1491
5	.1751	.1849	.1928	.1986	.2023	.2040	.2036	.2013	.1973	.1916
6	.1086	.1217	.1343	.1463	.1574	.1672	.1757	.1827	.1880	.1916
7	.0536	.0637	.0745	.0858	.0974	.1091	.1207	.1320	.1426	.1525
8	.0214	.0270	.0334	.0406	.0487	.0575	.0670	.0770	.0874	.0981
9	.0069	.0093	.0122	.0157	.0198	.0247	.0303	.0366	.0436	.0514
10	.0018	.0026	.0036	.0050	.0066	.0087	.0112	.0142	.0178	.0220
11	.0004	.0006	.0009	.0013	.0018	0025	.0034	.0045	.0060	.0077
12	.0001	.0001	.0002	.0003	.0004	.0006	.0008	.0012	.0016	.0022
13	.0000	.0000	.0000	.0000	.0001	.0001	.0002	.0002	.0004	.0005
14	.0000	.0000	.0000	.0000	.0000	.0000	.0000	.0000	.0001	.0001

r \ p	.31	.32	.33	.34	.35	.36	.37	.38	.39	.40
0	.0009	.0007	.0005	.0004	.0003	.0002	.0002	.0001	.0001	.0001
1	.0074	.0059	.0046	.0036	.0029	.0022	.0017	.0013	.0010	.0008
2	.0299	.0249	.0206	.0169	.0138	.0112	.0091	.0073	.0058	.0046
3	.0762	.0664	.0574	.0494	.0422	.0358	.0302	.0253	.0211	.0175
4	.1370	.1249	.1131	.1017	.0909	.0806	.0710	.0621	.0540	.0467
5	.1846	.1764	.1672	.1572	.1468	.1360	.1251	.1143	.1036	.0933
6	.1935	.1936	.1921	.1890	.1844	.1785	.1714	.1634	.1546	.1451
7	.1615	.1692	.1757	.1808	.1844	.1865	.1870	.1860	.1835	.1797
8	.1088	.1195	.1298	.1397	.1489	.1573	.1647	.1710	.1760	.1797
9	.0597	.0687	.0782	.0880	.0980	.1082	.1182	.1281	.1375	.1464
10	.0268	.0323	.0385	.0453	.0528	.0608	.0694	.0785	.0879	.0976
11	.0099	.0124	.0155	.0191	.0233	.0280	.0334	.0394	.0460	.0532
12	.0030	.0039	.0051	.0066	.0083	.0105	.0131	.0161	.0196	.0237
13	.0007	.0010	.0014	.0018	.0024	.0032	.0041	.0053	.0067	.0085
14	.0001	.0002	.0003	.0004	.0006	.0008	.0010	.0014	.0018	.0024
15	.0000	.0000	.0000	.0001	.0001	.0001	.0002	.0003	.0004	.0005
16	.0000	.0000	.0000	.0000	.0000	.0000	.0000	.0000	.0001	.0001

r \ p	.41	.42	.43	.44	.45	.46	.47	.48	.49	.50
0	.0000	.0000	.0000	.0000	.0000	.0000	.0000	.0000	.0000	.0000
1	.0006	.0004	.0003	.0002	.0002	.0001	.0001	.0001	.0001	.0000
2	.0037	.0029	.0022	.0017	.0013	.0010	.0008	.0006	.0004	.0003
3	.0144	.0118	.0096	.0077	.0062	.0049	.0039	.0031	.0024	.0018
4	.0400	.0341	.0289	.0243	.0203	.0168	.0138	.0113	.0092	.0074
5	.0834	.0741	.0653	.0572	.0497	.0429	.0368	.0313	.0265	.0222
6	.1353	.1252	.1150	.1049	.0949	.0853	.0751	.0674	.0593	.0518
7	.1746	.1683	.1611	.1530	.1443	.1350	.1254	.1156	.1058	.0961
8	.1820	.1829	.1823	.1803	.1771	.1725	.1668	.1601	.1525	.1442
9	.1546	.1618	.1681	.1732	.1771	.1796	.1808	.1806	.1791	.1762
10	.1074	.1172	.1268	.1361	.1449	.1530	.1603	.1667	.1721	.1762
11	.0611	.0694	.0783	.0875	.0970	.1066	.1163	.1259	.1352	.1442
12	.0283	.0335	.0394	.0458	.0529	.0606	.0688	.0775	.0866	.0961
13	.0106	.0131	.0160	.0194	.0233	.0278	.0328	.0385	.0448	.0518
14	.0032	.0041	.0052	.0065	.0082	.0101	.0125	.0152	.0185	.0222
15	.0007	.0010	.0013	.0017	.0022	.0029	.0037	.0047	.0059	.0074
16	.0001	.0002	.0002	.0003	.0005	.0006	.0008	.0011	.0014	.0018
17	.0000	.0000	.0000	.0000	.0000	.0001	.0001	.0002	.0002	.0003

n = 20

r \ p	.01	.02	.03	.04	.05	.06	.07	.08	.09	.10
0	.8179	.6676	.5438	.4420	.3585	.2901	.2342	.1887	.1516	.1216
1	.1652	.2725	.3364	.3683	.3774	.3703	.3526	.3282	.3000	.2702
2	.0159	.0528	.0988	.1458	.1887	.2246	.2521	.2711	.2818	.2852
3	.0010	.0065	.0183	.0364	.0596	.0860	.1139	.1414	.1672	.1901
4	.0000	.0006	.0024	.0065	.0133	.0233	.0364	.0523	.0703	.0898
5	.0000	.0000	.0002	.0009	.0022	.0048	.0088	.0145	.0222	.0319
6	.0000	.0000	.0000	.0001	.0003	.0008	.0017	.0032	.0055	.0089
7	.0000	.0000	.0000	.0000	.0000	.0001	.0002	.0005	.0011	.0020
8	.0000	.0000	.0000	.0000	.0000	.0000	.0000	.0001	.0002	.0004
9	.0000	.0000	.0000	.0000	.0000	.0000	.0000	.0000	.0000	.0001

n = 20 (Continued)									
r \ p	.11	.12	.13	.14	.15	.16	.17	.18	.19	.20
0	.0972	.0776	.0617	.0490	.0388	.0306	.0241	.0189	.0148	.0115
1	.2403	.2115	.1844	.1595	.1368	.1165	.0986	.0829	.0693	.0576
2	.2822	.2740	.2618	.2466	.2293	.2109	.1919	.1730	.1545	.1369
3	.2093	.2242	.2347	.2409	.2428	.2410	.2358	.2278	.2175	.2054
4	.1099	.1299	.1491	.1666	.1821	.1951	.2053	.2125	.2168	.2182
5	.0435	.0567	.0713	.0870	.1028	.1189	.1345	.1493	.1627	.1746
6	.0134	.0193	.0266	.0353	.0454	.0566	.0689	.0819	.0954	.1091
7	.0033	.0053	.0080	.0115	.0160	.0216	.0282	.0360	.0448	.0545
8	.0007	.0012	.0019	.0030	.0046	.0067	.0094	.0128	.0171	.0222
9	.0001	.0002	.0004	.0007	.0011	.0017	.0026	.0038	.0053	.0074
10	.0000	.0000	.0001	.0001	.0002	.0004	.0006	.0009	.0014	.0020
11	.0000	.0000	.0000	.0000	.0000	.0001	.0001	.0002	.0003	.0005
12	.0000	.0000	.0000	.0000	.0000	.0000	.0000	.0000	.0001	.0001

r \ p	.21	.22	.23	.24	.25	.26	.27	.28	.29	.30
0	.0090	.0069	.0054	.0041	.0032	.0024	.0018	.0014	.0011	.0008
1	.0477	.0392	.0321	.0261	.0211	.0170	.0137	.0109	.0087	.0068
2	.1204	.1050	.0910	.0783	.0669	.0569	.0480	.0403	.0336	.0278
3	.1920	.1777	.1631	.1484	.1339	.1199	.1065	.0940	.0823	.0716
4	.2169	.2131	.2070	.1991	.1897	.1790	.1675	.1553	.1429	.1304
5	.1845	.1923	.1979	.2012	.2023	.2013	.1982	.1933	.1868	.1789
6	.1226	.1356	.1478	.1589	.1686	.1768	.1833	.1879	.1907	.1916
7	.0652	.0765	.0883	.1003	.1124	.1242	.1356	.1462	.1558	.1643
8	.0282	.0351	.0429	.0515	.0609	.0709	.0815	.0924	.1034	.1144
9	.0100	.0132	.0171	.0217	.0271	.0332	.0402	.0479	.0563	.0654
10	.0029	.0041	.0056	.0075	.0099	.0128	.0163	.0205	.0253	.0308
11	.0007	.0010	.0015	.0022	.0030	.0041	.0055	.0072	.0094	.0120
12	.0001	.0002	.0003	.0005	.0008	.0011	.0015	.0021	.0029	.0039
13	.0000	.0000	.0001	.0001	.0002	.0002	.0003	.0005	.0007	.0010
14	.0000	.0000	.0000	.0000	.0000	.0000	.0001	.0001	.0001	.0002

r \ p	.31	.32	.33	.34	.35	.36	.37	.38	.39	.40
0	.0006	.0004	.0003	.0002	.0002	.0001	.0001	.0001	.0001	.0000
1	.0054	.0042	.0033	.0025	.0020	.0015	.0011	.0009	.0007	.0005
2	.0229	.0188	.0153	.0124	.0100	.0080	.0064	.0050	.0040	.0031
3	.0619	.0531	.0453	.0383	.0323	.0270	.0224	.0185	.0152	.0123
4	.1181	.1062	.0947	.0839	.0738	.0645	.0559	.0482	.0412	.0350
5	.1698	.1599	.1493	.1384	.1272	.1161	.1051	.0945	.0843	.0746
6	.1907	.1881	.1839	.1782	.1712	.1632	.1543	.1447	.1347	.1244
7	.1714	.1770	.1811	.1836	.1844	.1836	.1812	.1774	.1722	.1659
8	.1251	.1354	.1450	.1537	.1614	.1678	.1730	.1767	.1790	.1797
9	.0750	.0849	.0952	.1056	.1158	.1259	.1354	.1444	.1526	.1597
10	.0370	.0440	.0516	.0598	.0686	.0779	.0875	.0974	.1073	.1171
11	.0151	.0188	.0231	.0280	.0336	.0398	.0467	.0542	.0624	.0710
12	.0051	.0066	.0085	.0108	.0136	.0168	.0206	.0249	.0299	.0355
13	.0014	.0019	.0026	.0034	.0045	.0058	.0074	.0094	.0118	.0146
14	.0003	.0005	.0006	.0009	.0012	.0016	.0022	.0029	.0038	.0049
15	.0001	.0001	.0001	.0002	.0003	.0004	.0005	.0007	.0010	.0013
16	.0000	.0000	.0000	.0000	.0000	.0001	.0001	.0001	.0002	.0003

r \ p	.41	.42	.43	.44	.45	.46	.47	.48	.49	.50
0	.0000	.0000	.0000	.0000	.0000	.0000	.0000	.0000	.0000	.0000
1	.0004	.0003	.0002	.0001	.0001	.0001	.0001	.0000	.0000	.0000
2	.0024	.0018	.0014	.0011	.0008	.0006	.0005	.0003	.0002	.0002
3	.0100	.0080	.0064	.0051	.0040	.0031	.0024	.0019	.0014	.0011
4	.0295	.0247	.0206	.0170	.0139	.0113	.0092	.0074	.0059	.0046
5	.0656	.0573	.0496	.0427	.0365	.0309	.0260	.0217	.0180	.0148
6	.1140	.1037	.0936	.0839	.0746	.0658	.0577	.0501	.0432	.0370
7	.1585	.1502	.1413	.1318	.1221	.1122	.1023	.0925	.0830	.0739
8	.1790	.1768	.1732	.1683	.1623	.1553	.1474	.1388	.1296	.1201
9	.1658	.1707	.1742	.1763	.1771	.1763	.1742	.1708	.1661	.1602
10	.1268	.1359	.1446	.1524	.1593	.1652	.1700	.1734	.1755	.1762
11	.0801	.0895	.0991	.1089	.1185	.1280	.1370	.1455	.1533	.1602
12	.0417	.0486	.0561	.0642	.0727	.0818	.0911	.1007	.1105	.1201
13	.0178	.0217	.0260	.0310	.0366	.0429	.0497	.0572	.0653	.0739
14	.0062	.0078	.0098	.0122	.0150	.0183	.0221	.0264	.0314	.0370
15	.0017	.0023	.0030	.0038	.0049	.0062	.0078	.0098	.0121	.0148
16	.0004	.0005	.0007	.0009	.0013	.0017	.0022	.0028	.0036	.0046
17	.0001	.0001	.0001	.0002	.0002	.0003	.0005	.0006	.0008	.0011
18	.0000	.0000	.0000	.0000	.0000	.0000	.0001	.0001	.0001	.0002

use this table

Table 3

POISSON PROBABILITY DISTRIBUTION

r≥X	0.10	0.20	0.30	0.40	λ 0.50	0.60	0.70	0.80	0.90	1.00
0	.9048	.8187	.7408	.6703	.6066	.5488	.4966	.4493	.4066	.3679
1	.0905	.1637	.2222	.2681	.3033	.3293	.3476	.3595	.3659	.3679
2	.0045	.0164	.0333	.0536	.0758	.0988	.1217	.1438	.1647	.1839
3	.0002	.0011	.0033	.0072	.0126	.0198	.0284	.0383	.0494	.0613
4	.0000	.0001	.0003	.0007	.0016	.0030	.0050	.0077	.0111	.0153
5	.0000	.0000	.0000	.0001	.0002	.0004	.0007	.0012	.0020	.0031
6	.0000	.0000	.0000	.0000	.0000	.0000	.0001	.0002	.0003	.0005
7	.0000	.0000	.0000	.0000	.0000	.0000	.0000	.0000	.0000	.0001

r	1.10	1.20	1.30	1.40	λ 1.50	1.60	1.70	1.80	1.90	2.00
0	.3329	.3012	.2725	.2466	.2231	.2019	.1827	.1653	.1496	.1353
1	.3662	.3614	.3543	.3452	.3347	.3230	.3106	.2975	.2842	.2707
2	.2014	.2169	.2303	.2417	.2510	.2584	.2640	.2678	.2700	.2707
3	.0738	.0867	.0998	.1128	.1255	.1378	.1496	.1607	.1710	.1804
4	.0203	.0260	.0324	.0395	.0471	.0551	.0636	.0723	.0812	.0902
5	.0045	.0062	.0084	.0111	.0141	.0176	.0216	.0260	.0309	.0361
6	.0008	.0012	.0018	.0026	.0035	.0047	.0061	.0078	.0098	.0120
7	.0001	.0002	.0003	.0005	.0008	.0011	.0015	.0020	.0027	.0034
8	.0000	.0000	.0001	.0001	.0001	.0002	.0003	.0005	.0006	.0009
9	.0000	.0000	.0000	.0000	.0000	.0000	.0001	.0001	.0001	.0002

r	2.10	2.20	2.30	2.40	λ 2.50	2.60	2.70	2.80	2.90	3.00
0	.1225	.1108	.1003	.0907	.0821	.0743	.0672	.0608	.0550	.0498
1	.2572	.2438	.2306	.2177	.2052	.1931	.1815	.1703	.1596	.1494
2	.2700	.2681	.2652	.2613	.2565	.2510	.2450	.2384	.2314	.2240
3	.1890	.1966	.2033	.2090	.2138	.2176	.2205	.2225	.2237	.2240
4	.0992	.1082	.1169	.1254	.1336	.1414	.1488	.1557	.1622	.1680
5	.0417	.0476	.0538	.0602	.0668	.0735	.0804	.0872	.0940	.1008
6	.0146	.0174	.0206	.0241	.0278	.0319	.0362	.0407	.0455	.0504
7	.0044	.0055	.0068	.0083	.0099	.0118	.0139	.0163	.0188	.0216
8	.0011	.0015	.0019	.0025	.0031	.0038	.0047	.0057	.0068	.0081
9	.0003	.0004	.0005	.0007	.0009	.0011	.0014	.0018	.0022	.0027
10	.0001	.0001	.0001	.0002	.0002	.0003	.0004	.0005	.0006	.0008
11	.0000	.0000	.0000	.0000	.0000	.0001	.0001	.0001	.0002	.0002
12	.0000	.0000	.0000	.0000	.0000	.0000	.0000	.0000	.0000	.0001

r	3.10	3.20	3.30	3.40	λ 3.50	3.60	3.70	3.80	3.90	4.00
0	.0450	.0408	.0369	.0334	.0302	.0273	.0247	.0224	.0202	.0183
1	.1397	.1304	.1217	.1135	.1057	.0984	.0915	.0850	.0789	.0733
2	.2165	.2087	.2008	.1929	.1850	.1771	.1692	.1615	.1539	.1465
3	.2237	.2226	.2209	.2186	.2158	.2125	.2087	.2046	.2001	.1954
4	.1733	.1781	.1823	.1858	.1888	.1912	.1931	.1944	.1951	.1954

Charles Clark and Lawrence Schkade, *Statistical Methods for Business Decisions* (Cincinnati: South-Western Publishing Co., 1969), pp. 141-144, by Special Permission.

r	3.10	3.20	3.30	3.40	λ 3.50	3.60	3.70	3.80	3.90	4.00
5	.1075	.1140	.1203	.1264	.1322	.1377	.1429	.1477	.1522	.1563
6	.0555	.0608	.0662	.0716	.0771	.0826	.0881	.0936	.0989	.1042
7	.0246	.0278	.0312	.0348	.0385	.0425	.0466	.0508	.0551	.0595
8	.0095	.0111	.0129	.0148	.0169	.0191	.0215	.0241	.0269	.0298
9	.0033	.0040	.0047	.0056	.0066	.0076	.0089	.0102	.0116	.0132
10	.0010	.0013	.0016	.0019	.0023	.0028	.0033	.0039	.0045	.0053
11	.0003	.0004	.0005	.0006	.0007	.0009	.0011	.0013	.0016	.0019
12	.0001	.0001	.0001	.0002	.0002	.0003	.0003	.0004	.0005	.0006
13	.0000	.0000	.0000	.0000	.0001	.0001	.0001	.0001	.0002	.0002
14	.0000	.0000	.0000	.0000	.0000	.0000	.0000	.0000	.0000	.0001

r	4.10	4.20	4.30	4.40	λ 4.50	4.60	4.70	4.80	4.90	5.00
0	.0166	.0150	.0136	.0123	.0111	.0101	.0091	.0082	.0074	.0067
1	.0679	.0630	.0583	.0540	.0500	.0462	.0427	.0395	.0365	.0337
2	.1393	.1323	.1254	.1188	.1125	.1063	.1005	.0948	.0894	.0842
3	.1904	.1852	.1798	.1743	.1687	.1631	.1574	.1517	.1460	.1404
4	.1951	.1944	.1933	.1917	.1898	.1875	.1849	.1820	.1789	.1755
5	.1600	.1633	.1662	.1687	.1708	.1725	.1738	.1747	.1753	.1755
6	.1093	.1143	.1191	.1237	.1281	.1323	.1362	.1398	.1432	.1462
7	.0640	.0686	.0732	.0778	.0824	.0869	.0914	.0959	.1002	.1044
8	.0328	.0360	.0393	.0428	.0463	.0500	.0537	.0575	.0614	.0653
9	.0150	.0168	.0188	.0209	.0232	.0255	.0281	.0307	.0334	.0363
10	.0061	.0071	.0081	.0092	.0104	.0118	.0132	.0147	.0164	.0181
11	.0023	.0027	.0032	.0037	.0043	.0049	.0056	.0064	.0073	.0082
12	.0008	.0009	.0011	.0013	.0016	.0019	.0022	.0026	.0030	.0034
13	.0002	.0003	.0004	.0005	.0006	.0007	.0008	.0009	.0011	.0013
14	.0001	.0001	.0001	.0001	.0002	.0002	.0002	.0003	.0003	.0005
15	.0000	.0000	.0000	.0000	.0001	.0001	.0001	.0001	.0001	.0002

r	5.10	5.20	5.30	5.40	λ 5.50	5.60	5.70	5.80	5.90	6.00
0	.0061	.0055	.0050	.0045	.0041	.0037	.0033	.0030	.0027	.0025
1	.0311	.0287	.0265	.0244	.0225	.0207	.0191	.0176	.0162	.0149
2	.0793	.0746	.0701	.0659	.0618	.0580	.0544	.0509	.0477	.0446
3	.1348	.1293	.1239	.1185	.1133	.1082	.1033	.0985	.0938	.0892
4	.1719	.1681	.1641	.1600	.1558	.1515	.1472	.1428	.1383	.1339
5	.1753	.1748	.1740	.1728	.1714	.1697	.1678	.1656	.1632	.1606
6	.1490	.1515	.1537	.1555	.1571	.1584	.1594	.1601	.1605	.1606
7	.1086	.1125	.1163	.1200	.1234	.1267	.1298	.1326	.1353	.1377
8	.0692	.0731	.0771	.0810	.0849	.0887	.0925	.0962	.0998	.1033
9	.0392	.0423	.0454	.0486	.0519	.0552	.0586	.0620	.0654	.0688
10	.0200	.0220	.0241	.0262	.0285	.0309	.0334	.0359	.0386	.0413
11	.0093	.0104	.0116	.0129	.0143	.0157	.0173	.0190	.0207	.0225
12	.0039	.0045	.0051	.0058	.0065	.0073	.0082	.0092	.0102	.0113
13	.0015	.0018	.0021	.0024	.0028	.0032	.0036	.0041	.0046	.0052
14	.0006	.0007	.0008	.0009	.0011	.0013	.0015	.0017	.0019	.0022
15	.0002	.0002	.0003	.0003	.0004	.0005	.0006	.0007	.0008	.0009
16	.0001	.0001	.0001	.0001	.0001	.0002	.0002	.0002	.0003	.0003
17	.0000	.0000	.0000	.0000	.0000	.0001	.0001	.0001	.0001	.0001

r	6.10	6.20	6.30	6.40	λ 6.50	6.60	6.70	6.80	6.90	7.00
0	.0022	.0020	.0018	.0017	.0015	.0014	.0012	.0011	.0010	.0009
1	.0137	.0126	.0116	.0106	.0098	.0090	.0082	.0076	.0070	.0064
2	.0417	.0390	.0364	.0340	.0318	.0296	.0276	.0258	.0240	.0223
3	.0848	.0806	.0765	.0726	.0688	.0652	.0617	.0584	.0552	.0521
4	.1294	.1249	.1205	.1161	.1118	.1076	.1034	.0992	.0952	.0912
5	.1579	.1549	.1519	.1487	.1454	.1420	.1385	.1349	.1314	.1277
6	.1605	.1601	.1595	.1586	.1575	.1562	.1546	.1529	.1511	.1490
7	.1399	.1418	.1435	.1450	.1462	.1472	.1480	.1486	.1489	.1490
8	.1066	.1099	.1130	.1160	.1188	.1215	.1240	.1263	.1284	.1304
9	.0723	.0757	.0791	.0825	.0858	.0891	.0923	.0954	.0985	.1014
10	.0441	.0469	.0498	.0528	.0558	.0588	.0618	.0649	.0679	.0710
11	.0244	.0265	.0285	.0307	.0330	.0353	.0377	.0401	.0426	.0452
12	.0124	.0137	.0150	.0164	.0179	.0194	.0210	.0227	.0245	.0263
13	.0058	.0065	.0073	.0081	.0089	.0099	.0108	.0119	.0130	.0142
14	.0025	.0029	.0033	.0037	.0041	.0046	.0052	.0058	.0064	.0071

				λ					
r	6.10	6.20	6.30	6.40	6.50	6.60	6.70	6.80	6.90	7.00

r	6.10	6.20	6.30	6.40	6.50	6.60	6.70	6.80	6.90	7.00
15	.0010	.0012	.0014	.0016	.0018	.0020	.0023	.0026	.0029	.0033
16	.0004	.0005	.0005	.0006	.0007	.0008	.0010	.0011	.0013	.0014
17	.0001	.0002	.0002	.0002	.0003	.0003	.0004	.0004	.0005	.0006
18	.0000	.0001	.0001	.0001	.0001	.0001	.0001	.0002	.0002	.0002
19	.0000	.0000	.0000	.0000	.0000	.0000	.0001	.0001	.0001	.0001

				λ					
r	7.10	7.20	7.30	7.40	7.50	7.60	7.70	7.80	7.90	8.00

r	7.10	7.20	7.30	7.40	7.50	7.60	7.70	7.80	7.90	8.00
0	.0008	.0007	.0007	.0006	.0006	.0005	.0005	.0004	.0004	.0003
1	.0059	.0054	.0049	.0045	.0041	.0038	.0035	.0032	.0029	.0027
2	.0208	.0194	.0180	.0167	.0156	.0145	.0134	.0125	.0116	.0107
3	.0492	.0464	.0438	.0413	.0389	.0366	.0345	.0324	.0305	.0286
4	.0874	.0836	.0799	.0764	.0729	.0696	.0663	.0632	.0602	.0573
5	.1241	.1204	.1167	.1130	.1094	.1057	.1021	.0986	.0951	.0916
6	1468	.1445	.1420	.1394	.1367	.1339	.1311	.1282	.1252	.1221
7	.1489	.1486	.1481	.1474	.1465	.1454	.1442	.1428	.1413	.1396
8	.1321	.1337	.1351	.1363	.1373	.1381	.1388	.1392	.1395	.1396
9	.1042	.1070	.1096	.1121	.1144	.1167	.1187	.1207	.1224	.1241
10	.0740	.0770	.0800	.0829	.0858	.0887	.0914	.0941	.0967	.0993
11	.0478	.0504	.0531	.0558	.0585	.0613	.0640	.0667	.0695	.0722
12	.0283	.0303	.0323	.0344	.0366	.0388	.0411	.0434	.0457	.0481
13	.0154	.0168	.0181	.0196	.0211	.0227	.0243	.0260	.0278	.0296
14	.0078	.0086	.0095	.0104	.0113	.0123	.0134	.0145	.0157	.0169
15	.0037	.0041	.0046	.0051	.0057	.0062	.0069	.0075	.0083	.0090
16	.0016	.0019	.0021	.0024	.0026	.0030	.0033	.0037	.0041	.0045
17	.0007	.0008	.0009	.0010	.0012	.0013	.0015	.0017	.0019	.0021
18	.0003	.0003	.0004	.0004	.0005	.0006	.0006	.0007	.0008	.0009
19	.0001	.0001	.0001	.0002	.0002	.0002	.0003	.0003	.0003	.0004
20	.0000	.0000	.0001	.0001	.0001	.0001	.0001	.0001	.0001	.0002
21	.0000	.0000	.0000	.0000	.0000	.0000	.0000	.0000	.0001	.0001

				λ					
r	8.10	8.20	8.30	8.40	8.50	8.60	8.70	8.80	8.90	9.00

r	8.10	8.20	8.30	8.40	8.50	8.60	8.70	8.80	8.90	9.00
0	.0003	.0003	.0002	.0002	.0002	.0002	.0002	.0002	.0001	.0001
1	.0025	.0023	.0021	.0019	.0017	.0016	.0014	.0013	.0012	.0011
2	.0100	.0092	.0086	.0079	.0074	.0068	.0063	.0058	.0054	.0050
3	.0269	.0252	.0237	.0222	.0208	.0195	.0183	.0171	.0160	.0150
4	.0544	.0517	.0491	.0466	.0443	.0420	.0398	.0377	.0357	.0337
5	.0882	.0849	.0816	.0784	.0752	.0722	.0692	.0663	.0635	.0607
6	.1191	.1160	.1128	.1097	.1066	.1034	.1003	.0972	.0941	.0911
7	.1378	.1358	.1338	.1317	.1294	.1271	.1247	.1222	.1197	.1171
8	.1395	.1392	.1388	.1382	.1375	.1366	.1356	.1344	.1332	.1318
9	.1256	.1269	.1280	.1290	.1299	.1306	.1311	.1315	.1317	.1318
10	.1017	.1040	.1063	.1084	.1104	.1123	.1140	.1157	.1172	.1186
11	.0749	.0776	.0802	.0828	.0853	.0878	.0902	.0925	.0948	.0970
12	.0505	.0530	.0555	.0579	.0604	.0629	.0654	.0679	.0703	.0728
13	.0315	.0334	.0354	.0374	.0395	.0416	.0438	.0459	.0481	.0504
14	.0182	.0196	.0210	.0225	.0240	.0256	.0272	.0289	.0306	.0324
15	.0098	.0107	.0116	.0126	.0136	.0147	.0158	.0169	.0182	.0194
16	.0050	.0055	.0060	.0066	.0072	.0079	.0086	.0093	.0101	.0109
17	.0024	.0026	.0029	.0033	.0036	.0040	.0044	.0048	.0053	.0058
18	.0011	.0012	.0014	.0015	.0017	.0019	.0021	.0024	.0026	.0029
19	.0005	.0005	.0006	.0007	.0008	.0009	.0010	.0011	.0012	.0014
20	.0002	.0002	.0002	.0003	.0003	.0004	.0004	.0005	.0005	.0006
21	.0001	.0001	.0001	.0001	.0001	.0002	.0002	.0002	.0002	.0003
22	.0000	.0000	.0000	.0000	.0000	.0001	.0001	.0001	.0001	.0001

				λ					
r	9.10	9.20	9.30	9.40	9.50	9.60	9.70	9.80	9.90	10.00

r	9.10	9.20	9.30	9.40	9.50	9.60	9.70	9.80	9.90	10.00
0	.0001	.0001	.0001	.0001	.0001	.0001	.0001	.0001	.0001	.0000
1	.0010	.0009	.0009	.0008	.0007	.0007	.0006	.0005	.0005	.0005
2	.0046	.0043	.0040	.0037	.0034	.0031	.0029	.0027	.0025	.0023
3	.0140	.0131	.0123	.0115	.0107	.0100	.0093	.0087	.0081	.0076
4	.0319	.0302	.0285	.0269	.0254	.0240	.0226	.0213	.0201	.0189
5	.0581	.0555	.0530	.0506	.0483	.0460	.0439	.0418	.0398	.0378
6	.0881	.0851	.0822	.0793	.0764	.0736	.0709	.0682	.0656	.0631
7	.1145	.1118	.1091	.1064	.1037	.1010	.0982	.0955	.0928	.0901
8	.1302	.1286	.1269	.1251	.1232	.1212	.1191	.1170	.1148	.1126
9	.1317	.1315	.1311	.1306	.1300	.1293	.1284	.1274	.1263	.1251

228

r	9.10	9.20	9.30	9.40	λ 9.50	9.60	9.70	9.80	9.90	10.00
10	.1198	.1210	.1219	.1228	.1235	.1241	.1245	.1249	.1250	.1251
11	.0991	.1012	.1031	.1049	.1067	.1083	.1098	.1112	.1125	.1137
12	.0752	.0776	.0799	.0822	.0844	.0866	.0888	.0908	.0928	.0948
13	.0526	.0549	.0572	.0594	.0617	.0640	.0662	.0685	.0707	.0729
14	.0342	.0361	.0380	.0399	.0419	.0439	.0459	.0479	.0500	.0521
15	.0208	.0221	.0235	.0250	.0265	.0281	.0297	.0313	.0330	.0347
16	.0118	.0127	.0137	.0147	.0157	.0168	.0180	.0192	.0204	.0217
17	.0063	.0069	.0075	.0081	.0088	.0095	.0103	.0111	.0119	.0128
18	.0032	.0035	.0039	.0042	.0046	.0051	.0055	.0060	.0065	.0071
19	.0015	.0017	.0019	.0021	.0023	.0026	.0028	.0031	.0034	.0037
20	.0007	.0008	.0009	.0010	.0011	.0012	.0014	.0015	.0017	.0019
21	.0003	.0003	.0004	.0004	.0005	.0006	.0006	.0007	.0008	.0009
22	.0001	.0001	.0002	.0002	.0002	.0002	.0003	.0003	.0004	.0004
23	.0000	.0001	.0001	.0001	.0001	.0001	.0001	.0001	.0002	.0002
24	.0000	.0000	.0000	.0000	.0000	.0000	.0000	.0001	.0001	.0001

r	11.	12.	13.	14.	λ 15.	16.	17.	18.	19.	20.
0	.0000	.0000	.0000	.0000	.0000	.0000	.0000	.0000	.0000	.0000
1	.0002	.0001	.0000	.0000	.0000	.0000	.0000	.0000	.0000	.0000
2	.0010	.0004	.0002	.0001	.0000	.0000	.0000	.0000	.0000	.0000
3	.0037	.0018	.0008	.0004	.0002	.0001	.0000	.0000	.0000	.0000
4	.0102	.0053	.0027	.0013	.0006	.0003	.0001	.0001	.0000	.0000
5	.0224	.0127	.0070	.0037	.0019	.0010	.0005	.0002	.0001	.0001
6	.0411	.0255	.0152	.0087	.0048	.0026	.0014	.0007	.0004	.0002
7	.0646	.0437	.0281	.0174	.0104	.0060	.0034	.0019	.0010	.0005
8	.0888	.0655	.0457	.0304	.0194	.0120	.0072	.0042	.0024	.0013
9	.1085	.0874	.0661	.0473	.0324	.0213	.0135	.0083	.0050	.0029
10	.1194	.1048	.0859	.0663	.0486	.0341	.0230	.0150	.0095	.0058
11	.1194	.1144	.1015	.0844	.0663	.0496	.0355	.0245	.0164	.0106
12	.1094	.1144	.1099	.0984	.0829	.0661	.0504	.0368	.0259	.0176
13	.0926	.1056	.1099	.1060	.0956	.0814	.0658	.0509	.0378	.0271
14	.0728	.0905	.1021	.1060	.1024	.0930	.0800	.0655	.0514	.0387
15	.0534	.0724	.0885	.0989	.1024	.0992	.0906	.0786	.0650	.0516
16	.0367	.0543	.0719	.0866	.0960	.0992	.0963	.0884	.0772	.0646
17	.0237	.0383	.0550	.0713	.0847	.0934	.0963	.0936	.0863	.0760
18	.0145	.0256	.0397	.0554	.0706	.0830	.0909	.0936	.0911	.0844
19	.0084	.0161	.0272	.0409	.0557	.0699	.0814	.0887	.0911	.0888
20	.0046	.0097	.0177	.0286	.0418	.0559	.0692	.0798	.0866	.0888
21	.0024	.0055	.0109	.0191	.0299	.0426	.0560	.0684	.0783	.0846
22	.0012	.0030	.0065	.0121	.0204	.0310	.0433	.0560	.0676	.0769
23	.0006	.0016	.0037	.0074	.0133	.0216	.0320	.0438	.0559	.0669
24	.0003	.0008	.0020	.0043	.0083	.0144	.0226	.0329	.0442	.0557
25	.0001	.0004	.0010	.0024	.0050	.0092	.0154	.0237	.0336	.0446
26	.0000	.0002	.0005	.0013	.0029	.0057	.0101	.0164	.0246	.0343
27	.0000	.0001	.0002	.0007	.0016	.0034	.0063	.0109	.0173	.0254
28	.0000	.0000	.0001	.0003	.0009	.0019	.0038	.0070	.0117	.0181
29	.0000	.0000	.0001	.0002	.0004	.0011	.0023	.0044	.0077	.0125
30	.0000	.0000	.0000	.0001	.0002	.0006	.0013	.0026	.0049	.0083
31	.0000	.0000	.0000	.0000	.0001	.0003	.0007	.0015	.0030	.0054
32	.0000	.0000	.0000	.0000	.0001	.0001	.0004	.0009	.0018	.0034
33	.0000	.0000	.0000	.0000	.0000	.0001	.0002	.0005	.0010	.0020
34	.0000	.0000	.0000	.0000	.0000	.0000	.0001	.0002	.0006	.0012
35	.0000	.0000	.0000	.0000	.0000	.0000	.0000	.0001	.0003	.0007
36	.0000	.0000	.0000	.0000	.0000	.0000	.0000	.0001	.0002	.0004
37	.0000	.0000	.0000	.0000	.0000	.0000	.0000	.0000	.0001	.0002
38	.0000	.0000	.0000	.0000	.0000	.0000	.0000	.0000	.0000	.0001
39	.0000	.0000	.0000	.0000	.0000	.0000	.0000	.0000	.0000	.0001

Table 4

NORMAL PROBABILITY DISTRIBUTION

z	.00	.01	.02	.03	.04	.05	.06	.07	.08	.09
0.0	.0000	.0040	.0080	.0120	.0160	.0199	.0239	.0279	.0319	.0359
0.1	.0398	.0438	.0478	.0517	.0557	.0596	.0636	.0675	.0714	.0753
0.2	.0793	.0832	.0871	.0910	.0948	.0987	.1026	.1064	.1103	.1141
0.3	.1179	.1217	.1255	.1293	.1331	.1368	.1406	.1443	.1480	.1517
0.4	.1554	.1591	.1628	.1664	.1700	.1736	.1772	.1808	.1844	.1879
0.5	.1915	.1950	.1985	.2019	.2054	.2088	.2123	.2157	.2190	.2224
0.6	.2257	.2291	.2324	.2357	.2389	.2422	.2454	.2486	.2517	.2549
0.7	.2580	.2611	.2642	.2673	.2703	.2734	.2764	.2794	.2823	.2852
0.8	.2881	.2910	.2939	.2967	.2995	.3023	.3051	.3078	.3106	.3133
0.9	.3159	.3186	.3212	.3238	.3264	.3289	.3315	.3340	.3365	.3389
1.0	.3413	.3438	.3461	.3485	.3508	.3531	.3554	.3577	.3599	.3621
1.1	.3643	.3665	.3686	.3708	.3729	.3749	.3770	.3790	.3810	.3830
1.2	.3849	.3869	.3888	.3907	.3925	.3944	.3962	.3980	.3997	.4015
1.3	.4032	.4049	.4066	.4082	.4099	.4115	.4131	.4147	.4162	.4177
1.4	.4192	.4207	.4222	.4236	.4251	.4265	.4279	.4292	.4306	.4319
1.5	.4332	.4345	.4357	.4370	.4382	.4394	.4406	.4418	.4429	.4441
1.6	.4452	.4463	.4474	.4484	.4495	.4505	.4515	.4525	.4535	.4545
1.7	.4554	.4564	.4573	.4582	.4591	.4599	.4608	.4616	.4625	.4633
1.8	.4641	.4649	.4656	.4664	.4671	.4678	.4686	.4693	.4699	.4706
1.9	.4713	.4719	.4726	.4732	.4738	.4744	.4750	.4756	.4761	.4767
2.0	.4772	.4778	.4783	.4788	.4793	.4798	.4803	.4808	.4812	.4817
2.1	.4821	.4826	.4830	.4834	.4838	.4842	.4846	.4850	.4854	.4857
2.2	.4861	.4864	.4868	.4871	.4875	.4878	.4881	.4884	.4887	.4890
2.3	.4893	.4896	.4898	.4901	.4904	.4906	.4909	.4911	.4913	.4916
2.4	.4918	.4920	.4922	.4925	.4927	.4929	.4931	.4932	.4934	.4936
2.5	.4938	.4940	.4941	.4943	.4945	.4946	.4948	.4949	.4951	.4952
2.6	.4953	.4955	.4956	.4957	.4959	.4960	.4961	.4962	.4963	.4964
2.7	.4965	.4966	.4967	.4968	.4969	.4970	.4971	.4972	.4973	.4974
2.8	.4974	.4975	.4976	.4977	.4977	.4978	.4979	.4979	.4980	.4981
2.9	.4981	.4982	.4982	.4983	.4984	.4984	.4985	.4985	.4986	.4986
3.0	.4987	.4987	.4987	.4988	.4988	.4989	.4989.	.4989	.4990	.4990

Paul G. Hoel and Raymond J. Jessen, *Basic Statistics for Business and Economics* (New York: John Wiley and Sons, Inc., 1971), p. 412 by permission of the publishers.

Table 5

STUDENT DISTRIBUTION (t-distribution)

ν \ P	0.50	0.25	0.10	0.05	0.025	0.01	0.005
1	1.00000	2.4142	6.3138	12.706	25.452	63.657	127.32
2	0.81650	1.6036	2.9200	4.3027	6.2053	9.9248	14.089
3	0.76489	1.4226	2.3534	3.1825	4.1765	5.8409	7.4533
4	0.74070	1.3444	2.1318	2.7764	3.4954	4.6041	5.5976
5	0.72669	1.3009	2.0150	2.5706	3.1634	4.0321	4.7733
6	0.71756	1.2733	1.9432	2.4469	2.9687	3.7074	4.3168
7	0.71114	1.2543	1.8946	2.3646	2.8412	3.4995	4.0293
8	0.70639	1.2403	1.8595	2.3060	2.7515	3.3554	3.8325
9	0.70272	1.2297	1.8331	2.2622	2.6850	3.2498	3.6897
10	0.69981	1.2213	1.8125	2.2281	2.6338	3.1693	3.5814
11	0.69745	1.2145	1.7959	2.2010	2.5931	3.1058	3.4966
12	0.69548	1.2089	1.7823	2.1788	2.5600	3.0545	3.4284
13	0.69384	1.2041	1.7709	2.1604	2.5326	3.0123	3.3725
14	0.69242	1.2001	1.7613	2.1448	2.5096	2.9768	3.3257
15	0.69120	1.1967	1.7530	2.1315	2.4899	2.9467	3.2860
16	0.69013	1.1937	1.7459	2.1199	2.4729	2.9208	3.2520
17	0.68919	1.1910	1.7396	2.1098	2.4581	2.8982	3.2225
18	0.68837	1.1887	1.7341	2.1009	2.4450	2.8784	3.1966
19	0.68763	1.1866	1.7291	2.0930	2.4334	2.8609	3.1737
20	0.68696	1.1848	1.7247	2.0860	2.4231	2.8453	3.1534
21	0.68635	1.1831	1.7207	2.0796	2.4138	2.8314	3.1352
22	0.68580	1.1816	1.7171	2.0739	2.4055	2.8188	3.1188
23	0.68531	1.1802	1.7139	2.0687	2.3979	2.8073	3.1040
24	0.68485	1.1789	1.7109	2.0639	2.3910	2.7969	3.0905
25	0.68443	1.1777	1.7081	2.0595	2.3846	2.7874	3.0782
26	0.68405	1.1766	1.7056	2.0555	2.3788	2.7787	3.0669
27	0.68370	1.1757	1.7033	2.0518	2.3734	2.7707	3.0565
28	0.68335	1.1748	1.7011	2.0484	2.3685	2.7633	3.0469
29	0.68304	1.1739	1.6991	2.0452	2.3638	2.7564	3.0380
30	0.68276	1.1731	1.6973	2.0423	2.3596	2.7500	3.0298
40	0.68066	1.1673	1.6839	2.0211	2.3289	2.7045	2.9712
60	0.67862	1.1616	1.6707	2.0003	2.2991	2.6603	2.9146
120	0.67656	1.1559	1.6577	1.9799	2.2699	2.6174	2.8599
∞	0.67449	1.1503	1.6449	1.9600	2.2414	2.5758	2.8070

Paul G. Hoel and Raymond J. Jessen, *Basic Statistics for Business and Economics* (New York: John Wiley and Sons, Inc., 1971), p. 413 by permission of the publishers.

Table 6

CHI-SQUARE DISTRIBUTION

ν \ P	0.995	0.975	0.050	0.025	0.010	0.005
1	0.0⁴3927	0.0³9821	3.84146	5.02389	6.63490	7.87944
2	0.010025	0.050636	5.99147	7.37776	9.21034	10.5966
3	0.071721	0.215795	7.81473	9.34840	11.3449	12.8381
4	0.206990	0.484419	9.48773	11.1433	13.2767	14.8602
5	0.411740	0.831211	11.0705	12.8325	15.0863	16.7496
6	0.675727	1.237347	12.5916	14.4494	16.8119	18.5476
7	0.989265	1.68987	14.0671	16.0128	18.4753	20.2777
8	1.344419	2.17973	15.5073	17.5346	20.0902	21.9550
9	1.734926	2.70039	16.9190	19.0228	21.6660	23.5893
10	2.15585	3.24697	18.3070	20.4831	23.2093	25.1882
11	2.60321	3.81575	19.6751	21.9200	24.7250	26.7569
12	3.07382	4.40379	21.0261	23.3367	26.2170	28.2995
13	3.56503	5.00874	22.3621	24.7356	27.6883	29.8194
14	4.07468	5.62872	23.6848	26.1190	29.1413	31.3193
15	4.60094	6.26214	24.9958	27.4884	30.5779	32.8013
16	5.14224	6.90766	26.2962	28.8454	31.9999	34.2672
17	5.69724	7.56418	27.5871	30.1910	33.4087	35.7185
18	6.26481	8.23075	28.8693	31.5264	34.8053	37.1564
19	6.84398	8.90655	30.1435	32.8523	36.1908	38.5822
20	7.43386	9.59083	31.4104	34.1696	37.5662	39.9968
21	8.03366	10.28293	32.6705	35.4789	38.9321	41.4010
22	8.64272	10.9823	33.9244	36.7807	40.2894	42.7956
23	9.26042	11.6885	35.1725	30.0757	41.6384	44.1813
24	9.88623	12.4001	36.4151	39.3641	42.9798	45.5585
25	10.5197	13.1197	37.6525	40.6465	44.3141	46.9278
26	11.1603	13.8439	38.8852	41.9232	45.6417	48.2899
27	11.8076	14.5733	40.1133	43.1944	46.9630	49.6449
28	12.4613	15.3079	41.3372	44.4607	48.2782	50.9933
29	13.1211	16.0471	42.5569	45.7222	49.5879	52.3356
30	13.7867	16.7908	43.7729	46.9792	50.8922	53.6720
40	20.7065	24.4331	55.7585	59.3417	63.6907	66.7659
50	27.9907	32.3574	67.5048	71.4202	76.1539	79.4900
60	35.5346	40.4817	79.0819	83.2976	88.3794	91.9517
70	43.2752	48.7576	90.5312	95.0231	100.425	104.215
80	51.1720	57.1532	101.879	106.629	112.329	116.321
90	59.1963	65.6466	113.145	118.136	124.116	128.299
100	67.3276	74.2219	124.342	129.561	135.807	140.169

Paul G. Hoel and Raymond J. Jessen, *Basic Statistics for Business and Economics* (New York: John Wiley and Sons, Inc., 1971), p. 415 by permission of the publishers.

Table 7

F DISTRIBUTION

5% (Roman Type) and 1% (Boldface Type) Points for the Distribution of F

Each cell shows the 5% point (Roman type, upper value) over the 1% point (Boldface type, lower value).

v_2 \ v_1	1	2	3	4	5	6	7	8	9	10	11	12	14	16	20	24	30	40	50	75	100	200	500	∞
1	161 / 4052	200 / 4999	216 / 5403	225 / 5625	230 / 5764	234 / 5859	237 / 5928	239 / 5981	241 / 6022	242 / 6056	243 / 6082	244 / 6106	245 / 6142	246 / 6169	248 / 6208	249 / 6234	250 / 6258	251 / 6286	252 / 6302	253 / 6323	253 / 6334	254 / 6352	254 / 6361	254 / 6366
2	18.51 / 98.49	19.00 / 99.01	19.16 / 99.17	19.25 / 99.25	19.30 / 99.30	19.33 / 99.33	19.36 / 99.34	19.37 / 99.36	19.38 / 99.38	19.39 / 99.40	19.40 / 99.41	19.41 / 99.42	19.42 / 99.43	19.43 / 99.44	19.44 / 99.45	19.45 / 99.46	19.46 / 99.47	19.47 / 99.48	19.47 / 99.48	19.48 / 99.49	19.49 / 99.49	19.49 / 99.49	19.50 / 99.50	19.50 / 99.50
3	10.13 / 34.12	9.55 / 30.81	9.28 / 29.46	9.12 / 28.71	9.01 / 28.24	8.94 / 27.91	8.88 / 27.67	8.84 / 27.49	8.81 / 27.34	8.78 / 27.23	8.76 / 27.13	8.74 / 27.05	8.71 / 26.92	8.69 / 26.83	8.66 / 26.69	8.64 / 26.60	8.62 / 26.50	8.60 / 26.41	8.58 / 26.30	8.57 / 26.27	8.56 / 26.23	8.54 / 26.18	8.54 / 26.14	8.53 / 26.12
4	7.71 / 21.20	6.94 / 18.00	6.59 / 16.69	6.39 / 15.98	6.26 / 15.52	6.16 / 15.21	6.09 / 14.98	6.04 / 14.80	6.00 / 14.66	5.96 / 14.54	5.93 / 14.45	5.91 / 14.37	5.87 / 14.24	5.84 / 14.15	5.80 / 14.02	5.77 / 13.93	5.74 / 13.83	5.71 / 13.74	5.70 / 13.69	5.68 / 13.61	5.66 / 13.57	5.65 / 13.52	5.64 / 13.48	5.63 / 13.46
5	6.61 / 16.26	5.79 / 13.27	5.41 / 12.06	5.19 / 11.39	5.05 / 10.97	4.95 / 10.67	4.88 / 10.45	4.82 / 10.27	4.78 / 10.15	4.74 / 10.05	4.70 / 9.96	4.68 / 9.89	4.64 / 9.77	4.60 / 9.68	4.56 / 9.55	4.53 / 9.47	4.50 / 9.38	4.46 / 9.29	4.44 / 9.24	4.42 / 9.17	4.40 / 9.13	4.38 / 9.07	4.37 / 9.04	4.36 / 9.02
6	5.99 / 13.74	5.14 / 10.92	4.76 / 9.78	4.53 / 9.15	4.39 / 8.75	4.28 / 8.47	4.21 / 8.26	4.15 / 8.10	4.10 / 7.98	4.06 / 7.87	4.03 / 7.79	4.00 / 7.72	3.96 / 7.60	3.92 / 7.52	3.87 / 7.39	3.84 / 7.31	3.81 / 7.23	3.77 / 7.14	3.75 / 7.09	3.72 / 7.02	3.71 / 6.99	3.69 / 6.94	3.68 / 6.90	3.67 / 6.88
7	5.59 / 12.25	4.74 / 9.55	4.35 / 8.45	4.12 / 7.85	3.97 / 7.46	3.87 / 7.19	3.79 / 7.00	3.73 / 6.84	3.68 / 6.71	3.63 / 6.62	3.60 / 6.54	3.57 / 6.47	3.52 / 6.35	3.49 / 6.27	3.44 / 6.15	3.41 / 6.07	3.38 / 5.98	3.34 / 5.90	3.32 / 5.85	3.29 / 5.78	3.28 / 5.75	3.25 / 5.70	3.24 / 5.67	3.23 / 5.65
8	5.32 / 11.26	4.46 / 8.65	4.07 / 7.59	3.84 / 7.01	3.69 / 6.63	3.58 / 6.37	3.50 / 6.19	3.44 / 6.03	3.39 / 5.91	3.34 / 5.82	3.31 / 5.74	3.28 / 5.67	3.23 / 5.56	3.20 / 5.48	3.15 / 5.36	3.12 / 5.28	3.08 / 5.20	3.05 / 5.11	3.03 / 5.06	3.00 / 5.00	2.98 / 4.96	2.96 / 4.91	2.94 / 4.88	2.93 / 4.86
9	5.12 / 10.56	4.26 / 8.02	3.86 / 6.99	3.63 / 6.42	3.48 / 6.06	3.37 / 5.80	3.29 / 5.62	3.23 / 5.47	3.18 / 5.35	3.13 / 5.26	3.10 / 5.18	3.07 / 5.11	3.02 / 5.00	2.98 / 4.92	2.93 / 4.80	2.90 / 4.73	2.86 / 4.64	2.82 / 4.56	2.80 / 4.51	2.77 / 4.45	2.76 / 4.41	2.73 / 4.36	2.72 / 4.33	2.71 / 4.31

Degrees of freedom for denominator (v_2) — rows; Degrees of freedom for numerator (v_1) — columns.

Paul G. Hoel and Raymond J. Jessen, *Basic Statistics for Business and Economics* (New York: John Wiley and Sons, Inc., 1971), pp. 416-419 by permission of the publishers.

df																								
10	2.54 / 3.91	2.55 / 3.93	2.56 / 3.96	2.59 / 4.01	2.61 / 4.05	2.64 / 4.12	2.67 / 4.17	2.70 / 4.25	2.74 / 4.33	2.77 / 4.41	2.82 / 4.52	2.86 / 4.60	2.91 / 4.71	2.94 / 4.78	2.97 / 4.85	3.02 / 4.95	3.07 / 5.06	3.14 / 5.21	3.22 / 5.39	3.33 / 5.64	3.48 / 5.99	3.71 / 6.55	4.10 / 7.56	4.96 / 10.04
11	2.40 / 3.60	2.41 / 3.62	2.42 / 3.66	2.45 / 3.70	2.47 / 3.74	2.50 / 3.80	2.53 / 3.86	2.57 / 3.94	2.61 / 4.02	2.65 / 4.10	2.70 / 4.21	2.74 / 4.29	2.79 / 4.40	2.82 / 4.46	2.86 / 4.54	2.90 / 4.63	2.95 / 4.74	3.01 / 4.88	3.09 / 5.07	3.20 / 5.32	3.36 / 5.67	3.59 / 6.22	3.98 / 7.20	4.84 / 9.65
12	2.30 / 3.36	2.31 / 3.38	2.32 / 3.41	2.35 / 3.46	2.36 / 3.49	2.40 / 3.56	2.42 / 3.61	2.46 / 3.70	2.50 / 3.78	2.54 / 3.86	2.60 / 3.98	2.64 / 4.05	2.69 / 4.16	2.72 / 4.22	2.76 / 4.30	2.80 / 4.39	2.85 / 4.50	2.92 / 4.65	3.00 / 4.82	3.11 / 5.06	3.26 / 5.41	3.49 / 5.95	3.88 / 6.93	4.75 / 9.33
13	2.21 / 3.16	2.22 / 3.18	2.24 / 3.21	2.26 / 3.27	2.28 / 3.30	2.32 / 3.37	2.34 / 3.42	2.38 / 3.51	2.42 / 3.59	2.46 / 3.67	2.51 / 3.78	2.55 / 3.85	2.60 / 3.96	2.63 / 4.02	2.67 / 4.10	2.72 / 4.19	2.77 / 4.30	2.84 / 4.44	2.92 / 4.62	3.02 / 4.86	3.18 / 5.20	3.41 / 5.74	3.80 / 6.70	4.67 / 9.07
14	2.13 / 3.00	2.14 / 3.02	2.16 / 3.06	2.19 / 3.11	2.21 / 3.14	2.24 / 3.21	2.27 / 3.26	2.31 / 3.34	2.35 / 3.43	2.39 / 3.51	2.44 / 3.62	2.48 / 3.70	2.53 / 3.80	2.56 / 3.86	2.60 / 3.94	2.65 / 4.03	2.70 / 4.14	2.77 / 4.28	2.85 / 4.46	2.96 / 4.69	3.11 / 5.03	3.34 / 5.56	3.74 / 6.51	4.60 / 8.86
15	2.07 / 2.87	2.08 / 2.89	2.10 / 2.92	2.12 / 2.97	2.15 / 3.00	2.18 / 3.07	2.21 / 3.12	2.25 / 3.20	2.29 / 3.29	2.33 / 3.36	2.39 / 3.48	2.43 / 3.56	2.48 / 3.67	2.51 / 3.73	2.55 / 3.80	2.59 / 3.89	2.64 / 4.00	2.70 / 4.14	2.79 / 4.32	2.90 / 4.56	3.06 / 4.89	3.29 / 5.42	3.68 / 6.36	4.54 / 8.68
16	2.01 / 2.75	2.02 / 2.77	2.04 / 2.80	2.07 / 2.86	2.09 / 2.89	2.13 / 2.96	2.16 / 3.01	2.20 / 3.10	2.24 / 3.18	2.28 / 3.25	2.33 / 3.37	2.37 / 3.45	2.42 / 3.55	2.45 / 3.61	2.49 / 3.69	2.54 / 3.78	2.59 / 3.89	2.66 / 4.03	2.74 / 4.20	2.85 / 4.44	3.01 / 4.77	3.24 / 5.29	3.63 / 6.23	4.49 / 8.53
17	1.96 / 2.65	1.97 / 2.67	1.99 / 2.70	2.02 / 2.76	2.04 / 2.79	2.08 / 2.86	2.11 / 2.92	2.15 / 3.00	2.19 / 3.08	2.23 / 3.16	2.29 / 3.27	2.33 / 3.35	2.38 / 3.45	2.41 / 3.52	2.45 / 3.59	2.50 / 3.68	2.55 / 3.79	2.62 / 3.93	2.70 / 4.10	2.81 / 4.34	2.96 / 4.67	3.20 / 5.18	3.59 / 6.11	4.45 / 8.40
18	1.92 / 2.57	1.93 / 2.59	1.95 / 2.62	1.98 / 2.68	2.00 / 2.71	2.04 / 2.78	2.07 / 2.83	2.11 / 2.92	2.15 / 3.00	2.19 / 3.07	2.25 / 3.19	2.29 / 3.27	2.34 / 3.37	2.37 / 3.44	2.41 / 3.51	2.46 / 3.60	2.51 / 3.71	2.58 / 3.85	2.66 / 4.03	2.77 / 4.25	2.93 / 4.58	3.16 / 5.09	3.55 / 6.01	4.41 / 8.28
19	1.88 / 2.49	1.90 / 2.51	1.91 / 2.54	1.94 / 2.60	1.96 / 2.63	2.00 / 2.70	2.02 / 2.76	2.07 / 2.84	2.11 / 2.92	2.15 / 3.00	2.21 / 3.12	2.26 / 3.19	2.31 / 3.30	2.34 / 3.36	2.38 / 3.43	2.43 / 3.52	2.48 / 3.63	2.55 / 3.77	2.63 / 3.94	2.74 / 4.17	2.90 / 4.50	3.13 / 5.01	3.52 / 5.93	4.38 / 8.18
20	1.84 / 2.42	1.85 / 2.44	1.87 / 2.47	1.90 / 2.53	1.92 / 2.56	1.96 / 2.63	1.99 / 2.69	2.04 / 2.77	2.08 / 2.86	2.12 / 2.94	2.18 / 3.05	2.23 / 3.13	2.28 / 3.23	2.31 / 3.30	2.35 / 3.37	2.40 / 3.45	2.45 / 3.56	2.52 / 3.71	2.60 / 3.87	2.71 / 4.10	2.87 / 4.43	3.10 / 4.94	3.49 / 5.85	4.35 / 8.10
21	1.81 / 2.36	1.82 / 2.38	1.84 / 2.42	1.87 / 2.47	1.89 / 2.51	1.93 / 2.58	1.96 / 2.63	2.00 / 2.72	2.05 / 2.80	2.09 / 2.88	2.15 / 2.99	2.20 / 3.07	2.25 / 3.17	2.28 / 3.24	2.32 / 3.31	2.37 / 3.40	2.42 / 3.51	2.49 / 3.65	2.57 / 3.81	2.68 / 4.04	2.84 / 4.37	3.07 / 4.87	3.47 / 5.78	4.32 / 8.02
22	1.78 / 2.31	1.80 / 2.33	1.81 / 2.37	1.84 / 2.42	1.87 / 2.46	1.91 / 2.53	1.93 / 2.58	1.98 / 2.67	2.03 / 2.75	2.07 / 2.83	2.13 / 2.94	2.18 / 3.02	2.23 / 3.12	2.26 / 3.18	2.30 / 3.26	2.35 / 3.35	2.40 / 3.45	2.47 / 3.59	2.55 / 3.76	2.66 / 3.99	2.82 / 4.31	3.05 / 4.82	3.44 / 5.72	4.30 / 7.94
23	1.76 / 2.26	1.77 / 2.28	1.79 / 2.32	1.82 / 2.37	1.84 / 2.41	1.88 / 2.48	1.91 / 2.53	1.96 / 2.62	2.00 / 2.70	2.04 / 2.78	2.10 / 2.89	2.14 / 2.97	2.20 / 3.07	2.24 / 3.14	2.28 / 3.21	2.32 / 3.30	2.38 / 3.41	2.45 / 3.54	2.53 / 3.71	2.64 / 3.94	2.80 / 4.26	3.03 / 4.76	3.42 / 5.66	4.28 / 7.88
24	1.73 / 2.21	1.74 / 2.23	1.76 / 2.27	1.80 / 2.33	1.82 / 2.36	1.86 / 2.44	1.89 / 2.49	1.94 / 2.58	1.98 / 2.66	2.02 / 2.74	2.09 / 2.85	2.13 / 2.93	2.18 / 3.03	2.22 / 3.09	2.26 / 3.17	2.30 / 3.25	2.36 / 3.36	2.43 / 3.50	2.51 / 3.67	2.62 / 3.90	2.78 / 4.22	3.01 / 4.72	3.40 / 5.61	4.26 / 7.82
25	1.71 / 2.17	1.72 / 2.19	1.74 / 2.23	1.77 / 2.29	1.80 / 2.32	1.84 / 2.40	1.87 / 2.45	1.92 / 2.54	1.96 / 2.62	2.00 / 2.70	2.06 / 2.81	2.11 / 2.89	2.16 / 2.99	2.20 / 3.05	2.24 / 3.13	2.28 / 3.21	2.34 / 3.32	2.41 / 3.46	2.49 / 3.63	2.60 / 3.86	2.76 / 4.18	2.99 / 4.68	3.38 / 5.57	4.24 / 7.77

5% (Roman Type) and 1% (Boldface Type) Points for the Distribution of F

Degrees of freedom for numerator (v_1)

Degrees of freedom for denominator (v_2)	1	2	3	4	5	6	7	8	9	10	11	12	14	16	20	24	30	40	50	75	100	200	500	∞
26	4.22 / 7.72	3.37 / 5.53	2.89 / 4.64	2.74 / 4.14	2.59 / 3.82	2.47 / 3.59	2.39 / 3.42	2.32 / 3.29	2.27 / 3.17	2.22 / 3.09	2.18 / 3.02	2.15 / 2.96	2.10 / 2.86	2.05 / 2.77	1.99 / 2.66	1.95 / 2.58	1.90 / 2.50	1.85 / 2.41	1.82 / 2.36	1.78 / 2.28	1.76 / 2.25	1.72 / 2.19	1.70 / 2.15	1.69 / 2.13
27	4.21 / 7.68	3.35 / 5.49	2.96 / 4.60	2.73 / 4.11	2.57 / 3.79	2.46 / 3.56	2.37 / 3.39	2.30 / 3.26	2.25 / 3.14	2.20 / 3.06	2.16 / 2.98	2.13 / 2.93	2.08 / 2.83	2.03 / 2.74	1.97 / 2.63	1.93 / 2.55	1.88 / 2.47	1.84 / 2.38	1.80 / 2.33	1.76 / 2.25	1.74 / 2.21	1.71 / 2.16	1.68 / 2.12	1.67 / 2.10
28	4.20 / 7.64	3.34 / 5.45	2.95 / 4.57	2.71 / 4.07	2.56 / 3.76	2.44 / 3.53	2.36 / 3.36	2.29 / 3.23	2.24 / 3.11	2.19 / 3.03	2.15 / 2.95	2.12 / 2.90	2.06 / 2.80	2.02 / 2.71	1.96 / 2.60	1.91 / 2.52	1.87 / 2.44	1.81 / 2.35	1.78 / 2.30	1.75 / 2.22	1.72 / 2.18	1.69 / 2.13	1.67 / 2.09	1.65 / 2.06
29	4.18 / 7.60	3.33 / 5.52	2.93 / 4.54	2.70 / 4.04	2.54 / 3.73	2.43 / 3.50	2.35 / 3.33	2.28 / 3.20	2.22 / 3.08	2.18 / 3.00	2.14 / 2.92	2.10 / 2.87	2.05 / 2.77	2.00 / 2.68	1.94 / 2.57	1.90 / 2.49	1.85 / 2.41	1.80 / 2.32	1.77 / 2.27	1.73 / 2.19	1.71 / 2.15	1.68 / 2.10	1.65 / 2.06	1.64 / 2.03
30	4.17 / 7.56	3.32 / 5.39	2.92 / 4.51	2.69 / 4.02	2.53 / 3.70	2.42 / 3.47	2.34 / 3.30	2.27 / 3.17	2.21 / 3.06	2.16 / 2.98	2.12 / 2.90	2.09 / 2.84	2.04 / 2.74	1.99 / 2.66	1.93 / 2.55	1.89 / 2.47	1.84 / 2.38	1.79 / 2.29	1.76 / 2.24	1.72 / 2.16	1.69 / 2.13	1.66 / 2.07	1.64 / 2.03	1.62 / 2.01
32	4.15 / 7.50	3.30 / 5.34	2.90 / 4.46	2.67 / 3.97	2.51 / 3.66	2.40 / 3.42	2.32 / 3.25	2.25 / 3.12	2.19 / 3.01	2.14 / 2.94	2.10 / 2.86	2.07 / 2.80	2.02 / 2.70	1.97 / 2.62	1.91 / 2.51	1.86 / 2.42	1.82 / 2.34	1.76 / 2.25	1.74 / 2.20	1.69 / 2.12	1.67 / 2.08	1.64 / 2.02	1.61 / 1.98	1.59 / 1.96
34	4.13 / 7.44	3.28 / 5.29	2.88 / 4.42	2.65 / 3.93	2.49 / 3.61	2.38 / 3.38	2.30 / 3.21	2.23 / 3.08	2.17 / 2.97	2.12 / 2.89	2.08 / 2.82	2.05 / 2.76	2.00 / 2.66	1.95 / 2.58	1.89 / 2.47	1.84 / 2.38	1.80 / 2.30	1.74 / 2.21	1.71 / 2.15	1.67 / 2.08	1.64 / 2.04	1.61 / 1.98	1.59 / 1.94	1.57 / 1.91
36	4.11 / 7.39	3.26 / 5.25	2.86 / 4.38	2.63 / 3.89	2.48 / 3.58	2.36 / 3.35	2.28 / 3.18	2.21 / 3.04	2.15 / 2.94	2.10 / 2.86	2.06 / 2.78	2.03 / 2.72	1.98 / 2.62	1.93 / 2.54	1.87 / 2.43	1.82 / 2.35	1.78 / 2.26	1.72 / 2.17	1.69 / 2.12	1.65 / 2.04	1.62 / 2.00	1.59 / 1.94	1.56 / 1.90	1.55 / 1.87
38	4.10 / 7.35	3.25 / 5.21	2.85 / 4.34	2.62 / 3.86	2.46 / 3.54	2.35 / 3.32	2.26 / 3.15	2.19 / 3.02	2.14 / 2.91	2.09 / 2.82	2.05 / 2.75	2.02 / 2.69	1.96 / 2.59	1.92 / 2.51	1.85 / 2.40	1.80 / 2.32	1.76 / 2.22	1.71 / 2.14	1.67 / 2.08	1.63 / 2.00	1.60 / 1.97	1.57 / 1.90	1.54 / 1.86	1.53 / 1.84
40	4.08 / 7.31	3.23 / 5.18	2.84 / 4.31	2.61 / 3.83	2.45 / 3.51	2.34 / 3.29	2.25 / 3.12	2.18 / 2.99	2.12 / 2.88	2.07 / 2.80	2.04 / 2.73	2.00 / 2.66	1.95 / 2.56	1.90 / 2.49	1.84 / 2.37	1.79 / 2.29	1.74 / 2.20	1.69 / 2.11	1.66 / 2.05	1.61 / 1.97	1.59 / 1.94	1.55 / 1.88	1.53 / 1.84	1.51 / 1.81
42	4.07 / 7.27	3.22 / 5.15	2.83 / 4.29	2.59 / 3.80	2.44 / 3.49	2.32 / 3.26	2.24 / 3.10	2.17 / 2.96	2.11 / 2.86	2.06 / 2.77	2.02 / 2.70	1.99 / 2.64	1.94 / 2.54	1.89 / 2.46	1.82 / 2.35	1.78 / 2.26	1.73 / 2.17	1.68 / 2.08	1.64 / 2.02	1.60 / 1.94	1.57 / 1.91	1.54 / 1.85	1.51 / 1.80	1.49 / 1.78
44	4.06 / 7.24	3.21 / 5.12	2.82 / 4.26	2.58 / 3.78	2.43 / 3.46	2.31 / 3.24	2.23 / 3.07	2.16 / 2.94	2.10 / 2.84	2.05 / 2.75	2.01 / 2.68	1.98 / 2.62	1.92 / 2.52	1.88 / 2.44	1.81 / 2.32	1.76 / 2.24	1.72 / 2.15	1.66 / 2.06	1.63 / 2.00	1.58 / 1.92	1.56 / 1.88	1.52 / 1.82	1.50 / 1.78	1.48 / 1.75
46	4.05 / 7.21	3.20 / 5.10	2.81 / 4.24	2.57 / 3.76	2.42 / 3.44	2.30 / 3.22	2.22 / 3.05	2.14 / 2.92	2.09 / 2.82	2.04 / 2.73	2.00 / 2.66	1.97 / 2.60	1.91 / 2.50	1.87 / 2.42	1.80 / 2.30	1.75 / 2.22	1.71 / 2.13	1.65 / 2.04	1.62 / 1.98	1.57 / 1.90	1.54 / 1.86	1.51 / 1.80	1.48 / 1.76	1.46 / 1.72
48	4.04 / 7.19	3.19 / 5.08	2.80 / 4.22	2.56 / 3.74	2.41 / 3.42	2.30 / 3.20	2.21 / 3.04	2.14 / 2.90	2.08 / 2.80	2.03 / 2.71	1.99 / 2.64	1.96 / 2.58	1.90 / 2.48	1.86 / 2.40	1.79 / 2.28	1.74 / 2.20	1.70 / 2.11	1.64 / 2.02	1.61 / 1.96	1.56 / 1.88	1.53 / 1.84	1.50 / 1.78	1.47 / 1.73	1.45 / 1.70

50	1.44 / 1.68	1.46 / 1.71	1.48 / 1.76	1.52 / 1.82	1.55 / 1.86	1.60 / 1.94	1.63 / 2.00	1.69 / 2.10	1.74 / 2.18	1.78 / 2.26	1.85 / 2.39	1.90 / 2.46	1.95 / 2.56	1.98 / 2.62	2.02 / 2.70	2.07 / 2.78	2.13 / 2.88	2.20 / 3.02	2.29 / 3.18	2.40 / 3.41	2.56 / 3.72	2.79 / 4.20	3.18 / 5.06	4.03 / 7.17
55	1.41 / 1.64	1.43 / 1.66	1.46 / 1.71	1.50 / 1.78	1.52 / 1.82	1.58 / 1.90	1.61 / 1.96	1.67 / 2.06	1.72 / 2.15	1.76 / 2.23	1.83 / 2.35	1.88 / 2.43	1.93 / 2.53	1.97 / 2.59	2.00 / 2.66	2.05 / 2.75	2.11 / 2.85	2.18 / 2.98	2.27 / 3.15	2.38 / 3.37	2.54 / 3.68	2.78 / 4.16	3.17 / 5.01	4.02 / 7.12
60	1.39 / 1.60	1.41 / 1.63	1.44 / 1.68	1.48 / 1.74	1.50 / 1.79	1.56 / 1.87	1.59 / 1.93	1.65 / 2.03	1.70 / 2.12	1.75 / 2.20	1.81 / 2.32	1.86 / 2.40	1.92 / 2.50	1.95 / 2.56	1.99 / 2.63	2.04 / 2.72	2.10 / 2.82	2.17 / 2.95	2.25 / 3.12	2.37 / 3.34	2.52 / 3.65	2.76 / 4.13	3.15 / 4.98	4.00 / 7.08
65	1.37 / 1.56	1.39 / 1.60	1.42 / 1.64	1.46 / 1.71	1.49 / 1.76	1.54 / 1.84	1.57 / 1.90	1.63 / 2.00	1.68 / 2.09	1.73 / 2.18	1.80 / 2.30	1.85 / 2.37	1.90 / 2.47	1.94 / 2.54	1.98 / 2.61	2.02 / 2.70	2.08 / 2.79	2.15 / 2.93	2.24 / 3.09	2.36 / 3.31	2.51 / 3.62	2.75 / 4.10	3.14 / 4.95	3.99 / 7.04
70	1.35 / 1.53	1.37 / 1.56	1.40 / 1.63	1.45 / 1.69	1.47 / 1.74	1.53 / 1.82	1.56 / 1.88	1.62 / 1.98	1.67 / 2.07	1.72 / 2.15	1.79 / 2.28	1.84 / 2.35	1.89 / 2.45	1.93 / 2.51	1.97 / 2.59	2.01 / 2.67	2.07 / 2.77	2.14 / 2.91	2.22 / 3.07	2.35 / 3.29	2.50 / 3.60	2.74 / 4.08	3.13 / 4.92	3.98 / 7.01
80	1.32 / 1.49	1.35 / 1.52	1.38 / 1.57	1.42 / 1.65	1.45 / 1.70	1.51 / 1.78	1.54 / 1.84	1.60 / 1.94	1.65 / 2.03	1.70 / 2.11	1.77 / 2.24	1.82 / 2.32	1.88 / 2.41	1.91 / 2.48	1.95 / 2.55	1.99 / 2.64	2.05 / 2.74	2.12 / 2.87	2.21 / 3.04	2.33 / 3.25	2.48 / 3.56	2.72 / 4.04	3.11 / 4.88	3.96 / 6.96
100	1.28 / 1.43	1.30 / 1.46	1.34 / 1.51	1.39 / 1.59	1.42 / 1.64	1.48 / 1.73	1.51 / 1.79	1.57 / 1.89	1.63 / 1.98	1.68 / 2.06	1.75 / 2.19	1.79 / 2.26	1.85 / 2.36	1.88 / 2.43	1.92 / 2.51	1.97 / 2.59	2.03 / 2.69	2.10 / 2.82	2.19 / 2.99	2.30 / 3.20	2.46 / 3.51	2.70 / 3.98	3.09 / 4.82	3.94 / 6.90
125	1.25 / 1.37	1.27 / 1.40	1.31 / 1.46	1.36 / 1.54	1.39 / 1.59	1.45 / 1.68	1.49 / 1.75	1.55 / 1.85	1.60 / 1.94	1.65 / 2.03	1.72 / 2.15	1.77 / 2.23	1.83 / 2.33	1.86 / 2.40	1.90 / 2.47	1.95 / 2.56	2.01 / 2.65	2.08 / 2.79	2.17 / 2.95	2.29 / 3.17	2.44 / 3.47	2.68 / 3.94	3.07 / 4.78	3.92 / 6.84
150	1.22 / 1.33	1.25 / 1.37	1.29 / 1.43	1.34 / 1.51	1.37 / 1.56	1.44 / 1.66	1.47 / 1.72	1.54 / 1.83	1.59 / 1.91	1.64 / 2.00	1.71 / 2.12	1.76 / 2.20	1.82 / 2.30	1.85 / 2.37	1.89 / 2.44	1.94 / 2.53	2.00 / 2.62	2.07 / 2.76	2.16 / 2.92	2.27 / 3.13	2.43 / 3.44	2.67 / 3.91	3.06 / 4.75	3.91 / 6.81
200	1.19 / 1.28	1.22 / 1.33	1.26 / 1.39	1.32 / 1.48	1.35 / 1.53	1.42 / 1.62	1.45 / 1.69	1.52 / 1.79	1.57 / 1.88	1.62 / 1.97	1.69 / 2.09	1.74 / 2.17	1.80 / 2.28	1.83 / 2.34	1.87 / 2.41	1.92 / 2.50	1.98 / 2.60	2.05 / 2.73	2.14 / 2.90	2.26 / 3.11	2.41 / 3.41	2.65 / 3.88	3.04 / 4.71	3.89 / 6.76
400	1.13 / 1.19	1.16 / 1.24	1.22 / 1.32	1.28 / 1.42	1.32 / 1.47	1.38 / 1.57	1.42 / 1.64	1.49 / 1.74	1.54 / 1.84	1.60 / 1.92	1.67 / 2.04	1.72 / 2.12	1.78 / 2.23	1.81 / 2.29	1.85 / 2.37	1.90 / 2.46	1.96 / 2.55	2.03 / 2.69	2.12 / 2.85	2.23 / 3.06	2.39 / 3.36	2.62 / 3.83	3.02 / 4.66	3.86 / 6.70
1000	1.08 / 1.11	1.13 / 1.19	1.19 / 1.28	1.26 / 1.38	1.30 / 1.44	1.36 / 1.54	1.41 / 1.61	1.47 / 1.71	1.53 / 1.81	1.58 / 1.89	1.65 / 2.01	1.70 / 2.09	1.76 / 2.20	1.80 / 2.26	1.84 / 2.34	1.89 / 2.43	1.95 / 2.53	2.02 / 2.66	2.10 / 2.82	2.22 / 3.04	2.38 / 3.34	2.61 / 3.80	3.00 / 4.62	3.85 / 6.66
∞	1.00 / 1.00	1.11 / 1.15	1.17 / 1.25	1.24 / 1.36	1.28 / 1.41	1.35 / 1.52	1.40 / 1.59	1.46 / 1.69	1.52 / 1.79	1.57 / 1.87	1.64 / 1.99	1.69 / 2.07	1.75 / 2.18	1.79 / 2.24	1.83 / 2.32	1.88 / 2.41	1.94 / 2.51	2.01 / 2.64	2.09 / 2.80	2.21 / 3.02	2.37 / 3.32	2.60 / 3.78	2.99 / 4.60	3.84 / 6.64

Poisson

Table 8

NEGATIVE EXPONENTIAL FUNCTION

x	e^{-x}	x	e^{-x}	x	e^{-x}
0	1.000	1.5	.223	3.0	.050
.1	.905	1.6	.202	3.1	.045
.2	.819	1.7	.183	3.2	.041
.3	.741	1.8	.165	3.3	.037
.4	.670	1.9	.150	3.4	.033
.5	.607	2.0	.135	3.5	.030
.6	.549	2.1	.122	3.6	.027
.7	.497	2.2	.111	3.7	.025
.8	.449	2.3	.100	3.8	.022
.9	.407	2.4	.091	3.9	.020
1.0	.368	2.5	.082	4.0	.018
1.1	.333	2.6	.074	4.5	.011
1.2	.301	2.7	.067	5.0	.007
1.3	.273	2.8	.061	6.0	.002
1.4	.247	2.9	.055	7.0	.001

Paul G. Hoel and Raymond J. Jessen, *Basic Statistics for Business and Economics* (New York: John Wiley and Sons, Inc., 1971), p. 420 by permission of the publishers.

238

INDEX